MORPHOGENETICS OF KARST REGIONS

VARIANTS OF KARST EVOLUTION

by

LÁSZLÓ JAKUCS D. Sc. (Geog.)

A HALSTED PRESS BOOK

JOHN WILEY & SONS

NEW YORK

This book is the revised and enlarged version
of the original Hungarian

A KARSZTOK MORFOGENETIKÁJA
Akadémiai Kiadó, Budapest

Translated by

B. BALKAY

© Akadémiai Kiadó, Budapest 1977

Published in the U. S. A. in 1977 by HALSTED PRESS, a Division of
John Wiley & Sons, Inc., New York.
ISBN 0 470 98952 1

Library of Congress Cataloging in Publication Data
Jakucs, László
The Morphogenetics of Karst Regions.
Translation of A karsztok morfogenetikája.
"A Halsted Press book."
Bibliography: p.
Includes indexes.
1. Karst. I. Title.
GB600.J3413   551,4'4   76-40003

Printed in Hungary

CONTENTS

Introduction 7

I. THE PLACE OF KARST MORPHOLOGY IN SCIENCE

The karst concept 15

Meaning of the term karst morphogenetics 19

The place of karst morphogenetics among the geosciences 20

II. GENERAL CRITERIA OF KARSTIFICATION

Presentation of the problem 25

The concept of karst corrosion 26
 1. Carbonate dissolution of limestone 26
 2. Hydrocarbonate dissolution of limestone 28
 3. Non-karstic corrosion of limestone 48

Petrovariance as a factor of karst corrosion 54
 1. Specific features of limestone composition 55
 2. Influence of limestone crystallinity and lithostructure upon karst corrosion 63
 3. Influence of the lithology and limestone structure upon karst corrosion 68
 4. Dolomite corrosion 71
 5. Dissolution of gypsum and rock salt 78
 6. Karst corrosion of polymineral rocks 81

Epeirogenic movements as factors of karstification 86

Climatic control of karstification and the geomorphological consequences of climatic variance 103
 1. Karstification in the glacial and periglacial regions of geomorphology 117
 2. Karst corrosion in the temperate and Mediterranean zones 127
 3. Karst corrosion in the desert zone 129
 4. Tropical karstification 130
  a) Rain-forest karst 134
  b) Inselberg karst 134
  c) Karst cone and karst tower 135
  d) Intermontane karst plains 136
  e) Other characteristic tropical karst forms 137

5. Karst morphological consequences of soil microclimates   141
    a) Methods of testing soil gas for carbon dioxide content   152
    b) Examples of typical carbon dioxide contents in soil atmospheres of karst microspaces differing in biological and climatic features   157

Authigenic and allogenic karst evolution (the role of erosional variance in karst erosion)   166
    1. Features of authigenic karst erosion in the presence of an unchanging local baselevel of erosion   168
    2. Erosion of authigenic karst when accompanied by displacements of the local baselevel of karst erosion   172
    3. Allogenic (B-type) karst erosion   176

Influence of relief configuration upon the karst process (the geomorphological variance of karstification)   195

The anthropovariance of karstification   200
    1. Modifications in erosion due to changes in the natural plant cover of a karst region   201
    2. Modifications in erosional processes accompanying anthropogenic interference with the natural hydrology of a karst   207
    a) Problems connected with human interference with the intake capacity of shallow-holes   208
    b) Influence upon the karst process of human interference with karst springs   221
    c) Influence upon the karst process of the regulation of surface and underground stream channel sections   225
    d) Influence upon erosion of artificial dams   228

Thematic review of the theses put forward in this book   231

REFERENCES   245

INDEX OF NAMES   269

SUBJECT INDEX   271

INTRODUCTION

The upswing of science witnessed during the twentieth century is unprecedented in human history. Its rate has been especially fast in the last decade or two, as a natural consequence — but also, in certain respects, as a promoter — of social needs, and of research possibilities due to the broadening of the industrial and technical bases.

One of the most fundamental characteristics of our age in this respect is the replacement of both the instinctive and the purposeful quest for knowledge of earlier epochs by social demand as the prime mover determining the evolution of science.

Modern science is dominated by a complexity of outlook and research methods, leading to the analysis and verification of multilateral relationships between causes and effects, and of the objective laws of nature over a truly imposing range. The individual branches of science can boast of magnificent results in their own fields, precisely because they have learned to profit from the achievements and research conceptions of other branches.

Of the innumerable examples at hand, let it be sufficient to cite just a few of the most characteristic, such as cybernetics, blossoming into the science of our age by a fusion into a self-contained discipline with considerable unity of purpose and outlook, out of mathematics, physics, electronics, etc.; or molecular biology, achieving the abstraction of numerous functional laws of living matter by a highly complex synthesis of chemical, biological, medicinal, physical, and to a certain extent also mathematical traits of contemporary science; both have contributed decisively to the modelling of the geological sciences at large too. The research tools of classical geology teach us little about the endogenous events taking place in the earth's interior, noticeable on the surface merely by their effects. As soon as the conventional geological approach was compounded with physical, mathematical and experimental procedures and methods previously unexploited for this end, however, magnificent new results arose on both theoretical and practical levels.

Here are some concrete examples. Gravity, electrotelluric surveys, refraction seismics, etc. belong purely to the field of the physicist, but the results have a close bearing on the geologist's ideas. In the Soviet Union, hydrocarbon structures have recently been prospected by means of bacteriological analysis of the near-surface soil atmosphere. Researchers in the US have developed means for the mapping of palaeogeographical areas of erosion on the basis of the radioactive properties of various lithofacies. The palaeomagnetism trapped in the crystal grains of magmatic rocks permits us to take a stand concerning continental movements that took place millions of years ago. The causes and laws of change of local anomalies of gravity are investigated by artificial Earth satellites. Nor would it be difficult to continue this enumeration.

In the science of our fathers, such interdisciplinary relationships would have been inconceivable: today we regard them as obvious, rely on them, and are looking for new ones.

The recently evolved geosciences of our age reflect their underlying complexity even in their names: geophysics, geochemistry, geomechanics, radiogeology, climatic geomorphology, geokinetics, hydrogeology, hydrometeorology, etc.

The range of meaningful interdisciplinary approaches is far from exhausted as yet. The more abundant the information accumulating in individual branches of science, and the more modern and manifold the special methods of investigation, the more intense the trend of differentiation within those branches. This will give rise to further and further perspectives concerning forms of interaction and also the need for realizing them, partly on a spontaneous basis, and partly under the pressure of social demand. Breath-taking as the present evolution of science and technology may seem, we are standing merely at the outset of a tremendous process, unfathomable as to the depth and breadth of its perspectives.

In the author's opinion, it follows that physical geography and the narrower subject of this book, karst geomorphology, cannot be satisfied by the description and recording of land forms, and their conventional analysis, even if this be most circumspect and painstaking. And although new regional data and records of forms may usefully contribute to the data bank of science, the modernization of our knowledge of nature should not be expected in our days to be the fruit predominantly of a series of great descriptive and detailed regional monographs of physical geography.

Our excellent predecessors in karst research (CVIJIĆ 1893, 1895, 1918, 1923, 1924/1—2, 1926, GRUND 1903, 1912/2, 1914, MARTEL 1908, KATZER 1909/1, CHOLNOKY 1916, 1917, 1928, 1932/2, 1939, KREBS 1929, O. LEHMANN 1932, ABSOLON 1909, 1911, 1914, ECKERT 1896, 1898, KRUBER 1913, 1922, etc.) have given comprehensive and fundamental descriptions of karst phenomena: they elaborated on — and debated with some ardour — the natural and anthropogenic processes resulting in the sculpture of today's land forms. Even to our critical eyes, their regional monographs appear as classics of permanent value in geographical literature. Still, their ideas concerning the origin of karst forms are not acceptable without qualification; their geomorphological approaches tended to be one-sided, based on purely visual comparisons with empirically derived information concerning areas of different surface morphologies, on a territorial application of the principle of uniformitarianism, and on logical speculation. Their interpretations of forms lacked, of course, the backing that today's geomorphology receives from modern physics, chemistry, soil biology, microclimatology, etc. as well as any analysis of the genetic implications of their achievements; information indispensable for the current trends of complex analysis.

The physical geographer (deliberately avoiding the term geomorphologist here) must get rid of a particularly heavy burden of inherited views and ideas if he is to find the right way in the complex world of karst phenomena. There is doubtless no other discipline within geomorphology that is weighted down with so many disputable interpretations of forms, and controversial, unsolved problems, as the field of karst morphology, where even the basic data figuring as axioms in the interpretative deduction of form types may require reassessment.

To substantiate the truth of the above statement, let it suffice to cite here as illustration the striking contrast between the theorems of Corbel's climato-geomorphologic dynamics (CORBEL 1959), and the actual zonal distribution of karst regions and karst forms on this planet (ZUBASHCHENKO 1947, H. LEHMANN 1948, 1954/1—2, 1956, RATHJENS 1951, KOSACK 1952, P. Z. SZABÓ 1957, BIROT 1959, BALÁZS 1962/1—2, 1963/1), or the fundamental revision and modernization of views in the second half of this century concerning the mechanism of chemical dissolution of limestone (TROMBE 1952, MILLER 1952, BÖGLI 1956/2, 1957, 1960, ERNST 1961, MARKÓ 1961).

The application to karst morphology of modern science with its bias towards the experimental will necessarily bring about certain more or less revolutionary changes of view; these will tend to receive a greater share of the limelight, the more fundamental the problems that they concern. And it would seen that the number of fundamental truths of waning actuality in the theory of karst phenomena is still fairly large, as the early classical theories of interpretation were largely based on feeling, instinct and intuition, and if a theorem was not refuted by everyday evidence visible to the naked eye, it soon attained the rank of a scientific dogma. Some of the dogmas of karst morphology were inherited ready-made even by the founders of progressive geomorphology (LOMONOSOV, HUMBOLDT, DOKU-CHAEV, RICHTHOFEN, DAVIS, PENCK, etc.); these were rooted in the folklore concerning the often mysterious, phantasy-exciting karst phenomena, or in another respect, in the colourful but not always adept, nor any too moderate descriptions of the early speleologists.

In effect the early approaches to karst phenomena came, with a few exceptions, from the side of speleological exploration (MARTEL, ABSOLON, CASTERET, etc.): the fast-swelling body of regional-speleological information soon became, owing to its disproportionate mass impact, one of the primary yardsticks of the morphogenetic evaluation of karst regions, and a determinant of the place of karst research in the realm of science as a whole.

Even in this century, the interest of workers in karst regions has been tied down predominantly by caverns; it was precisely owing to the perspective distortion of these details looming in the foreground that they tended to disregard the importance of a genetic and comparative synthesis of the processes controlling the evolution of the karst matrix, and of the broad range of land forms connected with it.

In Hungary, the essence of this problem was formulated by BULLA (1954/1, p. 459):

"The karstic erosion of limestone, that is, the evolution of karst peneplains in limestone mountains, is an extremely complex process, clarified only in some details thus far; its analytical clarification will require the development of new research tools and their application to geomorphology. It is in particular from geochemistry that karst morphology may expect promotive assistance. In this context, research into the dynamisms of karst evolution acquires especial importance. Such research has been rather sporadic to date. Even its methods lack development. The research that has been carried out so far has fallen into the serious error of deriving the process as a whole either from the structure of limestone regions, or from the physical and chemical properties of limestone, or from the laws of motion of water in limestone. This approach to research — the isolated separate examination of each karst phenomenon and each component of karstification in itself — can provide only details, but will not lead to a full understanding of the process. Karstic erosion as a whole cannot be interpreted except in terms of an indivisible, dialectic interplay of limestone and water. In such a context, the karst and the dialectics of its sculpture are in effect little known as yet."

All this signifies, then, on a conceptual level that any novel research aimed at providing a modern interpretation of karst phenomena must not be oriented towards either pure geology or pure geomorphology; nor may it serve the aims solely of the hydrogeologist, climatologist or possibly the geochemist: the view to be sought is a complex synthetic one which will permit the joint critical evaluation and the correct weighting of the evidence and arguments furnished by geochemistry, hydrology, geomorphology, geohistory, etc.

In the quest for laws of general validity, any attempt at synthesis had to be preceded by the collection of material evidence. The abundance of the data collected over the last decade or two makes its classification and critical sifting worth-while, in addition to an evaluation of the more recent morphogenetic theories and viewpoints, while matching them, if possible, to one's own observations and conclusions.

The task facing us is therefore a responsible and an honourable one. Armed with the knowledge and research tools of all the branches of science auxiliary to physical geography, we shall attempt to develop traditional karst morphology into karst morphogenetics, and to justify this change of term by an adequate change in content.

This is not, of course, an easy thing to do. The subject matter of all the auxiliary disciplines required — each of which is undergoing a modern evolution at a tremendous rate — is beyond the grasp of any single person. The gigantic task of a modern reassessment of the subject matter of our own discipline will demand a purposeful and well-co-ordinated, prolonged effort on the part of the well-organized research staffs of various scientific institutions. Still, if he has enough faith in the correctness of his reading of evolutionary trends as determined by the nature of our age, even the individual may, with some self-confidence, attempt an in-depth reassessment of at least some partial problems, especially if he is ready to accept physical geography as a synthetic branch of science suitable for providing a unity of purpose, a beacon to show the way in the otherwise unchartable wilderness of information in the most diverse fields of science. The scientist must have faith that this beacon will provide the light by which the spots of colour — the geological, geophysical, geokinetical, hydrological, chemical, pedologic, climatologic, etc. evidence gleaned from the study of Nature — will merge into a harmonic whole, in which the various colours of the spectrum fuse into a beam of light illuminating novel inductions and relationships. In this way we feel justified in expecting to arrive at a genetic interpretation of karst phenomena worthy of today's level of human knowledge.

So much for the credo of this work or, more prosaically, for its statement of aims.

The Author

I. THE PLACE OF KARST MORPHOLOGY IN SCIENCE

THE KARST CONCEPT

The word "karst" was originally an orographic proper name, denoting the northern part of the Dinarids from the Julian Alps to the sources of the river Una. It was only later that it was abstracted into a general conceptual term of physical geography. This is perhaps why it is so hard to outline its exact phenomenological content, and also why most of the definitions so far propounded are, in the eyes of modern science, wanting in some respect.

Relevant literature presents, among others, the following propositions.

"Karst is a geographic concept subsequently altered into a geomorphologic technical term. Today those regions are called karst that exhibit the same features as the Karst in the geographic sense. These features tend to manifest themselves on rocks that are comparatively readily soluble, with little or no residue. These rocks include rock salt, gypsum and limestone. The first two rarely appear in substantial masses on the surface, but limestone abounds. Hence, all the true karsts of some magnitude are in limestone regions." (DUDICH sen., 1932.)

Another definition of the karst was given by KADIĆ (1939): "Limestone regions rich in caverns were observed first and most thoroughly in the Karst region of Krain, Istria and Croatia; this is why any other region exhibiting these same features is called a karst, and the phenomena observed in karst regions are called karst phenomena."

Even though the above definitions do conform to fact, they do not express all the essential properties of a karst. They have the shortcoming — to name just one — that they lack any reference to evolution and the continuous modelling of the karst; they present it as a frozen set of features corresponding to a fixed instant of evolution. On the other hand, the definitions cannot make any claim at completeness for the added reason that they do not rise to the level where the universal essence detaches itself from the concrete and individual. Thus, any person not acquainted with the Karst in Krain, Istria, etc. will not, on reading the above two definitions, acquire an understanding of the general karst concept. Although "karst" as a technical term of geomorphology was introduced into science as described above, from today's viewpoint it is unsatisfactory to regard the reference to the semantic origin of the term as a correct conceptual definition of the karst in general.

A definition with a typically speleological orientation was given by KESSLER (1957), who stated karst phenomena to be simply "phenomena connected with the subterranean activity of precipitations" in limestone mountains. This is, however, an arbitrary highlighting of just another facet of the karst's essence, its relationship to a single agency, the underground activity of precipitations.

Almost identical with the above is VENKOVITS' definition (1960/2):

"In today's terminology, we mean by the term karst a portion of the earth's solid crust, made up of rocks affected more than the average by the dissolving power of surface or underground waters."

To gain an insight into the entire karst process, however, a number of factors other than precipitation have to be correctly assessed, including for example the structural and diagenetic history of the rock, the volume of rock available for karstification, its position above or below its surroundings, the ecological types of its flora, the climate of the region, the quality of the soil cover, the influence of the fauna, etc. These are all essential factors of interaction, closely interdetermined, which assume a decisive role by the interplay of their often opposed influences, and determine in their turn the resultant direction of karst evolution, the characteristic unfolding of its life cycle, different in each case studied. If we consider just the peculiarities of the rock and the dissolving power of precipitation, we find no explanation of the multitude of karst forms, such as the tropical cone karst (H. LEHMANN 1948, 1954/2, 1956, WISSMANN 1954, P. Z. SZABÓ 1957) or the karst of the tjäle zone (MAKSIMOVICH 1947, GVOZDETSKY 1950, BOTS 1957, CORBEL 1959). Nor could we interpret the homologies of the various karst brush wood associations (P. JAKUCS 1955, 1956) that, in a final analysis, are also phenomena linked with the karst process.

In another paper, KESSLER (1932) included under the term karst phenomena "those phenomena that are peculiar to mountains made up of rocks capable of residueless dissolution".

This definition, however, is not wholly satisfactory either, since it is not expressive of the process and its conditions. One of the essential features of a mountain of rock salt, for example, a rock soluble without residue, is a salt taste. Nevertheless, a salt taste is not a karst feature. In loess, on the other hand, which is far from being soluble without a residue, a set of well-defined karst phenomena may appear (BULLA 1932, 1954/2, PÉCSI 1967), which justify our speaking of the karstification of loess.

Without denying the usefulness in their own time and place of the definitions just cited, or their role in promoting the advance of science, we must point out that the prevailing state of evolution in karst science and speleology demands a more profound, more essential definition.

It was H. LEHMANN (1948, 1954/1, 1956) in Europe who assessed the many facets of terrestrial climatic zoning in its importance for relief forming, and more specifically for karst evolution. We are therefore justified in regarding these authors as the founders and developers of the school of climatic (karst) morphology.

Following in Bulla's footsteps, P. Z. SZABÓ (1956, 1957) further developed the climatic-morphologic-regional system of karsts. He already knew that "karstification is not a simple process. The peculiar geomorphological products of dissolution, that is, the factors determining the quality of the phenomena, vary according to the climatic zoning. Except for the properties and the structure of the rock, the factors imposing the essential peculiarities of a karst region are decisively climatic. It is the intensity and characteristic distribution of the various climatic factors over the years that have determined the zonal structural differences. The principal relief-modelling climatic factors including temperature, humidity, precipitation and vegetational cover vary not only from one place to another, but also with time; as the geomorphological process advances, they continually change in a quantitative way. Therefore, in every climatic zone there is something that is dying off and something else that is arising. This holds for land forms, too. Under the laws of morphological evolution, the dying and the arising are linked in an irreconcilable antithesis. Deprived of its climatical *raisons d'être*, the land form, the karst form, will die away and disappear sooner or later. Due attention to this rule is the fundamental condition of the successful study of climatically controlled land forms."

With all this in mind, we outline the definition of karst required in our examinations as follows:

Karst is a stage, with a characteristic appearance, in the development of dominantly limestone mountain-forming rock, together with the natural phenomena associated with it, whose origin and evolution are the complex result of a peculiar petrographic constitution, and an interplay in space and time of various geological, geographical, climatological and biological causes and environmental conditions.

Karst as a category, then, is an environmental situation. On the other hand, karstification is a process resulting from a temporal succession of events and phenomena, as determined by the laws governing karst evolution.

Since, by the above, karst is an instantaneous cross-section at a given instant of the process of evolution called karstification, the karst concept is discrete and relative, as opposed to the concept of karstification which has a connotation of motion, change and evolution, thus being in closer conceptual affinity with the actual world.

The phenomena of morphology, hydrology, biology, etc., or groups of such phenomena (including sink-holes, poljes, dolines, caverns, lapies, specific associations of plants and animals, forms of human habitation and ways of life, etc.) more or less persistently specified as karst phenomena (which, even if not so specified, are the direct consequences of karst evolution always and everywhere, and must therefore be counted among the attributes of karst) do not exhaust the much broader range of essential karst phenomena.

The karst phenomena accessible to study are merely the external expressions of an intrinsic state. Our understanding of the essence of karst and its processes will thus be the more profound, the more complex our approach to the object studied, the more facets it discloses of the relationships in space and time, the cause and effects, the unity of the internal contradictions in the phenomenon and the struggle for supremacy among their various tendencies. Karst evolution, for instance, does not take place either on the surface or in the caverns accessible to us, but in the entire inaccessible three-dimensional volume of the karst rock, and in the manifold relationships of this mass with the non-karstic environment, including the variations in these relationships. Moreover, in order that our approach be truly genetic, it has to reckon continually with time as a fourth dimension.

The definition of the karst concept as a state of evolution, dependent on certain conditions, of a mountain-sized mass of limestone does not preclude the manifestation of karst phenomena on other rocks similar in some aspects to limestone, under similar influences and conditions. The purpose of this science is to find and specify the properties and conditions that interact in the most general way in the widest possible space over the longest possible span of time, which give rise to karstification as a process. Diverse aspects of this process are studied by various branches of science using their peculiar and distinctive methods, including karst morphology, karst hydrology, karst biology, karst geology, karst geochemistry, karst petrography, etc. The conceptual unity of how we see the process as a whole, however, is provided by the discipline of karst morphogenetics.

MEANING OF THE TERM KARST MORPHOGENETICS

The term karst morphogenetics is the result of a formal conceptual joining of the component terms*; it means the science of the origin of karst forms.

This compound term has not, except for certain earlier publications of the present author (1956/1, 1960/2), figured so far in international physical-geographical literature. The corresponding term in common use is karst morphology. This traditional technical term, however, is less demanding as to content; it smacks to some extent of a more or less morphogenetic characterization, suggesting a purely descriptive approach to karst forms, owing to a connotation acquired early in the history of the word.

In studying the publications of today's geographers and geologists concerned with karst phenomena, however, we are struck by the fact that the majority of them are largely concerned not only with morphological traits but also with climate, lithologic and hydrologic environment, and causal problems of geochemistry and, indeed, of geomechanics, etc. These publications are richer in content and on a higher level than mere karst morphology in the strict sense: even though a tacit one, this is decisively a morphogenetic approach, with a strong emphasis on the genetic aspect. We are thus justified in using the term karst morphogenetics, coined by the present author to indicate a new branch of science engendered by a fully ripened necessity in the evolution and enrichment of science.

---

* *Karst morphogenetics* is a word compounded from the components karst, morphology and genetics, each of which has a concrete meaning of its own. The meaning of the term karst was analysed in some detail above; morphology means the science of forms, and genetics the science of origins.

THE PLACE OF KARST MORPHOGENETICS AMONG THE GEOSCIENCES

Karst morphogenetics as a branch of science is an organic inseparable part of physical geography, and more specifically of geomorphology, its concern being with the specific processes of erosion of a distinct group of rocks participating in the constitution of the earth's crust. Now, since the land-forms subject to karst morphogenetic study are under a well-defined litho-logic control, we must agree in the main with BULLA, who places karst morphology in the group of lithomorphology within geomorphology as a whole (1954/2).

This is but a half-truth, however, lithology in itself is not a sufficient cause for the evolution of a karst. Another prime requisite is a suitable climate, without which no karst will form even in lithologically suitable regions. In the deserts of Africa, Asia and Australia, for example, there are extensive limestone areas without any karst forms; and, despite the presence of a lithologic bias towards karstification, one observes a karstophobic set of forms of erosion comparable with those in any other lithology (regs, sphinx rocks, deflated tablelands, buttes, etc.). Hence, karst morpho-genetics must necessarily study the effects of azonal petrographic and zonal climatic factors; it therefore constitutes an important chapter of climatic geomorphology, too.

Of course, the above-discussed relationships are merely the most essential, but by no means the only co-ordinates of karst morphology in the field of geomorphology as a whole; karst forms also have manifold functional con-nections with problems studied by other branches of physical geography, primarily hydrogeography and biogeography.

These connections tend to occupy the foreground of interest, especially when the problem is approached not from aspects of the corrosive karst process proper, but conversely, from the viewpoint of landform analysis of karst configurations effectively constituting the relief under study; it is usually observed where the modelling of any set of karst forms is due not only to the conventional karstifying processes, but also to a greater or lesser extent to the factors of erosion common in non-karstic regions, so that the set of forms is always essentially complex.

The relative intensities of the individual processes are of course decisive, but even these are climatically controllable. An example is PÉCSI's pioneer-ing system (1967), which groups the exogenous agencies active in influencing the modelling of karst forms in particular, and karst landscapes in general, as follows.

1. *Karst corrosion*
   a) carbonate dissolution
   b) hydrocarbonate disso-
      lution
2. *Chemical weathering*
   a) CO_2-containing solu-
      tions due to soil gen-
      esis
   b) organic processes in
      the soil
   c) weathering due to in-
      organic acids
3. *Calcification* (the precipitation of calcium carbonate)
4. *Mechanical comminution*
   a) by solar energy
   b) by ice formation
   c) by the formation of
      crystals

1. *Sheetwash*
   a) sheetwash proper
   b) surface corrosion of
      the transported waste
2. *Mass wasting*
   a) corrasion on the slope
      due to creeping scree
   b) rockslides (e.g. in cav-
      erns, dolines, etc.)

1. *Linear flow of water*
   a) hydraulic action
   b) removal of matter,
      fluvial transport
   c) corrasion of riverbed
      by waste
   d) attrition of waste
   e) corrosion by flowing
      water

The karst phenomena whose processes of evolution are analysed by karst morphogenetics are partly superficial, but partly subterranean. This duality would not in itself constitute a sufficient reason for a further subdivision of our discipline, since the superficial and subterranean phenomena are largely interconnected. The reason for the *de facto* existence of the duality is tradition. There is the somewhat paradoxical situation that the evolution

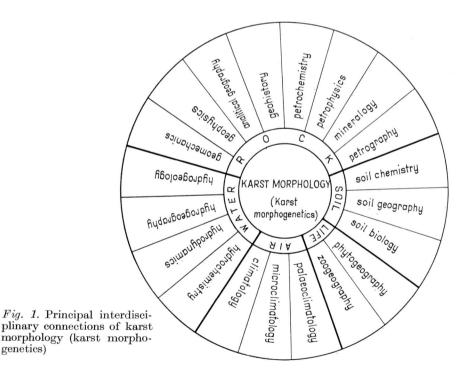

Fig. 1. Principal interdisciplinary connections of karst morphology (karst morphogenetics)

of geospeleology (a part) preceded the evolution of karst morphology (the whole) both in time and in content; indeed, even within speleology as a whole, *geospeleology* gained a great deal of independence vis-à-vis *archaeospeieology*, concerned with the archaeological exploration of caverns, and *biospeleology*, studying the life forms contained in them.

Thus it is understandable that many modern speleological works fail to reflect modern theories of karst morphology, whereas geomorphological works, on the contrary, clarify problems by utilizing a broad range of geospeleological evidence, even when concerned with only superficial processes of karst genesis.

Figure 1 is a comprehensive illustration of the most important disciplines related to karst morphogenetics. The information provided by these ancillary disciplines is indispensable for the understanding of karst phenomena.

It is expedient to distinguish in this context primary and secondary, that is, direct and indirect ancillary disciplines. From the former the geomorphologist frequently borrows methods and tools, whereas he will merely use certain statements and documents of those in the second group.

This is not a rigid classification, however. The number of potential interdisciplinary connections is vast. Depending on the time and the place, an enormous variety of these potential connections may be realized. The evolution of science discovers new relationships almost day by day so that, in the unravelling of the infinitely complex tangle of causes and effects, any constraint to stay within the confines of any specific discipline must be considered a burden. The scientist engrossed in his quest for the essence of the phenomena will perceive almost as a material presence the profound truth of Engels' statement that 'everything is connected with everything' and 'any change in any object will entail a change in every other object'. He will be deeply contented if he can find among the almost infinite number of threads the most essential, most robust one.

II. GENERAL CRITERIA OF KARSTIFICATION

PRESENTATION OF THE PROBLEM

Karstification is a complex natural process controlled by several interconnected factors. What we mean by this is not merely that the modelling of karst forms may be due, in addition to the corrosive action of water, to other processes of erosion (variable in time and space), but also that even the factors determining the quality and intensity of the purely corrosive, 'classic' karst processes depend on several variable conditions of their own. According to J. BÜDEL (1963), the most decisive of the regionally and temporally variable controllers of the corrosive karst process include the nature of the rock (*petrovariance*), tectonic structure (*epeirovariance*) and climatic conditions (*climatovariance*). It has lately been proved that the nature of the geographical environment (the relationship of the karst region to its non-karstic surroundings) will also influence the corrosion process qualitatively; this directs attention to another factor, erosional variance (ROGLIĆ 1956, 1957, 1960, L. JAKUCS 1956/1—2, 1960/1—2, 1968/1—2). In addition to these, another factor requiring elucidation is geomorphological variance, which incorporates such features of the karstifying rock as the permeability of its surface cover, the relative position of the karst water table, the absolute size of the connected karst mass, the relief energy of the ground surface, etc. The remaining agencies, such as the anthropogenetic influence, may also play a decisive role in controlling corrosion, although their effects are usually fairly local.

In the following, we shall review in detail the above-mentioned circumstances controlling karst corrosion. It is reasonable, however, to precede this with a clarification of the basic concept, an unequivocal definition of karst corrosion. The chemical interpretation of karst corrosion must be one of our priority subjects, all the more so, since the recent considerable advances in our theoretical knowledge has rendered the usual textbook theories out of date.

Even though the process of karstification is not restricted to limestone, since the peculiar karst phenomena of dissolution may appear in other rocks, the classic definitions were justified in associating karst with limestone, since some 80 to 90 per cent of all karst regions on earth are in limestone regions (KOSACK 1952); hence, of all the rocks soluble in water, it is the dissolution of limestone that results in the most numerous and most conspicuous karst phenomena.

THE CONCEPT OF KARST CORROSION

By karst corrosion we mean the peculiar erosion by dissolution primarily of limestone (and, in a broader sense, of other rocks readily soluble without residue in water).

The dissolution of limestone in water may be the result of any one or any combination of three distinct processes: (a) carbonate dissolution in pure (distilled) water, (b) bicarbonate dissolution — the dissolution of limestone in water containing carbon dioxide ((a) and (b) are distinguished by specific quantitative and qualitative properties, but both processes are reversible), and (c) the dissolution of limestone by other chemical agents, largely soil acids of organic origin. In this last case, the new calcium compound entering the solution is not as a rule reversible to $CaCO_3$.

1. CARBONATE DISSOLUTION OF LIMESTONE

The dissociated ions of calcite ($CaCO_3$) remain unaffected when dissolved in distilled water; that is, dissolution is expressed by the following reversible relationship:

$$CaCO_3 \rightleftharpoons Ca^{++} + CO_3^{--} \tag{1}$$

This process results in a state of equilibrium between the solid phase ($CaCO_3$), the solvent (H_2O) and the dissolved ions; the concentrations of these latter can be characterized by the solubility product K_1 (TILLMANNS 1932, MILLER 1952). K_1 is a variable index more or less proportional to the solution temperature, but depending also on certain features of the solid phase. For instance, the index for orthorhombic bipyramidal $CaCO_3$ (aragonite) is higher than that for trigonal calcite (SCHOELLER 1956).

Table 1 lists some published data concerning the magnitude and range of variability of the solubility index.

As regards the time required for limestone to dissolve in pure water, there is some controversy in the literature. HARRASOWITZ (1954), BÖGLI (1956/2, 1960), H. LEHMANN (1956, 1960), BAUER (1964) and FRANKE (1967) state this reaction to be an exceedingly fast one. This is confirmed by field studies, at least according to the authors cited: none of the water samples collected from limestone surfaces contained less dissolved $CaCO_3$ than the values figuring in the table, although the rainwater collected e.g. by the Austrian Bauer was *in statu nascendi*, running down lapies rills, in contact for no longer than a few seconds with the limestone surface. On this basis,

Bögli (1960, 1963/3) estimated about one second as the time required for primary carbonate dissolution. (For more on this problem see the following section on hydrocarbonate dissolution.)

Table 1

The solubilities of the various crystal lattice types of $CaCO_3$

Author (year)	Temp. °C	Dissolved $CaCO_3$ in mg/l		
		calcite	aragonite	amorphous
Schloesing (1872)	8·7	10·0	—	—
Schloesing (1872)	16·0	13·1	—	—
Schloesing (1872)	25·0	14·3	—	—
Charlot and Enschwiller (1939)	—	12·4	—	—
Trombe (1952)	16·0	16·0	—	—
Hodgman (1955)	cold	14·25	—	—
Hodgman (1955)	warm	18·75	—	—
Schoeller (1956)	25·0	14·33	15·28	14·45
Schoeller (1956)	50·0	15·04	16·16	15·15
Schoeller (1956)	100·0	17·79	19·02	18·16

According to Markó (1962), however, these results prove not the fast rate of dissolution, but the fact that, under the conditions of sampling, ionic diffusion was particularly fast — ionic diffusion being the process that removes dissolved molecules or ions from the saturated layer adhering to the rock surface into the running water. Naturally then, conditions of diffusion are optimum in the thin layers of sheetwash running down the rock surface; in Markó's interpretation, this may account for the considerable dynamism of dissolution.

Gerstenhauer and Pfeffer (1966), on the other hand, on the basis of their own extensive examinations, go so far as to cast doubt on the reliability of Bögli's analytical data. Working in the laboratory, these authors measured the rates of dissolution of limestone samples taken from all over the world, and did not observe rapid saturation: on the contrary (cf. Fig. 7), they found dissolution times longer by several orders of magnitude. In order to attain a concentration of 13 mg/l, for instance, some water samples had to be in contact with the rock for as long as a full day, which is all the more striking since the water they used contained some carbon dioxide, which accelerates dissolution.

These apparently irreconcilable differences of several orders of magnitude might possibly be due to differences in the analytical procedures used by the various authors. We shall avoid going into details here (these can be found in Merck (1956), Müller (1962) and Gerstenhauer (1969), and shall point out only that Bögli and Franke used the Wartha—Lunge process with a methylorange indicator, whereas Gerstenhauer and Pfeffer used the titriplex III (chalcone carboxylic acid) method. It seems to us that Gerstenhauer and Pfeffer's ideas are closer to fact, as the indicator used by them is specific for calcium ions, a readily observed change of colour being obtained even at very low concentrations.

Incidentally, the significance in nature of the carbonate dissolution process is rather subordinate, since pure (almost distilled) water simply does not occur in the earth's hydrosphere. Phreatic waters entering into consideration for effective karst corrosion — and indeed even rain water — invariably contain a certain amount of dissolved substances, and the compositions and concentrations of these substances may decisively affect the solubility of limestone in the water.

Of all the chemicals occurring in natural waters, the literature puts the greatest emphasis on the role of carbon dioxide (CO_2), since even a water fairly low in CO_2 may dissolve several times the amount of calcium carbonate as in pure water.

2. HYDROCARBONATE DISSOLUTION OF LIMESTONE

The dissolution of limestone in water containing carbon dioxide is termed hydrocarbonate dissolution: the ions formed from the carbon dioxide in the solution enter into chemical reaction with the limestone; as a result, the highly-soluble calcium bicarbonate $Ca(HCO_3)_2$ is formed, which exists only in aqueous solution (KYRLE 1923, TILLMANNS 1932, CHOLNOKY 1940).

As current views on the genesis of karst processes would be incomprehensible even taxonomically without a review of the up-to-date theories of the physico-chemical relationships of hydrocarbonate dissolution of limestone in water, we shall have to examine this problem in some detail.

Hydrocarbonate dissolution, and its reverse, the precipitation of the dissolved lime out of the solution, are invariably controlled by the carbon dioxide saturation of the water or of the solution involved in the dissolution or precipitation. To a first approximation, it is sufficient to state that water entering into contact with a limestone can dissolve more $CaCO_3$, the higher its original CO_2 content. That is, increase of the CO_2 content of the water increases its dissolving power; on the other hand, if the CO_2 concentration is reduced (e.g. by evaporation), the water may become saturated with $CaCO_3$, and part of the previously dissolved $CaCO_3$ may precipitate out (calcareous oozes, stalactites, calcareous tufa, etc.).

The total dissolved CO_2 content of a natural water may vary over a wide range, and since the CO_2 content of the water and its dissolving power for calcium carbonate are directly proportional, the interpretation of the *corrosive potential of any given water* requires first and foremost an assessment of the conditions affecting its CO_2 content when in contact with the rock.

$$CO_2 \text{ (gaseous in the atmosphere)} \rightleftharpoons CO_2 \text{ (absorbed in water)} \quad (2)$$

Carbon dioxide saturation in water is affected by the following factors:

(1) The relative CO_2 content of the atmosphere (gas phase) in contact with the water, expressed in terms of the partial pressure of carbon dioxide, $p\,CO_2$.

(2) The common temperature of the solvent and the gas, at which the dissolution process takes place.

28

(3) The hydrostatic pressure acting simultaneously upon the solvent and the gas space in contact with it.

(4) The time available for dissolution.

This reveals that dissolution and evaporation of CO_2 from the water are complex functions of a number of variables; a change in any one of the above factors immediately displaces the equilibrium in one direction or the other.

Although the factors influencing the dissolution of CO_2 are in complex interplay in nature, to gain a clearer insight it is useful to consider the influences of the factors one by one.

By the Henry—Dalton law (1803) the absorptive capacity of a solvent for various gases in contact with it varies directly as the partial pressure (p) of each gas and inversely as the temperature. Accordingly, the amount of CO_2 that can be absorbed by water can be calculated using the formula

$$\text{absorbed } CO_2 \text{ (g/l)} = L.p.1{\cdot}9634 \qquad (3)$$

where the numerical coefficient $1{\cdot}9634$ is equal to the weight in grams of one litre of CO_2 at one atm and 20 °C, p is the partial pressure of CO_2 and L is the temperature-dependent solubility or *absorption coefficient* of CO_2 gas. The values of L for some temperatures that may prevail during karstification are listed in *Table 2*.

Table 2

Absorption coefficients of CO_2 (L) at various temperatures

Temperature of solution, °C							
0	5	10	15	17	20	25	30
1·713	1·424	1·194	1·019	0·958	0·878	0·765	0·665

Using eq. (3), SCHLOESING (1872) calculated and tabulated the saturation concentrations of carbon dioxide in water for various temperatures and partial pressures of CO_2. His results are listed in *Table 3* for the ranges of variables that interest us.

Table 3 reveals, for example, that at a temperature of 5 °C, rain falling through the air may absorb about 0·84 mg/l CO_2 at the partial pressure of 0·0003 (equivalent to a carbon dioxide content of 0·03 per cent) usual in the atmosphere. In warmer air, e.g. at 30 °C, common in the tropics and not rare in summer even in our latitudes, the amount of CO_2 that can be absorbed is less, i. e. 0·39 mg/l.

On the other hand, in the tropics where the production of CO_2 in the soil is intense all the year round, owing to the decay of abundant organic matter and to further processes of pedogenesis and biogenesis, the CO_2 content of the air at ground level may attain fairly high values. For instance, from air at 22 °C H. LEHMANN in 1955 collected in Cuba rainwater which contained 2·5 mg/l CO_2, considered by Lehmann as atmospheric in origin;

Table 3

Solubility of CO_2 in water at temperatures and partial pressures encountered on the surface of the earth

Atmospheric pCO_2	Total CO_2 (mg/l) soluble in water at the temperatures (°C) below							
	0	5	10	15	17	20	25	30
0·0001	0·34	0·28	0·23	0·20	0·19	0·17	0·15	0·13
0·0003	1·01	0·84	0·70	0·60	0·56	0·52	0·45	0·39
0·0005	1·68	1·40	1·17	1·00	0·94	0·86	0·74	0·65
0·00075	2·52	2·09	1·76	1·50	1·41	1·28	1·12	0·98
0·001	3·36	2·80	2·34	2·00	1·88	1·72	1·49	1·31
0·0015	5·04	4·19	3·51	3·00	2·82	2·58	2·24	1·96
0·002	6·73	5·59	4·69	4·00	3·76	3·45	3·01	2·61
0·0025	8·40	6·99	5·85	5·00	4·70	4·28	3·73	3·28
0·005	16·8	13·98	11·7	10·0	9·4	8·57	7·46	6·56
0·075	25·2	20·9	17·6	15·0	14·1	12·8	11·2	9·79
0·01	33·6	28·0	23·5	20·0	18·8	17·2	14·9	13·1
0·02	67·3	55·9	46·9	40·0	37·6	34·5	30·0	26·1
0·03	101	83·9	70·4	60·0	56·5	51·7	45·1	39·2
0·04	135	112	93·8	80·1	75·6	69·0	60·0	52·2
0·05	168	140	117	100	94·1	86·2	74·6	65·3
0·06	202	168	141	120	113	103	90·0	78·4
0·07	236	196	164	140	132	121	105	91·4
0·08	269	224	188	160	151	138	120	104
0·09	303	252	211	180	169	155	135	118
0·1	336	280	235	200	188	172	149	131
0·2	673	559	469	400	376	342	300	261

by SCHLOESING's table, this would correspond to a partial atmospheric pressure of about 0·0016 (H. LEHMANN 1956).

Strikingly high atmospheric CO_2 contents (0·15 per cent) corresponding to this partial pressure have not so far been verified by simultaneous air analysis, however, and hence the origin purely by atmospheric diffusion of such a high concentration of CO_2 has not yet been adequately documented. The CO_2 concentration may have been raised by minute grains of spray due to the break-up of rain drops hitting the ground with high impact energy, as it is well known that the spray component of the aerosols thus formed is comparatively rich in soil ions (CAUER 1954, L. JAKUCS 1953/1, 1959/3). However, one of the partial causes of the phenomenon may conceivably be that the pCO_2 of the rain is controlled not by the temperature of the altitude zone where the rain samples are taken, but by the substantially lower temperatures prevailing at a height of several thousand metres, where the rain first condensed.

The fact that the chemical composition of rainwater samples collected not far above the ground is significantly modified by the above effects (especially by the aerosol effect, possibly by as much as an order of magnitude) is proved by similar observations made in the temperate zone and even on high mountains (BÖGLI 1960 and BAUER 1964 in the Alps, CZÁJLIK 1961 in Hungary) that gave CO_2 contents in the same range (1·32 to 3·63 mg/l) for rain samples taken close to the ground.

Even these elevated values, however, are insufficient to cause a significant hydrocarbonate dissolution in limestone, since (cf. *Table 4*) merely to equal

Table 4

Bound and accessory CO$_2$ demands when hydrocarbonate solution forms from a limestone

CaCO$_3$ mg/l	Bound CO$_2$	Accessory CO$_2$ at the temperatures (°C) below							
		5	7	9	10	11	12	15	20
8·92	3·85	—	—	—	—	—	—	—	—
17·85	7·70	—	—	—	—	—	0·01	0·01	0·01
26·77	11·5	0·03	0·03	0·04	0·04	0·04	0·04	0·04	0·05
35·70	15·6	0·07	0·07	0·07	0·08	0·08	0·08	0·09	0·10
44·52	19·4	0·14	0·15	0·16	0·17	0·17	0·18	0·19	0·23
53·55	23·5	0·23	0·24	0·26	0·26	0·27	0·28	0·30	0·35
62·47	27·3	0·38	0·41	0·44	0·45	0·46	0·48	0·51	0·59
71·40	31·5	0·54	0·58	0·61	0·63	0·65	0·67	0·73	0·84
80·32	35·3	0·79	0·84	0·89	0·92	0·95	0·97	1·06	1·23
89·25	39·2	1·06	1·11	1·18	1·21	1·25	1·28	1·40	1·62
98·17	43·0	1·39	1·52	1·61	1·65	1·71	1·75	1·91	2·21
107·1	47·1	1·82	1·93	2·04	2·10	2·17	2·23	2·43	2·81
116·0	50·9	2·27	2·50	2·65	2·73	2·81	2·89	3·15	3·64
124·8	55·0	2·90	3·08	3·26	3·36	3·45	3·56	3·88	4·48
133·8	58·8	3·60	3·82	4·04	4·16	4·28	4·41	4·81	5·56
142·8	62·7	4·30	4·56	4·83	4·97	5·12	5·27	5·57	6·64
151·7	66·5	5·22	5·53	5·86	6·03	6·21	6·40	7·48	8·06
160·6	70·6	6·14	6·51	6·90	7·10	7·31	7·53	8·21	9·49
169·6	74·4	7·29	7·73	8·19	8·43	8·70	8·96	9·75	11·2
178·5	78·5	8·45	8·96	9·49	9·77	10·1	10·4	11·3	13·1
187·4	82·5	9·92	10·4	11·0	11·3	11·7	12·1	13·2	15·2
196·3	86·5	11·4	11·9	12·7	13·0	13·4	13·8	15·1	17·4
205·3	90·4	13·0	13·6	14·5	14·9	15·3	15·8	17·3	19·9
214·2	94·2	14·6	15·4	16·4	16·8	17·3	17·8	19·5	22·5
223·1	98·1	16·6	17·5	18·6	19·1	19·7	20·2	22·1	25·6
232·0	102·1	18·6	19·7	20·8	21·5	22·1	22·7	24·6	28·7
241·0	106·0	20·9	22·1	23·4	24·1	24·8	25·5	27·9	32·3
249·9	110·0	23·2	24·6	26·1	26·8	27·6	28·4	31·0	35·9
258·8	113·9	25·9	27·4	29·1	29·9	30·3	31·7	34·6	40·0
267·7	117·9	28·6	30·3	32·1	33·0	34·0	35·0	38·2	44·2
276·7	121·8	31·6	33·4	35·4	36·5	37·5	38·6	42·2	48·8
285·6	125·6	34·6	36·6	38·8	40·0	41·1	42·3	46·2	53·4
294·5	129·5	38·0	41·3	42·7	44·0	45·2	46·5	50·3	58·7
303·3	133·5	41·5	44·0	46·6	48·0	49·4	50·8	55·5	64·1
321·3	141·3	49·3	52·3	55·4	57·0	58·7	60·4	65·9	76·2
330·2	145·2	53·5	56·8	60·1	61·9	63·7	65·6	71·6	82·8
339·1	149·2	57·8	61·3	64·9	66·8	68·8	70·8	77·3	89·4
348·0	153·1	62·6	66·4	70·3	72·4	74·5	76·7	83·7	96·9
357·0	157·1	67·5	71·5	75·8	78·0	80·3	82·7	90·2	104·3
365·9	161·0	72·9	77·2	81·9	84·3	86·7	89·3	97·5	112·7
374·7	165·0	78·4	83·0	88·0	90·6	93·2	96·0	104·8	121·1
383·8	168·9	84·3	89·2	94·6	97·4	100·2	103·2	112·6	130·2
392·2	173·5	90·2	95·5	101·3	104·3	107·3	110·5	120·5	139·3
401·6	176·9	96·5	102·2	108·3	112·5	114·8	118·2	128·9	149·0
410·5	180·7	102·8	108·9	115·4	118·8	122·3	125·9	137·4	158·8
419·5	184·6	109·8	116·3	123·3	126·9	130·7	134·5	146·8	169·7
428·4	188·5	116·8	123·8	131·2	135·1	139·1	143·2	156·2	180·6
437·3	192·4	124·5	131·9	139·8	143·9	148·2	152·5	166·8	192·4
446·2	196·4	132·2	140·1	148·4	152·8	157·7	161·9	176·6	204·2
455·2	200·3	140·3	148·7	157·6	162·2	167·0	171·9	187·5	216·8
464·1	204·2	148·5	157·4	166·8	171·7	176·8	182·0	198·5	229·5
473·0	208·1	159·0	166·9	176·8	182·0	187·4	192·9	210·5	243·3

31

Table 4 (cont.)

CaCO₃ mg/l	Bound CO₂	Accessory CO₂ at the temperatures (°C) below							
		5	7	9	10	11	12	15	20
481·9	212·1	166·5	176·4	186·9	192·4	198·1	203·9	222·5	257·2
490·8	216·0	176·1	186·6	197·7	203·6	209·6	215·7	235·4	272·1
499·8	220·0	185·7	196·8	209·6	214·8	221·1	227·6	248·3	287·0
508·7	223·9	196·1	207·8	220·2	226·7	233·4	240·3	263·1	303·0
517·6	227·9	206·5	218·8	231·9	238·7	245·8	253·0	276·0	319·1
526·6	231·8	217·3	229·8	244·0	251·2	258·6	266·2	290·4	335·8
535·5	235·7	228·1	241·8	256·2	263·8	271·5	279·5	304·9	352·5
553·4	243·5	251·9	266·9	282·9	291·2	299·8	307·9	336·6	389·2
571·2	251·2	276·5	293·0	310·5	319·6	329·1	338·0	369·5	427·2
589·0	259·2	303·3	321·5	340·7	350·7	361·0	370·8	405·4	468·7
606·9	267·1	331·9	351·8	372·8	383·8	395·1	405·8	443·6	512·9
624·7	275·0	362·8	384·5	407·5	419·5	431·8	443·5	484·9	560·6
642·6	282·7	394·1	417·6	442·5	455·6	469·0	481·7	526·6	608·8
660·3	290·6	428·1	453·6	480·7	494·9	509·5	523·3	572·1	661·4
678·3	298·5	464·0	491·7	521·1	536·5	552·3	567·2	620·1	716·9
696·1	306·2	500·8	530·7	562·5	579·0	596·1	602·2	669·3	773·8
714·0	314·1	540·6	572·9	607·1	625·0	643·4	660·9	722·5	835·3
731·8	322·0	582·5	617·3	654·1	673·4	693·3	712·0	778·5	900·0
749·7	330·0	627·0	664·4	704·1	724·8	746·2	766·4	837·9	968·7
767·5	337·7	671·8	711·9	754·5	776·7	799·6	821·2	897·8	1038
785·4	345·6	720·1	763·1	808·7	832·9	857·1	880·3	962·4	1112
803·2	353·5	770·5	816·6	865·3	890·8	917·1	941·9	1029	1190
821·1	361·2	822·0	871·1	923·1	950·3	978·4	1004	1098	1271
838·8	369·1	877·1	929·5	985·1	1014	1044	1072	1172	1355
856·8	377·0	934·7	990·5	1049	1080	1112	1142	1249	1444
874·6	385·0	995·6	1055	1118	1151	1185	1217	1330	1538
892·5	392·7	1056	1119	1186	1221	1257	1291	1411	1632

the dissolution potential of carbonate dissolution (simple dissociation as per eq. (1), with a maximum possible concentration of about 13 mg/l $CaCO_3$ in the water), at 17 °C the rain should contain some 6 mg/l of absorbed CO_2, which would require a tenfold or so increase in the partial pressure of atmospheric CO_2. In contrast, the ground and karst waters of nature, the primary agents of karst corrosion, are invariably much richer in CO_2 (frequently above 100 mg/l). It is beyond any doubt, therefore, that the precipitation falling on the ground derives its high carbon dioxide content from the soil it seeps through, and not from the atmosphere.

High partial pressures of CO_2 in soil gas, e.g. in the soils covering limestone rock, were recorded long ago by pedological research (SCHLOESING 1872, FODOR 1875, WOLLNY 1880, BOUSSINGAULT and LÉVY 1853, etc.).

We shall return to a more detailed study of the soil gas, i.e. of the gas mixture filling the pores of the soil, but it is convenient here to point out that, according to the relevant pedological research, the CO_2 content of the soil gas, especially in humus soils rich in organic matter, is usually higher than 1 per cent and in a fair number of cases may exceed even 10 per cent. This is one of the most important factors of karst corrosion, since the precipitation falling upon and seeping into the ground immediately comes into contact with the soil gas over an enormous interface area (by forming films on the soil grains). The water thus attains the saturation level corresponding to the partial pressure of CO_2 in the soil gas even in the top layer of the soil.

Geographers concerned with karst genesis early became aware of the controlling role of the soil gas in the dissolution of limestone. At the turn of this century KNEBEL (1906) gave a careful analysis of this interaction, but a causal connection between the nature of the soil and the dissolution potential of the ground water had been assumed much earlier than that. Thus, for example, the Hungarian IMRE VASS in 1831, in a detailed evaluation of the stalactite formation theory of PARROT, LAND and SOMMER, expressed an opinion that was very close to our current views of the problem. These authors attributed the formation of stalactites to dissolution by precipitation seeping through the layer of 'rotten plants and garden soil saturated with carbonic acid'.

CHOLNOKY (1940) was another author to stress the role of carbon dioxide in the soil, in causing aggressivity of ground water: "It is known that in the soil there is a continuous process of decay, of slow oxidation resulting in the formation of carbonic acid gas. This gas then condenses on the grains of the soil skeleton, which are invariably of an adsorptive nature. Rainfall after a dry spell gives out a 'smell of rain': this is the characteristic odour of the gases displaced by the raindrops from the surfaces of the soil grains. It can be proved that at such times the bottom layer of the atmosphere over the rain-wetted area is always rather high in carbonic acid gas. Consequently, much carbonic acid gas will enter the fallen rain here, assisted by the dynamic pressure of the impacting raindrops. The water carries this high gas content into the fissures of the rock." (loc. cit. p. 1006.)

According to the measurements of Trombe in France and Jäckly in Switzerland (TROMBE 1951/2, 1952, 1956), local concentrations of CO_2 gas in the soil layers overlying karstic rocks may attain 10 and as much as 25 per cent: such values do not occur anywhere else in the atmosphere.

Careful and painstaking research into the variation of the CO_2 content of soil gas and the laws governing it was carried out by FEHÉR (1954): more recently (in 1967 and 1972), the present author performed measurements on Hungarian and Yugoslav karst soils. These investigations revealed that the soil gas reacts very rapidly and sensitively to both micro- and macroclimatic changes; it exhibits differences at any given time even within one and the same locus of observation (a single doline), depending on the nature of the vegetation and even, as regards the rhizosphere (the zone of the plant roots), on the individual plant species.

We shall return to these problems later.

The above considerations obviously imply that the infiltrating precipitation, which, by dissolving limestone, controls the entire process of karst evolution, invariably acquires its carbonic acid content, essential for the dynamism of corrosion, in the topsoil layers. This means that, in any region, the rate of karst denudation by corrosion is controlled not only by the quantity of infiltrating precipitation, but primarily by the biological and other pedogenic processes of the soil covering the surface.

It should be pointed out that the water seeping from the humus topsoil into the fissures of the limestone does not, as a rule, encounter in the fissure system of the rock any gases significantly different in consumption and concentration from the soil gas. The downward-seeping water consequently retains virtually unchanged the carbonic acid concentration it acquired in the soil, until it emerges into a well-aerated cavern or on the surface; there it gives off part of its carbon dioxide content, till equilibrium with the lower CO_2 concentration of the new environment is established.

The temperature of water seeping down the joints within a limestone mass progressing towards the mature karst stage does not as a rule change significantly, since at the same time the vertical water-conducting fissure system is well known to be the means of heat exchange by convection, too; consequently, a uniform temperature equal to the mean annual temperature of the region reigns in the entire zone above the karst water table. Hence, the thermal factor of absorption of CO_2 into the water does not play a significant role except in the topsoil layer, where its influence accords to the values listed in Table 3.

It should be pointed out, however, that even the extreme range of soil temperatures occurring in nature affects the CO_2 concentration much less than the difference in partial pressure, since at any pCO_2 water at 0 °C can at best dissolve twice the amount of CO_2 soluble in water at 20 °C. Hence, in considering the karst dynamic significance of the thermal factor, we shall probably be right if, in agreement with most of today's workers in climatic karst morphogeny (H. LEHMANN, TROMBE, BÖGLI, WISSMANN, GVOZDETSKY, etc.), we assess the influence of the temperature ranges typical of the earth's individual climatic zones not in the direct Schloesingian sense, but in terms of their indirect action via intensified pedogenetic processes, soil atmospheres with higher pCO_2 and an increased rate of material transport (intensity of dissolution). In other words, although the warm rains of the tropics may, owing to their higher temperature, absorb less CO_2 gas than, for example, the cold meltwaters of the polar regions, this is outweighed many times over by the fact that at the same time the higher temperatures of the tropics entail both an accelerated dissolution and a much enhanced production of CO_2 by the more intense inorganic and organic processes of soil evolution. Overall, the chances for a water to acquire a high saturation in CO_2 will be much better in the tropical regions.

This immediately provides us with a well-founded, unequivocal approach to the international dispute initiated by the ominous declarations of CORBEL (1959); Corbel was wrong, and H. Lehmann and the climatic geomorphologists following in his footsteps, who not only broke down the climatic factor into a temperature factor and a precipitation factor, were able, in the true spirit of Dokuchaev, to account for every aspect (geomorphological, pedologic, biological, hydrological, chemical, etc.) of climatic zonality, and indeed even for the complex interplay of these factors.

Of the factors controlling the absorption in water of atmospheric CO_2 and of soil gas, we have studied so far the roles of partial gas pressure and of temperature. There remain the factors of pressure and time.

The absorption of carbon dioxide in water is clearly promoted by increasing pressure. It is sufficient to recall the common household soda syphon which is an obvious experimental verification of this statement. We also know that the natural conditions prevailing in a karst region allow a fairly broad range of pressures, primarily as a result of the periodicity of precipitation; consequently, the fissures of the rock are filled at times with soil gas, and at other times with water seeping down from the soil, depending on whether the soil layer is saturated with water or not.

In periods of abundant precipitation, the fissures in the limestone are filled with water. As soon as the descending water supply is interrupted, these fissure fillings moving downwards under gravity create a mild suction above themselves, which is sufficient to draw in the soil gas. The next rain, of course, refills the soil-side "entrances" of these fissures and this new filling pushes downward the gas-mixture bubbles thus formed. In hairline cracks, where adhesion and capillary-forces predominate over the arrangement of phases by density, there will be a downward passage of alternating liquid and gas phases, somewhat on the model of a mercury thermometer with a broken mercury column.

Even at this stage, the hydrostatic pressure influencing the equilibrium of the water-and-gas system will change, for the water film adhering to the fissure walls by capillary-forces would have no cause to move downward if no pressure differential acted upon it. However, these pressure modifications would not be sufficient to significantly modify the equilibrium of water and carbon dioxide as established in the soil. Nevertheless, sooner or later, the downward-moving water attains a depth where it can find no further free downward passage, either because of the presence of an impermeable, unfissured footwall rock, or because all the fissures are already saturated with water. The water reaching that depth is thus dammed up and, together with the gas bubbles contained in it, of necessity seeks means of lateral escape.

This is not so simple, however, because the fissures called upon to drain horizontally (linearly or areally) the waters that seep down to the karst water table in a spatial (three-dimensional) system of fissures are, in the early stages of karst evolution, neither more spacious nor better developed than the preceding spatial system. The alternating sections of water and gas are thus exposed to increased hydrostatic pressure, the increase being the greater, the more abundant the supply of water from above and the more restricted the means of lateral escape. Hence, there develops within the karst a zone of high-pressure flowing karst water (L. JAKUCS 1960/2, 1968/1—2) in which the water is further enriched in carbon dioxide, the pressure as it were injecting the gas mix into the solution.

In this zone, then, where the fissures and cavities draining the flow are all filled with water, pressures of several bars may prevail (confirmed by mining experience: cf. ALBEL, 1950). The pressure is especially high at the bottom of horizontal karst-water flow zones. Our observations show that pressures in excess of 10 bars are not unusual here, especially in a young karst.

We shall discuss the problem in more detail later, but it should be pointed out here that both the order of magnitude and the mechanism of action of pressure may be accounted for by a modification of eq. (3). By the classical gas laws of Boyle and Mariotte the volume of a given mass of gas varies inversely as the pressure. This means that the coefficient 1·9634 in eq. (3) is not a constant: it holds at a pressure of one atmosphere, and has to be doubled if the pressure acting on the gas is 2 atm, multiplied by ten if it is 10 atm, etc.

Hence, in the hypothetical case that pCO_2 remains constant, that is, the composition of the gas mixture is unchanged, the total amount of CO_2 gas absorbed by water at 10 °C, 5 atm pressure and $pCO_2 = 0\cdot002$ increases above the value of $4\cdot69$ mg/l furnished by Table 3, to $1\cdot194 \times \times 0\cdot002 \times 5 \times 1\cdot9634 = 23\cdot45$ mg/l. Since this figure is precisely five times the quantity of CO_2 absorbed from an atmosphere at 1 atm, we may say that, within limits, *the CO_2-absorbing capacity of water varies directly as the pressure* (Henry's law).

It would be wrong, however, to neglect a highly important factor that considerably modifies the scope of the above relationship, especially under karst conditions: in a confined two-component system (water and gas trapped in a karst fissure) the composition of the original gas mixture changes in the sense that the higher the pressure, the lower the partial tension of CO_2 in the gas space becomes, since the absorption coefficients (L) of the different gases involved are different: those of the gases playing a significant role in a karst situation are invariably much lower than those of CO_2 (oxygen: $0\cdot031$, nitrogen: $0\cdot015$, CO_2: $0\cdot0878$, all at 20 °C).

Consequently, increasing pressure removes all the carbon dioxide fairly quickly from the heterogeneous gas mixture, and even higher pressures achieve little in the way of further augmenting the total CO_2 content of the solution. We are therefore of the opinion that, as far as the absorption of carbon dioxide in karst water is concerned, it is the lower range of pressure increases (1 to 10 atm) that plays the main role, whereas in the range of pressure acting on deep karst waters, often close to 100 atm, a unit increase of pressure affects the dissolution of CO_2 comparatively much less.

Owing to the differences in the absorption coefficients of the three atmospheric gases, the composition of the original gas mixture is changed significantly; at quite high pressures little CO_2 remains and nitrogen, the least soluble gas, predominates. (This is why nitrogen always predominates in the gas bubbles contained in the waters of karst springs surging up from great depths.)

Thus the substantial increase in CO_2 absorption due to the increase in hydrostatic pressure is a significant factor of karst evolution; it controls, among other factors, the depth of deep karst corrosion (at the level of embryonic cave formation) by what may be termed the secondary aggressivity of the water.

Obviously, any subsequent fall in pressure (when the water enters a more spacious cavern or emerges to the surface, where its further motion is determined by the slope) expels the gases which entered the water under pressure, and this secondary increase in hydrocarbonate corrosive potential ceases.

In such surroundings, moreover, the water is not only relieved of the excess hydrostatic load, but also comes into contact with a pCO_2 much lower than in the soil it infiltrated initially. Hence, a further quantity of CO_2 escapes, proportional to the difference in pCO_2 between the two atmospheres, until a new equilibrium controlled by the new pCO_2 (and the new temperature) has set in, as described by eq. (3).

In the literature, another role of pressure has been discussed, too. For instance, DUDICH (1932) emphasized the significance of changes in the water's surface tension. A drop of water emerging from a karst fissure onto a cavern roof builds up a surface tension; water streaming down slopes and dashed into spray in cataracts is relieved of some pressure; this facilitates and, what is more important, accelerates the escape of the excess CO_2 content.

This consideration leads us to the fourth important factor determining CO_2 absorption: the time required for the development of equilibrium between the dissolved CO_2 and the CO_2 in the atmosphere in contact with the solution; that is, the time to establish the equilibrium of eq. (3).

A formula can be devised to express this duration, but unfortunately we still cannot calculate it satisfactorily in practice: it is the complex resultant of a number of factors, all variable in their own right, and some of them inaccessible to any precise mathematical formulation. Let us itemize just a few of these factors, merely by way of illustration.

The process leading to equilibrium is accelerated by the following condition: increase of the area of the gas-to-liquid interface; increase of temperature; turbulent motion of the gas in contact with the liquid; turbulent agitation of the liquid. The various adsorptive surfaces present in the reaction space (e.g. mineral and organic soil particles) promote or hinder absorption according to their specific properties. The rate of absorption in water differs according to whether it is in contact with limestone or not, since in the presence of limestone hydrocarbonate dissolution may start simultaneously with CO_2 absorption, thereby maintaining at least some of the absorption potential of the water. It would be no problem at all to cite further influencing factors.

This problem may justifiably be regarded as one of the most difficult ones as far as the interpretation of the corrosion process is concerned. It is nevertheless one of the key problems of climatic karst-morphogenetic analysis, and one of the fundamental modulators of the dynamism of limestone dissolution.

* * *

We have so far examined the dissolution of CO_2 merely in terms of the interaction of a liquid and a gas phase, that is, without considering the presence of a solid phase, the limestone rock in the case under investigation. Our next task is to analyse the dissolution process characterized by the simultaneous presence of all three phases.

It is clear that the introduction of this new factor further complicates the equilibrium relationships and interactions, all the more so, since we are faced here not just with simple dissolution and/or dissociation, but with an interplay of chemical changes in close causal relationship with the dissociation equilibrium and other equilibria of physical dissolution.

A fraction of the CO_2 absorbed in water (0·7 per cent of it at 4 °C, according to HOLLUTA 1927, and PIA 1953) turns into carbonic acid:

$$CO_2 + H_2O \rightleftharpoons H_2CO_3 \tag{4}$$

As soon as the water containing the carbonic acid comes into contact with $CaCO_3$, reaction occurs to produce calcium hydrocarbonate by dissolution of the limestone:

$$CaCO_3 + H_2CO_3 \rightleftharpoons Ca(HCO_3)_2 \tag{5}$$

The carbonic acid bound to calcium is, of course, replaced by CO_2 physically dissolved in the water (while this lasts), so that practically the entire absorbed CO_2 content of the water participates in the process of limestone dissolution.

According to calculations by Tillmanns and Heublein (TILLMANNS 1932, 1940), the equilibrium in eq. (5) tends to shift to the right-hand side whenever the CO_2 concentration diminishes. In dilute solutions, with 10 to 15 mg/l total dissolved CO_2, the equilibrium lies to the right; in more concentrated solutions equilibrium is achieved while part of the total absorbed CO_2 content is still free, since at higher concentrations an increasing quantity of so-called *accessory or equilibrium carbonic acid is required* to keep the dissolved hydrocarbonate in solution.

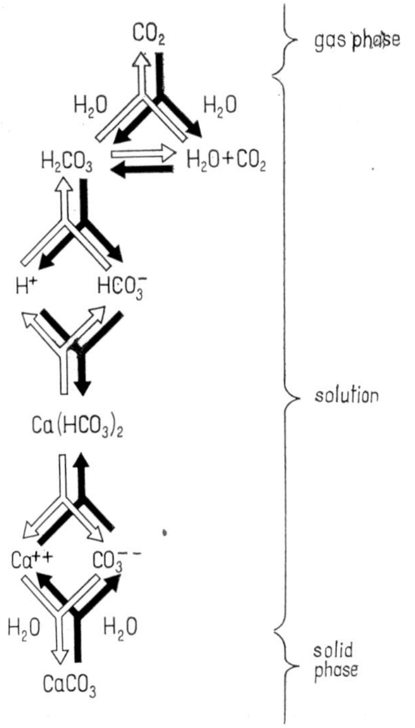

The principal relationships and equilibria controlling the dissolution and precipitation of $Ca(HCO_3)_2$ are presented in *Figure 2*.

Each milligram of CO_2 dissolved in the water can dissolve 2·2723 mg of $CaCO_3$, irrespective of the temperature of the system. Hence, at low concentrations, where the amount of accessory carbonic acid is negligible, the dissolution potential of the water as regards limestone rock can be calculated simply from its total dissolved CO_2 content. Water in contact with an average atmosphere characterized by $pCO_2 = 0·0003$ at 10 °C can dissolve 0·70 mg/l CO_2, and this permits the dissolution of $2·2723 \times 0·7 = 1·59$ mg/l of limestone, without requiring the addition of any further CO_2.

Of course, if there is solid $CaCO_3$ present, an equilibrium solution so low in calcium carbonate is inconceivable even under laboratory conditions, since, to start with, the solution contains the ca. 13 mg/l of calcium carbonate due to primary carbonate dissolution, as per eq. (1). A further factor to be kept in mind is that natural ground waters also contain oxygen in addition to car-

Fig. 2. Principal components of the chemical conditions of hydrocarbonate limestone dissolution. Displacements of equilibria indicated by black arrows entail dissolution; those indicated by white arrows indicate calcium carbonate precipitation. At any given time, the system may be displaced either along black or along white arrows only

bon dioxide; oxygen is converted by bacterial and inorganic processes of oxidation in the soil into further CO_2, resulting in an increased CO_2 level in the water (TUĆAN 1933, CHRAMUSHEV 1941, VENKOVITS 1949/1).

At higher concentrations, the dissolution process is complicated only inasmuch as the hydrocarbonate reaction may not use up all the CO_2 in the water, part of which must be left over to ensure the equilibrium of the system. It should be noted, however, that the required accessory carbonic acid level is a function not only of the concentration of dissolved calcium carbonate, but also of the temperature of the reaction space.

By the above considerations, then, CO_2 absorbed in water assumes the following forms in the presence of $CaCO_3$, all of which may exist side by side in aqueous solution:

1. Calcium hydrocarbonate.

2. Accessory or equilibrium carbonic acid, required to keep the hydrocarbonate in solution.

3. Any excess carbon dioxide (i.e. CO_2 over and above the concentration required to keep the hydrocarbonate in solution) plays the role of aggressive carbonic acid. The term 'aggressive' is used because this fraction of CO_2, not being required to maintain equilibrium, permits the water to dissolve more calcium carbonate.

In the knowledge of the distribution of the actual CO_2 content among these three functionally different forms of carbonic acid, one may decide whether a given solution is capable of further dissolution, whether it is in a state of equilibrium, or conversely, whether it is supersaturated and tends to precipitate out some of its calcium carbonate content.

Earlier international chemical and hydrogeological literature gave accessory carbonic acid indices only for water at 17 °C (TILLMANNS 1932, LAPT'EV 1939, TROMBE 1951/2, 1952, BÖGLI 1960, etc.), but Sz. PAPP (1954, 1956) calculated the accessory carbonic acid contents of waters in calcium carbonate — carbonic acid equilibrium for all important concentrations and temperatures. Table 4, derived from his work, lists the values most frequently required in karst research.

This table also permits us to form an idea as to the influence of temperature upon solubility: water with a given total CO_2 content dissolves less calcium carbonate at higher temperatures, since the amount of accessory carbonic acid required to keep the calcium hydrocarbonate in solution is then higher. For instance, water in $CaCO_3$—CO_2 equilibrium, containing 957 mg/l of CO_2 at 5 °C (of which 330 mg/l is bound in the hydrocarbonate and 627 mg/l is the accessory carbonic acid) dissolves an amount of $Ca(HCO_3)_2$ corresponding to 749·7 mg/l of solid $CaCO_3$. At the higher temperature of 14 °C, this same water, containing the same amount of CO_2, is supersaturated: its total CO_2 content of 957 mg/l is in this case divided up into 306·2 mg/l of bound CO_2 and 650·8 mg/l of accessory CO_2; accordingly, the equivalent $CaCO_3$ content of the water cannot exceed 696·1 mg/l. Hence, each litre of the solution will precipitate 749·7 − 696·1 = 53·6 mg $CaCO_3$.

These conditions are illustrated by the complex graph of *Figure 3*, a plot of the values listed in Table 4. By reference to the total CO_2 content of the water on the abscissa and the concentration of dissolved calcium carbonate

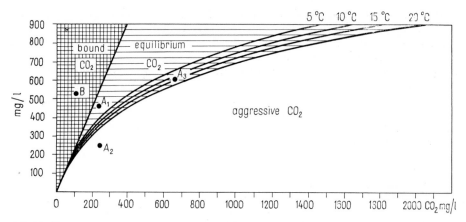

Fig. 3. Concentrations of bound and equilibrium free carbonic acid in waters where calcium carbonate—carbonic acid is in equilibrium at 5, 10, 15 and 20 °C

on the ordinate, one obtains points whose positions immediately reveal the chemical nature of the water investigated.

If, for instance, the total CO_2 is 250 mg/l and the dissolved $CaCO_3$ 450 mg/l (as represented in the figure by the point A_1), it is obvious that the water is strongly supersaturated and will precipitate $CaCO_3$. If, on the other hand, the dissolved $CaCO_3$ content is only 250 mg/l, with its plot (A_2) in the undersaturated zone, the water is strongly aggressive. A third water, represented by the point A_3, is in equilibrium at 12 °C: it becomes aggressive when cooled and suparsaturated when warmed up.

A water sample with a plot in the region of bound CO_2 (e.g. B) is an impossibility.

It should be pointed out that an aggressive water will not necessarily dissolve more calcium carbonate, because equilibrium can also be established by the evaporation of some of its CO_2 content, provided that this is possible.

The question as to which of the two alternatives is realized is decided by the complicated interaction of a number of factors. In a confined system, with no means for the CO_2 to escape into the atmosphere, equilibrium is established in any case by the dissolution of further calcium carbonate, i.e. by a more intense corrosion. (This is why even slightly aggressive water confined in a pipe network has such a high corrosion potential!)

A measure of the aggressivity of water can be derived from Table 4 if its carbonate hardness* and its total CO_2 content are known.

---

* The *carbonate hardness* of a water is a function of the sum of its calcium and magnesium hydrocarbonate contents. One *German degree of hardness* is equivalent to 10 mg/l CaO, which is in turn equivalent to 17·85 mg/l $CaCO_3$. For example, a water having a hardness of 22 German degrees contains $17·85 \times 22 = 392·7$ mg/l of $CaCO_3$ in hydrocarbonate solution, provided its hardness is due exclusively to calcium carbonate.

Using Tables 3 and 4, the karst scientist may draw further conclusions of considerable interest. Thus, he may calculate *the intensity of calcium carbonate transport,* provided the pCO_2 of the soil atmosphere, decisive for the chemical nature of the water in the infiltration zone, can be established. Let us illustrate this type of application of the tables with an example.

In the soil, the water was in contact with gas of $pCO_2 = 0.08$, and it was this partial pressure at the gas—water interface that determined the water—CO_2 equilibrium. The soil temperature was 5 °C in the period of infiltration. The water therefore contains 224 mg/l total CO_2 (cf. Table 3). Migrating in the fissures of the limestone, this aggressive water effects dissolution, until it attains $CaCO_3$—CO_2 equilibrium in its downward journey. The equilibrium concentration of $CaCO_3$ can be established from Table 4, by finding the bound and accessory fractions at 5 °C of a total CO_2 content of 224 mg/l: adding together the various pairs of values of bound CO_2 and accessory CO_2 at 5 °C, one finds a sum reasonably close to the 224 mg/l looked for. In the present case, the best approximation to 224 mg/l is 157.1 mg/l bound CO_2 plus 67.5 mg/l accessory CO_2. It only remains now to find the corresponding $CaCO_3$ concentration in the first column of Table 4, which gives 357 mg/l.

However, this merely reveals the dissolution potential of the water, which is not necessarily equal to the actual concentration of $CaCO_3$, except in favourable cases. In addition, the amount of $CaCO_3$ that a saturated solution will precipitate under given conditions, e.g. in a cavern, requires further calculation.

For instance, if the karst water discussed above emerges into a cavern where the atmosphere has $pCO_2 = 0.02$ at a temperature of 10 °C, equilibrium corresponding to the CO_2 content of this atmosphere will be reached in time, which means that, from Table 3, the total CO_2 content of the water will decrease to 46.9 mg/l (the rest will escape). Now, by the procedure already discussed, we have to find in Table 4 the $CaCO_3$ concentration corresponding to a situation with

bound CO_2 + equilibrium CO_2 (10 °C) = 46.9 mg/l.

We find in fact that the water exposed to this new set of conditions cannot retain more than about 100 mg/l $CaCO_3$ in solution. The difference, $357 - 100 = 257$ mg/l, is the figure looked for, representing the amount of calcium carbonate transferred by the water from one point of the karst to another.

It must be pointed out that although the procedure just outlined will often provide a fair approximation, these calculations cannot always be regarded as realistic, since in nature a number of additional factors will be involved, such as the time factor, other gases (primarily oxygen dissolved in the water), the influence of humic and rhizogenic acids present in the organic matter decay zone; in the present state of our knowledge, these defy all efforts at quantification. Their influence, variable from one case to the next, may affect the intensity of limestone dissolution fairly substantially.

In a different context, Table 4 further reveals that, whereas the concentration of CO_2 bound in the hydrocarbonate is a linear function of the amount of dissolved $CaCO_3$, the concentration of accessory carbonic acid is not; a unit increment in the dissolved $CaCO_3$ demands a much greater increment in the accessory carbonic acid content at a higher than at a lower dissolved $CaCO_3$ content. This relationship is quantified by Tillmanns' formula:

$$\text{accessory } CO_2 = \frac{(\text{bound } CO_2)^3}{K_t} \tag{6}$$

where the factor K_t is constant as long as the temperature is constant.

41

All this leads to the straightforward conclusion that the mixing of any two hydrocarbonate solutions individually in equilibrium (e.g. a natural ground water and a karst water), makes part of their joint accessory carbonic acid content superfluous, with the consequence that the solution becomes aggressive. Depending on the conditions, the excess CO_2 either evaporates or dissolves further $CaCO_3$. As a result, a secondary phenomenon of dissolution may arise, which may be termed mixing corrosion. Its existence was first pointed out by LAPT'EV (1939), but its significance for karst evolution was not given due attention until BÖGLI (1963/1—2) and ERNST (1964).

The increased aggressivity due to the mixing of solutions is the stronger, the greater the difference in the pre-mixing hydrocarbonate concentrations of the two solutions. The influence of the temperature factor is minor.

Let us verify the above findings by applying Table 4 to a concrete example. Let the solutions A and B to be mixed together have the following equilibrium parameters before mixing:

Solution A (9 °C)	$CaCO_3$ content of the hydrocarbonate solution	151·7 mg/l
	Bound CO_2 content	66·5 mg/l
	Accessory carbonic acid content	5·8 mg/l
Solution B (9 °C)	$CaCO_3$ content of the hydrocarbonate solution	508·7 mg/l
	Bound CO_2 content	223·9 mg/l
	Accessory carbonic acid content	220·2 mg/l

Assuming for simplicity that the mixture is composed of one litre of A and one of B, we obtain two litres of solution C composed as follows:

Solution C
(9 °C)

$CaCO_3$ content of hydrocarbonate solution

$$\frac{151\cdot7 + 508\cdot7}{2} = 330\cdot2 \text{ mg/l}$$

Bound CO_2 content

$$\frac{66\cdot5 + 223\cdot9}{2} = 145\cdot2 \text{ mg/l}$$

Accessory CO_2 content

$$\frac{5\cdot8 + 220\cdot2}{2} = 113\cdot0 \text{ mg/l}$$

From the CO_2 values in Table 4 corresponding to the $CaCO_3$ concentration of solution C, 330·2 mg/l, we perceive that the bound CO_2 remains unaffected, but that the accessory carbonic acid requirement of solution C at 9 °C is only 60·1 mg/l. Hence, the mixing of the two waters results in the liberation, *in statu nascendi*, of 113·0 − 60·1 = 62·9 mg/l CO_2 from solution C. This CO_2 fraction is, of course, aggressive.

The above procedure has been used to calculate (*Table 5*) the amounts of CO_2 (mg/l) liberated on the 1:1 mixing of waters at 10 °C, with carbonate hardness in the range 0 to 50 degrees.

Table 5

Aggressive CO_2 (mg/l) produced on the mixing of equal parts of waters of different hardnesses, severally at equilibrium, in the hardness range from 0 to 50 German degrees (G.d.)

	0 G.d.	5 G.d.	10 G.d.	15 G.d.	20 G.d.	25 G.d.	30 G.d.	35 G.d.	40 G.d.	45 G.d.	50 G.d.
0 G.d.	0										
5 G.d.	0·5	0									
10 G.d.	3·7	1·3	0								
15 G.d.	12·4	7·3	2·4	0							
20 G.d.	29·2	20·6	10·8	3·1	0						
25 G.d.	57·4	43·9	28·8	14·9	2·7	0					
30 G.d.	98·8	80·8	58·8	35·8	18·1	4·7	0				
35 G.d.	157	132	102	73·5	45·2	22·3	6·0	0			
40 G.d.	234	200	164	126	87·6	64·1	24·8	5·8	0		
45 G.d	333	293	247	198	149	102	61·4	30·3	7·7	0	
50 G.d.	448	407	351	292	230	169	117	70·1	32·4	7·8	0

43

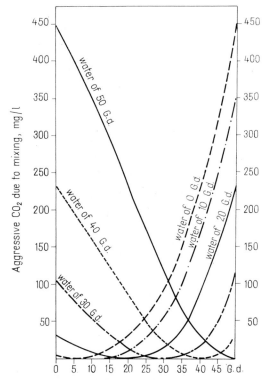

Fig. 4. Abundance in mg/l of aggressive CO_2 forming on the 1:1 mixing of karst waters of various hardnesses at 10 °C

Figure 4 is a plot of these same values, from which values not specified in the table can be found by interpolation.

It has been stated that temperature differences will not have a substantial effect on the amount of aggressive carbonic acid liberated on mixing. This is illustrated by the following example.

Let solution A, as defined above, be kept at 9 °C, but let solution B be warmed to 15 °C, all other conditions remaining the same. As a result, solution C is at 12 °C.

At this higher temperature, the accessory CO_2 content of solution B will now be 262·1 mg/l, as opposed to the original 220·2 mg/l. The other parameters of the solutions remain unaffected. The total free CO_2 content of solution C now becomes

$$\frac{5\cdot86 + 262\cdot1}{2} = 133\cdot9 \text{ mg/l}$$

Since the accessory carbonic acid content of solution C at 12 °C is 65·5 mg/l, mixing liberates 113·9 − 65·6 = 68·3 mg/l CO_2, that is, only 5·4 mg/l more than in the preceding case where all three solutions were at 9 °C.

The amount of increasingly aggressive CO_2 is the greater, the greater the temperature difference between the two solutions. For instance, if in the example discussed above the temperature of A is 5 °C, while that of B is 15 °C, it may readily be computed that the resulting water at 10 °C liberates 60·6 mg/l of aggressive CO_2, that is, 7·8 mg/l more than in the case where all solutions were at 9 °C.

Figure 5 is a diagram based on a number of similar calculations, indicating in mg/l the amounts of CO_2 *in statu nascendi*, liberated on the 1 : 1 mixing of distilled water (rainwater) and waters of various hardness, all in equilibrium, in systems at 5, 10 and 20 °C.

Of course, not all the CO_2 liberated on mixing is available to dissolve further $CaCO_3$, since part of it is required to maintain the newly dissolved $CaCO_3$ in solution. The question of importance to the karst scientist, as to how much additional limestone will be dissolved by the aggressive CO_2 liberated on the mixing of two solutions, can be answered by using Table 4 once more, in the following way.

Let us add together all the bound and accessory CO_2 contents of the solution A and B, and divide the result by two for reference to one litre of solution C. Now let us select that row in Table 4 where the sum of the bound

44

plus the corresponding accessory CO_2 approximately equals the value thus found. The amount of $CaCO_3$ that may undergo secondary dissolution in one litre of solution C can now be obtained, by subtracting from the $CaCO_3$ concentration figuring in the selected row the actual $CaCO_3$ concentration of C (the arithmetic mean of the concentrations in A and B).

As an example, consider once more the waters A and B, both at 9 °C. The total CO_2 concentration in $C = A + B$ is

$$\frac{66 \cdot 5 + 5 \cdot 8 + 223 \cdot 9 + 220 \cdot 2}{2}$$

$$= 258 \cdot 2 \text{ mg/l}$$

The actual $CaCO_3$ concentration of this same solution C was found above to be 330·2 mg/l.

Considering one by one the corresponding pairs of bound and accessory carbonic acid concentrations in the "bound" column and in the "accessory" column for 9 °C of Table 4, it is found that 258·2 mg/l total CO_2 corresponds at equilibrium to 166·7 mg/l bound and 91·5 mg/l accessory CO_2.

The amount of $CaCO_3$ soluble in the resulting solution C can now readily be calculated using the expression $N . V$, where N is the concentration of bound CO_2 in mg/l, and V is the constant 2·2723.

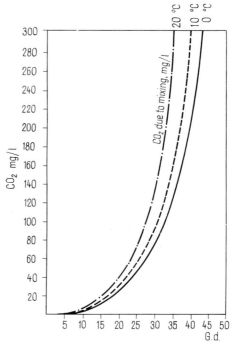

Fig. 5. Calcium carbonate liberated *in statu nascendi* on the mixing of a soft water containing no dissolved chemicals with waters of various carbonate hardnesses at equilibrium, in systems at 5, 10 and 20 °C

Hence, in the present case, under the new conditions, solution C may dissolve 166·8 . 2·2723 = 378·8 mg/l of $CaCO_3$; that is, its secondary corrosion potential due to mixing is 378·8 − 330·2 = 48·0 mg/l of limestone.

Opinions in the literature differ as to the role played dy mixing corrosion in karst evolution. According to the Swiss researcher Bögli (1963/1—2), considered today the leading authority in this field, this factor does not have any significance outside the zone where, deep in the karst, passages are entirely filled with water, because any aerated space is in contact with the water, this latter tends to lose its CO_2 recently increased in aggressivity by evaporation. Conversely, it has been shown by Hungarian workers among others (Gánti 1957, Maucha 1960/2, Czájlik 1961, Ernst 1964), on the basis of many observations and analyses, that cavern waters that appear richly oversaturated can affect recent corrosion even in quite spacious cavern passages.

Clearly, the point can be decided once and for all by investigating the respective rates of gas dissolution and diffusion; in this context we feel the views of Franke (1965), Ernst (1964) and Balázs (1966) to be the most realistic. These authors consider that the mixing of karst waters of different

45

hardnesses may enhance the dissolution potential even if the water is in contact with free air, because the evaporation of CO_2 from the solution takes place across the water–air interface, that is, areally and hence comparatively slowly, whereas the rate of mixing of the two confluent components is two-dimensional with both components in turbulent motion; hence, rock surface is in continual contact with water molecules.

It is rightly pointed out by BALÁZS (*loc. cit.*, p. 184) that "the greatest differences in concentration in the waters of our karst caves may arise when hard karst waters stagnating in the depths are mixed with flood waters of snowmelt or sudden summer rainstorms". According to Balázs, apart from any aggressivity that the descending waters may have picked up during their downward journey, each such event may dissolve several hundred kilograms of limestone by mixing corrosion.

Many details of this process, and especially its actual intensity under natural conditions, will not be clarified in a definitive manner until further data have been painstakingly collected and interpreted. However, it may be stated that mixing corrosion, as a significant facet of the hydrocarbonate solution process, plays a major role in karst evolution.

However multilateral our analysis of the complex interplay of factors controlling the relationship of the CO_2 content of the atmosphere and the carbonic acid content of the water, and also that of the latter and the concentration of dissolved calcium carbonate, there is still one highly important equilibrium left undiscussed, notably that between the CO_2 in the atmosphere and the solution in calcium carbonate—carbonic acid equilibrium. This highest-order equilibrium of hydrocarbonate dissolution requires the longest time to be established, so long in fact that under natural conditions it remains unattained in many cases.

The fundamental idea is that the carbonic acid used in producing the hydrocarbonate in solution appears as a deficit in the primary dual system air—water, initiating the waterward migration of further amounts of CO_2 from the atmosphere. This means that the CO_2 bound in the form of hydrocarbonate, associated to calcium and magnesium and thereby removed from the absorption equilibrium, in its turn enters into an equilibrium relationship with the accessory carbonic acid content of the solution (as per eq. (6)); thus, it is this latter that must find its equilibrium level with regard to the pCO_2 of the air (as per eq. (3)). That is, the advance of the limestone-dissolution process reacts back, in the sense of Figure 2, as far as the air in contact with the solution, and entails the absorption of further CO_2 from the air.

In the final analysis then, a body of water in contact with a body of limestone will keep on absorbing more and more CO_2 until equilibrium according to eq. (3) is achieved between the CO_2 in the atmosphere and the accessory carbonic acid content of the solution. This does not mean that Table 3 (after Schloesing) is useless, but merely introduces the restriction that if there is any dissolved calcium carbonate present, then the table must be referred to the equilibrium concentrations of CO_2 at the prevailing temperature as listed in Table 4.

Let us reconsider here an example already treated above.

The average atmosphere with $pCO_2 = 0\cdot0003$ gives rise at equilibrium to an absorbed CO_2 content of $0\cdot84$ mg/l at 5 °C. It has been seen that the hydrocarbonate dissolution potential of water saturated in an average atmosphere is very slight indeed, provided this concentration of CO_2 is considered to be entirely stationary. However, if the water has the means and the time to absorb further CO_2 from the atmosphere, at the rate that the CO_2 content originally absorbed is being used up to form hydrocarbonates, this process may go on until the hydrocarbonate concentration in the water attains equilibrium with the $0\cdot84$ mg/l CO_2, now playing the role of accessory carbonic acid. The hydrocarbonate concentration in question is equivalent to $81\cdot97$ mg/l $CaCO_3$ (found by interpolation from Table 4).

This is why even the softest karst waters, encountered in fully denuded karst regions and high-mountain karsts above the snow limit, contain 80 to 100 mg/l of dissolved calcium carbonate. According to BALÁZS (1963/1), the Cadisha source emerging from the naked karst mass of the 3000 m high Kornet es Saouda in Lebanon contains in fact no more than 104 mg/l $CaCO_3$. The karst spring Lodowe Zrodlo in the Polish Western Carpathians contains 75 to 85 mg/l $CaCO_3$. H. Kessler found 80 to 100 mg/l $CaCO_3$ in karst waters sampled from the depths of the barren Albanian karst with a top-level altitude of 2000 m. Karst waters with similar low concentrations have also been mentioned by BAUER (1964) from the Austrian Alps and TELL (1961) from Sweden.

The order of magnitude of these values agree fairly well with the results of theoretical values calculated along different lines (MILLER 1952, MÁNDY 1954, GÁNTI 1957, ERNST 1961, MARKÓ 1961, FRANKE 1967).

* * *

The time requirements of the chain of reactions underlying *hydrocarbonate dissolution* have been discussed by BÖGLI (1960, 1963/3). He stated that as far as the duration of the process is concerned, it is useful to subdivide hydrocarbonate dissolution of limestone into four stages, as follows:

In a *first*, very brief *stage*, simple physical dissolution of limestone takes place as per eq. (1). This is preceded by the partial transformation of the CO_2 absorbed by the water into carbonic acid, that is, its dissociation into H^+ and HCO_3^- ions. The first phase takes approximately one second.

The *second stage*, involving the association of the carbonate ions (CO_3^{--}) from the limestone with the H^+ ions of the carbonic acid, cannot be separated in time from the first stage. Nevertheless, the equilibrium established in the first stage is upset by the removal of CO_3^{--} ions, which must necessarily be succeeded by the physical (carbonate) dissolution of more limestone.

Moreover, the second phase also upsets the equilibrium between physically and chemically bound CO_2. As a result, the third stage of the process is initiated without delay, consisting essentially in the transformation of the CO_2 gas in physical solution into carbonic acid.

BÖGLI found that this *third stage* requires about one minute, during which the original CO_2 content of the water is used up for the hydrocarbonate dissolution of limestone. According to Bögli, this signals the start of the fourth stage, involving the absorption of more CO_2 from the atmosphere.

47

The sequence of dissolution reactions now proceeds until a chain of definitive equilibria sets in, dominated by the highest-order equilibrium between the calcium carbonate in hydrocarbonate solution on the one hand, and the CO_2 of the atmosphere in contact with the water on the other.

Hence, all in all, the dynamism of limestone dissolution in the fourth stage is determined by the rate of absorption of CO_2, which is very slow. Bögli suggests that the establishment of the final equilibrium takes 24 to 60 hours. Frear and Johnston too give several days.

One of the essential factors controlling rates of absorption and diffusion is temperature: low temperatures tend to slow down gas absorption, whereas high temperatures may accelerate it several-fold (owing to the higher velocity, and hence the larger number of gas molecules impacting on the interface).

In the view of Feitknecht, generally accepted nowadays, in aqueous solution reaction rates are roughly doubled for each temperature increase of 10 °C. However, the duration of absorption (or of diffusion, if the reaction proceeds in the other direction) is also influenced substantially by the area of the interface per unit volume of water. Accordingly, the greater the specific surface available for gas diffusion (water droplets, spray, a cascade, etc.) the faster will be the gas exchange. The reaction rate is also affected by hydrostatic pressure, as already discussed.

It was pointed out in our treatment of carbonate dissolution that certain modern research by GERSTENHAUER and PFEFFER (1966) (to be discussed in more detail later) seems to contradict Bögli's ideas concerning dissolution rates, questioning in particular the validity of Bögli's statements about stages 1, 2 and 3. Thus, even if we retain Bögli's four stages for its illustrative and didactic merits, we must keep in mind that the individual stages in nature never occur in succession, but invariably simultaneously and in mutual interplay: that is, the stages as such do not in fact exist. The link of the entire chain of reaction shown in Figure 2 which has the lowest rate, the bottleneck as it were, is the one represented by the uppermost arrow, the exchange between the water and the atmosphere. Accordingly, it might be most appropriate to state the problem by saying that the rate of hydrocarbonate dissolution in the three-phase system is determined *ab initio* by the total capacity of this absorption (or diffusion) reaction. We have already discussed the essential factors and controlling conditions of this process in some detail.

3. NON-KARSTIC CORROSION OF LIMESTONE

Whereas the simple physical (carbonate) and chemical (hydrocarbonate) dissolution of limestone may simply be considered under karstic corrosion, corrosive denudation due to other chemical agencies comes under the heading of *the non-karstic chemical decomposition of limestone*.

This group includes a large number of chemical reactions, mainly of the exchange type, resulting from the interaction with limestone of chemical reagents liberated in various types of soil. Some are dominated by the organic and inorganic products (largely acids) of the aerobic or anaerobic decay of vegetal and animal substances in the humus level of the soil, as well as by the chemically related products of the plant roots and soil microorganisms; others by the products of inorganic decomposition processes in the soil. The chemical agencies liberated by all these pedological processes, simply grouped together under the term non-karstic corrosive agencies, convert the limestone into a radically different calcium-containing compound, which is either carried away in solution, or remains in situ for a longer or shorter time as a solid reaction product.

Modern textbooks on pedology, agrochemistry and soil biology dwell extensively upon the characteristic processes of humification of various soils and various soil horizons, which are influenced decisively in their dynamism by climatic conditions. The aerobic decay of organic matter in the soil and the metabolic processes of the soil microorganisms produce the following chemical agencies of importance for limestone corrosion: formic acid, oxalic acid, acetic acid, propionic acid, lactic acid, secretions of various roots and, of course, the extensively discussed carbonic acid, all of which give rise to various calcium salts upon interaction with limestone.

At present it is too early to assess the individual dynamisms of these agencies in their action upon limestone, all the more so, since in the soil they act in concert and simultaneously, and since their quantitative proportions in the soil solution differ from one region to the next. Their overall effect, however, is much easier to judge. Let it suffice to cite in this context one of the classic experiments in biochemistry, the germination of a grain on a slab of marble: even after a short time, the minute root will leave a visible trace on the smooth marble surface (SACHS 1865).

The most important corrosive organic acids produced by the aerobic decay of vegetal and animal substances (the anaerobic too, but at a much reduced rate) are fulvic and crenic acids, which are especially active if the soil reaction is acidic (under aerobic conditions); their salts produced during limestone corrosion tend to stay in solution.

Limestone is equally strongly attacked by the humic and huminic acids of the soil, but their reaction products tend to precipitate in acidic medium.

The inorganic acids and salts resulting from the biochemical or inorganic processes of weathering in the soil also play an important role in limestone corrosion. Of these, sulphuric acid and nitric acid, both strong acids, are characterized by the fact that their reaction with limestone is irreversible even in very dilute solutions:

$$CaCO_3 + H_2SO_4 \longrightarrow CaSO_4 + H_2O + CO_2 \tag{7}$$

$$CaCO_3 + 2HNO_3 \longrightarrow Ca(NO_3)_2 + H_2O + CO_2 \tag{8}$$

These acids may exist in the soil from a number of processes. For instance, sulphuric acid is most often a product of the oxidation — inorganic or biochemical (brought about by sulphur bacteria) — of sulphides (e.g. pyrites) and hydrogen sulphide (H_2S); these latter compounds may in turn result from the decay, most often anaerobic, of the vestiges of living organisms and/or the chemical decomposition of certain inorganic soil constituents. According to FEHÉR (1954), the achromatic sulphur bacteria, including the genera *Achromatium, Beggiatoa, Thiotrix, Thioploca*, etc., split off sulphur from H_2S (resulting from the decay of proteins), store it in the form of droplets in their plasma, and subsequently burn it to derive energy for the assimilation of carbon.

In outline, the process operates as follows:

$$2H_2S + O_2 \longrightarrow 2H_2O + 2S \tag{9}$$
$$2S + 3O_2 + 2H_2O \rightarrow 2H_2SO_4 \quad (+244 \text{ cal})$$

The mechanism of the oxidation of hydrogen sulphide by *purple bacteria* is a somewhat complicated process. These are aerobic organisms, and oxidize hydrogen sulphide and assimilate it chemosynthetically. However, the bacteriochlorophyll and bacterioerythrin contained in their plasma permit them to exploit the energy of solar radiation to allow photosynthetic assimilation. Using hydrogen sulphide and solar light energy, they convert CO_2 into formaldehyde:

$$H_2S + 2H_2O + 2CO_2 \longrightarrow 2HCHO + H_2SO_4 \tag{10}$$

The most common sulphur bacteria living in the soil include the genera *Thiocystis, Thiospirillum, Rhabdomonas, Rhodothece*, etc.

Nitric acid in the soil originates most often from ammonia, present mainly as a result of organic decay. Ammonia is oxidized to acids corrosive to limestone by bacteria living in the soil. VINOGRADSKY proved as early as 1892 that nitrification in the soil is performed by two groups of metabiotically collaborating bacteria: one group produces nitrous acid, and the other converts it into nitric acid, by the following reactions:

$$2NH_3 + 3O_2 \longrightarrow 2HNO_2 + 2H_2O \quad (+156 \cdot 6 \text{ cal}) \tag{11}$$

$$2HNO_2 + O_2 \longrightarrow 2HNO_3 \quad (+43 \cdot 6 \text{ cal}) \tag{12}$$

Of course, neither the nitrous nor the nitric acid remains free for long in the soil: they react more or less immediately with the cations of the soil or the limestone, to form nitrites or nitrates [eq. (8)].

It should be mentioned that the soil may also absorb a certain amount of nitric acid from the atmosphere. As pointed out by FINDEISEN (1939), HARRASOWITZ (1954), KILINSKI (1958) and REITER (1960), summer rain almost invariably contains some nitric acid, formed in the atmosphere by the electrical discharges accompanying thunderstorms. Even though there is no method suitable for demonstrating the contribution to karst corrosion of acids of such origin, we must assume that, especially in the tropics where electrical discharges occur with some regularity, this amount of acid may contribute significantly.

Of the various non-karstic processes of corrosion utilizing soil solutions as a vehicle, one should also mention phosphate solutions, which also have a substantial corrosive potential. For instance, calcium diphosphate reacts with limestone to yield calcium hydrophosphate:

$$CaCO_3 + Ca(H_2PO_4)_2 \rightarrow 2CaHPO_4 + H_2O + CO_2 \tag{13}$$

50

Ammonium phosphate, notable for its occurrence in the rendzina soils over limestone as a decay product of animal tissues, acts upon limestone as follows:

$$3CaCO_3 + 2(NH_4)_3PO_4 \longrightarrow Ca_3(PO_4)_2 + 3(NH_4)_2CO_3 \qquad (14)$$
$$\text{(solid)} \qquad \text{(solution)} \qquad \text{(solid)} \qquad \text{(solution)}$$

Taking the molar volume of the product (tricalcium phosphate) as 100, we find the volume of the original $3CaCO_3$ to be 110·7; hence, this exchange reaction is accompanied by a decrease of volume, and may therefore take place even deep within the limestone texture. In general, if a freshly formed compound takes up less space than the original compound, empty space results around the new product (the pore volume of the rock increases, opening up the rock for the infiltration of further aggressive solution; this process may effect the total conversion of the original substance to a considerable depth).

This holds for any exchange reaction giving rise to solid end-products where the products have a greater density than the original solid components. For instance, an iron salt may react with limestone according to

$$CaCO_3 + FeSO_4 \longrightarrow CaSO_4 + FeCO_3 \qquad (15)$$

Of course, this exchange reaction takes place not only with sulphate, but with any iron compound of a strong acid, all the more since the molar volume of iron carbonate (siderite), 30·9, is less than that of calcium carbonate (36·9), and the exchange reaction involves one molecule of each.

The above example, of course, is the classic case of the replacement of limestone by iron salts.

A circumstance worthy of note is that the hard siderite crust forming at the interface of soil and limestone cannot retard the action of iron sulphate upon the deeper limestone horizons, as it is soon dissolved by the soil solution rich in carbonic acid; in the presence of water and oxygen (the rendzina soil over the karst is a suitable medium for this) the ferrous carbonate is sooner or later oxidized to ferric oxide, which accumulates in the soil either as dark red hematite, Fe_2O_3, or as brown geothite, $2Fe_2O_3 \cdot 3H_2O$:

$$2FeCO_3 + 1/2O_2 \longrightarrow Fe_2O_3 + 2CO_2 \qquad (16)$$

$$4FeCO_3 + O_2 + 3H_2O \longrightarrow (Fe_2O_3)_2 \cdot (H_2O)_3 + 4CO_2 \qquad (17)$$

It is probable that many other similar replacement reactions take place on the pattern of the replacement of limestone by siderite. The formation of glauconite and of chert nodes, and the replacement of calcite crystals by pseudomorphs of *base-metal sulphides* (e.g. pyrites) may be the results of equivalent processes. Elie de Beaumont was probably right when he attributed the subsequent dolomitization of limestone in contact with sea water to a phenomenon of this sort. In this case, calcium carbonate is attacked by the magnesium chloride of sea water, and the well-known double salt is formed. The reaction may take place deep in the rock, since the density of the double carbonate (V_2), less soluble than either pure calcium or pure magnesium carbonate, is higher that that of calcite (V_1):

$$MgCl_2 + 2CaCO_3 \longrightarrow CaCO_3 \cdot MgCO_3 + CaCl_2 \tag{18}$$

(solution)   (solid)   (solid)   (solution)

$2V_1 = 73.8$ $V_2 = 63.6$

Another potential factor in the non-karstic corrosion of limestone is ammonium sulphate, sometimes fairly abundant in the soil:

$$CaCO_3 + (NH_4)_2SO_4 \rightleftharpoons CaSO_4 + (NH_4)_2CO_3 \tag{19}$$

It should be noted, however, that this reaction takes place according to the upper arrow only if the compounds on the right-hand side of the equation are present in much lower concentrations than those on the left-hand side; that is, if the continuous removal of the calcium sulphate and ammonium carbonate produced is ensured by some agency such as ground water flow or consumption by the biosphere. If, on the other hand, the concentrations are higher on the right-hand side, the reaction proceeds in the sense of the lower arrow (BECK 1968).

An interesting type of corrosion may be due to the aluminium sulphate content of the soil:

$$6CaCO_3 + Al_2(SO_4)_3 + 6H_2O \longrightarrow 3CaSO_4 + 3Ca(HCO_3)_2 +$$
$$+ 2Al(OH)_3 \tag{20}$$

It should be pointed out that this reaction takes place only in neutral or acidic medium, since in a basic medium the aluminium sulphate, which is hydrolyzed to acidic products in an aqueous environment, is at first used up in neutralizing the basicity of the soil:

$$Al_2(SO_4)_3 + 3Na_2CO_3 + 3H_2O \longrightarrow 3Na_2SO_4 +$$
$$+ 2Al(OH)_3 + CO_2 \tag{21}$$

In order to present an image as complete as possible of the non-karstic processes of limestone corrosion, largely neglected in earlier karst literature, it must be added that the various ions of the soil solution influence the dynamism of dissolution not only by giving rise to chemical bonds under suitable conditions, but by simple mass action too, indirectly controlling the efficacy of hydrocarbonate dissolution merely by their presence. It is known that the solubility of a salt is reduced in the presence of another salt containing the same ion, whereas a salt made up of different ions increases solubility. For instance, the solubility of sodium chloride is reduced by magnesium chloride, whereas alkali chlorides (NaCl, KCl) in water improve the solubility of calcium carbonate, calcium phosphate, etc. The solubility of $CaCO_3$ is augmented in a similar manner if the soil solution contains magnesium chloride, for instance.

According to our present knowledge, the hydrocarbonate dissolution of limestone is reduced by the presence of other dissolved carbonates as a result of the reduction of the parameter K_t in eq. (6); this means in effect an increase in the quantity of accessory carbonic acid required to keep the calcium carbonate in solution. Thus natural karst waters, which invariably also contain carbonates of other cations, usually need more free carbonic acid than calculated from their carbonate hardness.

This increase in carbonic acid demand is not normally very significant in practice because, especially in hard waters which tend to contain other carbonates too, the increase is only a small percentage of the rather high concentration of accessory carbonic acid. Furthermore, the reduction in solubility of $CaCO_3$ due to the presence of other calcium salts or carbonates can be more than offset by the influence of salts having no common ion with $CaCO_3$; these are invariably present in all karst waters, and most of them increase the solubility of $CaCO_3$. All this means that, statistically anyway, the data in Table 4, calculated on the basis of eq. (6), give a fair approximation to reality in most actual cases.

This short chapter is insufficient to exhaust all the potential factors that may affect the non-karstic corrosion of limestone in nature. We have only indicated the most important components that manifest themselves by their objective effects. It should be added, however, that the further elucidation of all the data concerning the detail and the ranges of intensity of these processes remains a considerable future challenge for karst science. The results may be of great benefit to karst science, possibly to the extent that some of the fundamental axioms of karst evolution will have to be scrapped. Primarily, however, we may expect from this analysis a fresh impetus to assess the rambling complex of problems of denudation dynamics in the karst regions of the various climatic zones.

PETROVARIANCE AS A FACTOR OF KARST CORROSION

The branch of geomorphology concerned with the peculiar differences in landscape sculpture due to differences in petrographic constitution under otherwise identical conditions of denudation over equal spans of time is called petromorphology. The idea has been formulated by B. BULLA (1954/1) as follows. "Petromorphology elucidates the influence of petrographic constitution, and of the variations in petrographic constitution, upon the evolution of landscape forms. Petrology is, then, the science of landform facies based on the material (petrographic and lithologic) differences in the rocks forming the earth's surface."

In the following discussion (*loc. cit.* pp. 441—481), Bulla extends this precise definition by presenting and comparing specific sets of denudation forms of the most important groups of rocks. It is no insult to his esteemed fundamental scholarship that today we can no longer be satisfied with a mere outline of the main problems; a much more detailed and profound analysis of these is now demanded. Such an analysis, however, is lacking from even the most recent handbooks of geomorphology. THORNBURY (1956), MAULL (1958), KETTNER (1959), LOUIS (1964) etc. restrict discussion to an exposition of the most conspicuous and generally typical denudational features of rock groups or rocks (limestone, dolomite, granite, basalt, sandstone, loess, clay, gypsum, rock salt, etc.), relegating the consequences of minor structural or compositional differences at best to a subordinate position. Nonetheless, a host of data available today go to prove that slight variances in petrography, traceable within the individual narrower categories of petrographic classification, often insignificant in a purely petrographic context, will sometimes affect the dynamics and even the nature of denudation more strongly than the broad fundamental categories of rock classification.

This is especially true of carbonate rocks, whose hardly detectable specific features may be reflected in the set of forms of corrosive denudation. This was already recognized by GRUND, who stated (1914, p. 634): "Just as we may distinguish rocks as soft and hard in their resistance to erosion, limestone and dolomite rocks behave differently as regards corrosion, since limestone may be easy or difficult to dissolve, depending on the purity of the rocks."

With the above ideas in mind, and within the general scope of the term limestone, the rock most important for karst evolution, let us now investigate in somewhat more detail the minor variance that may play a significant role in affecting karst denudation either qualitatively or quantitatively.

54

1. SPECIFIC FEATURES OF LIMESTONE COMPOSITION

Limestone as a rock belongs to the group of monomineralic rocks. Its essential constituent is the mineral form calcite of the chemical compound calcium carbonate ($CaCO_3$).

In fact, some limestones occurring in nature do not include any other constituent than calcite, whereas others contain various amounts of magnesite, as an accessory constituent, and other contaminations. These latter most often include iron oxide, different clay minerals, grains of sand, various inclusions of silica gel, bitumen, etc. In so-called pure limestone, the total content of accessories and contaminants is 1 per cent or less, whereas in highly impure limestones it may amount to 15 or more weight percent. Such limestones are called sandy, clayey (marly), cherty, dolomitic, etc. Indeed, if the non-calcite components gain the upper hand, we have to speak of calcareous sandstone, marl, calcareous dolomite, etc.

Accessories and contaminants exert a considerable influence on the behaviour of limestone under corrosion. The analysis of a limestone's composition may therefore be highly informative as to the interpretation of certain processes of karst genesis. It is often necessary to determine:

1. the contaminant-to-carbonate ratio of a calcareous rock,
2. the cation distribution (Ca:Mg ratio) of its carbonate minerals,
3. the composition and mineralogical nature of its contaminants.

The carbonate mass of the limestone is dissolved without residue in dilute hydrochloric acid according to the reaction

$$CaCO_3 + 2HCl \longrightarrow CaCl_2 \text{ (in solution)} + H_2O + CO_2 \qquad (22)$$

Any residue is composed of the non-carbonatic contaminants, which can readily be separated for study by this simple means.

Table 6 presents the chemical compositions of some type of limestone, showing the proportions of accessory and contaminating constituents.

Ideally pure limestone (calcite) is composed of 56 per cent CaO and 44 per cent CO_2. Limestone approaching this ideal is exceedingly rare in nature.

The contaminants of limestone, insoluble in dilute hydrochloric acid, will not as a rule dissolve in ground water or karst water either, and may therefore accumulate as substantial masses of residues during the evolution of limestone reliefs, thereby playing a decisive, controlling role in the karstification process. The various deposits and fillings of caverns are also composed largely of these insoluble residues (BÖGLI 1963/2, LAIS 1941, KUKLA-LOŽEK 1958).

The most widespread foreign component in limestone is shown by Table 6 to be magnesium carbonate, whose presence must be expected in most limestones. Its quantity is highly variable, and nature presents the full range from chemically pure limestone to chemically pure dolomite, in which the molar ratio $CaCO_3$ to $MgCO_3$ is 1:1, corresponding to a weight per cent ratio of 54·35:45·65. Further widespread components include SiO_2, Al_2O_3 and Fe_2O_3, all in concentrations lower than that of $MgCO_3$. Other components tend to be less abundant and less ubiquitous.

Theoretical speculation as to the influence of mineralogical composition upon the solubility of a limestone gives equivocal results, as illustrated by the contradictory findings of the relevant calculations (GÁNTI 1957, MARKÓ 1961); the reason is presumably that differences in constitution may or may not be accompanied by features of crystallinity and lattice structure that also affect the dynamism of dissolution. This is why paramount importance must be ascribed to experimental investigation aimed at comparing rates of dissolution of known types of limestone under indentical conditions.

Of the Hungarian authors, mention should be made of MÁNDY and his interesting investigations into the comparative solubilities of limestones of various geological ages, and of Upper Triassic "Hauptdolomite", in aqueous solutions saturated with CO_2 under the partial pressure of the atmosphere, flowing down rock faces of various slopes. His experimental findings have confirmed, and shed new light upon, the ancient tenet of observation and theory that the solubility of dolomite is much less than that

Table 6

Chemical compositions of various types of limestone

Sample designation	Percentage of				
	CaO	CO_2	MgO	SiO_2	Al_2O_3
Recent Corallian limestone from *Bermudas* (after CLARKE)	55·16	43·74	0·20	0·23	*
Calc. tufa from *Ivanovo-Voznesensk area* (after SHVETSOV)	54·30	44·45	0·16	0·37	0·65
Average composition of 345 limestone samples (after CLARKE)	42·61	41·58	7·90	5·19	0·81
Average composition of 498 limestone types used as building stones (after CLARKE)	40·60	35·58	4·49	14·09	1·75
North Caucasian Cretaceous limestone (after RENGARTEN)	50·11	39·75	0·39	5·70	2·38
Cretaceous limestone from the *Bryansk area* (after DOBROV)	52·40	43·56	0·48	1·00	0·90
White Cretaceous limestone (biancone) from near *Lake Garda* (after BLANCK and WEISSE)	54·50	43·29	1·20	0·76	0·17
Grey Cretaceous limestone (biancone) from near *Lake Garda* (after BLANCK and WEISSE)	52·02	43·29	2·10	2·12	0·27
Liassic limestone from *Gerecse Hills, Hungary* (after GEDEON)	53·11	42·80	*	0·29	3·61
Russet "calcare ammonitico" from *South Alps* (after BLANCK and WEISSE)	52·78	41·80	0·30	0·426	0·76
Pink "calcare ammonitico" from *South Alps* (after BLANCK and WEISSE)	55·05	42·96	*	0·153	0·38
Triassic (Wetterstein) limestone from *Aggtelek Hills* (JAKUCS)	53·19	43·96	2·00	0·61	0·14
Lower Carboniferous limestone from *Moscow Basin* (after SHVETSOV)	55·44	44·11	0·02	0·10	0·07
Carboniferous cherty limestone from south flank of *Moscow Basin* (after SHVETSOV)	41·18	32·34	*	26·44	0·21

* = in traces only

of any limestone. Incidentally, this difference in solubility is the greater, the longer the duration of the contact between rock and solvent (*Fig. 6*).

MÁNDY further recorded substantial differences in solubility between dolomites from various localities. Unfortunately, he did not publish the geochemical data of his limestone or dolomite samples, thus precluding any assessment of the causal connexion between solubility and composition.

Considerably more can be learned about this problem from the Germans GERSTENHAUER and PFEFFER (1966), who performed a series of tests at the laboratory of the Institute of Geography, University of Frankfurt-Main, with a view to settling the problem once and for all. On 46 samples of limestone of various ages, collected from various localities, they first performed a quantitative analysis of the $CaCO_3$ and $MgCO_3$ content; then, after grinding to minus 2 mm, they exposed the samples for 28 hours to water at room temperature, saturated with the CO_2 content of the atmosphere. They subsequently determined rates of dissolution. Their results,

| sample containing | | | | | | | | | Total % |
Fe_2O_3	TiO_2	MnO	K_2O	Na_2O	P_2O_5	SO_3	Cl	H_2O	
*	—	—	—	—	—	—	—	0·54	99·87
*	—	—	—	—	—	—	—	—	99·93
0·54	0·06	0·05	0·33	0·05	0·04	0·13	0·02	0·77	100·09
0·77	0·08	0·03	0·58	0·62	0·42	0·14	0·01	1·18	100·34
0·24	—	—	—	—	—	—	—	—	98·55
—	—	—	—	—	—	*	—	—	98·34
0·01	—	—	—	—	—	—	—	—	99·96
0·04	—	—	—	—	—	—	—	—	99·94
*	—	—	—	—	—	—	—	—	99·91
0·08	—	—	—	—	—	—	—	—	99·98
0·05	—	—	—	—	—	—	—	—	99·97
0·06	—	*	—	—	—	—	—	—	99·96
0·07	—	—	—	—	*	—	—	—	99·81
*	—	—	—	—	—	—	—	—	100·17

Table 7

Composition and dissolution behaviour of limestone samples studied by GERSTEN-HAUER and PFEFFER (1966)

No.	Sampling site	Geological age	Composition (%)			CaCO₃ mg/l over 28 h
			CaCO₃	MgCO₃	Others	
1.	Carrara (Apuane Alps)	Triassic	98·0	2·0	0·0	31
2.	Copoya (Chiapas, Mexico)	Oligocene	81·8	2·0	16·2	18
3.	Pan-American highway, 1187 kilometre, Chiapas, Mexico	Middle Cretaceous	89·4	4·8	5·8	20
4.	Macuspana (Tabasco, Mexico)	Oligocene	92·7	4·8	2·5	24
5.	Canon (Chiapas, Mexico)	Oligocene	93·2	4·0	2·6	26
6.	Poaná (Tabasco, Mexico)	Upper Cretaceous	93·9	3·7	2·4	25
7.	Morelia (Chiapas, Mexico)	Middle Cretaceous	97·4	1·0	1·6	41
8.	Val de Travers, Jura of Neuenburg	Malm	93·2	3·8	3·0	27
9.	Val de Brevine, Jura of Neuenburg	Malm	91·3	4·8	3·9	23
10.	Val de Brevine, Jura of Neuenburg	Malm	92·8	4·9	2·3	23
11.	Les Sognettes, Jura of Neuenburg	Malm	84·8	4·9	10·3	22
12.	Soyaló (Chiapas, Mexico)	Middle Cretaceous	92·0	3·8	4·2	26
13.	Bochil (Chiapas, Mexico)	Middle Cretaceous	90·9	4·9	4·2	22
14.	Teopisca (Chiapas, Mexico)	Quaternary	87·0	8·4	4·6	18
15.	Eube (German Mountains)	"Muschelkalk"	87·0	8·4	4·6	18
16.	Glattalp (Swiss Alps)	Lower Cretaceous	95·0	3·4	1·6	26
17.	Ibid.	Lower Cretaceous	93·4	4·7	1·9	22
18.	Monte Cavallo (Venetian Prealps)	Cretaceous	91·0	4·9	4·1	20
19.	Ibid.	Cretaceous	89·4	9·9	0·7	16
20.	Ibid.	Cretaceous	91·0	8·6	0·4	19
21.	Ibid.	Cretaceous	84·6	9·7	5·7	16
22.	Ibid.	Cretaceous	88·9	4·9	6·2	21
23.	Ibid.	Cretaceous	87·9	9·9	2·2	17
24.	Ibid.	Cretaceous	94·4	2·8	2·8	17
25.	Ibid.	Cretaceous	95·0	3·0	2·0	28
26.	Ibid.	Eocene	92·6	4·6	2·8	22
27.	Ibid.	Eocene	87·0	8·9	4·1	18
28.	Ibid.	Eocene	89·4	10·0	0·6	15
29.	Ibid.	Cretaceous	90·4	8·8	0·8	19
30.	Ibid.	Eocene	96·0	0·7	3·4	40
31.	Ibid.	Cretaceous	94·1	4·1	1·8	23
32.	Longarone (Piave Valley)	Jurassic	90·9	4·3	4·8	16
33.	Paranuzzi (Venetian Prealps)	Eocene	92·4	5·0	2·6	20
34.	Torrente Pentina (Venetian Prealps)	Triassic	95·8	4·2	0·0	22
35.	Ibid.	Jurassic	92·0	8·0	0·0	16
36.	Ibid.	Triassic	88·3	4·8	6·9	21
37.	Campo Felice (Abruzzi)	Lower Miocene	97·0	2·0	1·0	20
38.	Campo di Rovere (Abruzzi)	Lower Miocene	97·2	2·1	0·7	22
39.	Campo Felice (Abruzzi)	Middle Miocene	84·5	9·7	5·8	22
40.	Campo Saline (Abruzzi)	Cretaceous	87·3	8·6	3·1	14
41.	Campo di Rovere (Abruzzi)	Lower Miocene	90·6	4·4	5·0	12
42.	Piano di Ovindoli (Abruzzi)	Middle Miocene	92·0	4·9	3·1	22
43.	Ibid.	Middle Miocene	90·0	4·0	6·0	22
44.	Campo Saline (Abruzzi)	Lower Miocene	85·0	1·0	5·0	22
45.	Campo Felice (Abruzzi)	Cretaceous	99·0	1·0	0·0	26
46.	Ibid.	Cretaceous	91·5	7·6	0·9	18

58

obtained with exemplary care and by the most modern chemical and technological means, are presented in *Table 7*.

For some of the samples, Gerstenhauer and Pfeffer also presented dissolution-rate diagrams covering spans of time in excess of 28 h. These highly instructive diagrams are given in the present *Figure 7*.

Both Table 7 and Fig. 7 reveal that the differences in solubility between different limestones may attain one order of magnitude. Another remarkable phenomenon is that the progress of dissolution likewise exhibits specific differences, since the breaks in the dissolution-rate diagrams for the various samples cannot be correlated.

In order to clarify the relationship between rock composition and dissolution behaviour, Gerstenhauer constructed another

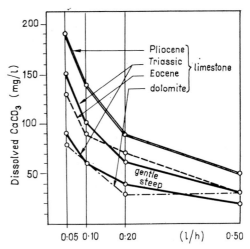

Fig. 6. Rates of dissolution of Triassic "Hauptdolomite" and various limestones in tap water saturated with carbonic acid. The abscissa gives the quantity of water dripping onto the rock-sample surface. Dissolution of Triassic limestone is presented separately for gentle and steep runoff slopes, in order to reveal the resulting difference in corrosion rates (after MÁNDY 1954)

diagram (*Fig. 8*), a plot of the percentage $CaCO_3$ content of the rock vs. the amount of $CaCO_3$, in mg/l, dissolved in the solution over 28 hours. The scatter of the points thus plotted, however, revealed no underlying regularity. This is one of the principal implications of this series of tests: even though the rates of dissolution of limestones of various compositions do exhibit some slight dependence on the $CaCO_3$ content of the rock, this factor in itself is incapable of accounting for the variance in solubility.

If we plot the above dissolution rates against the $MgCO_3$ rather than the $CaCO_3$ content of the rock (*Fig. 9*), however, we obtain a much less irregular distribution, with a comparatively narrow dissolution band including the large majority of the points. This is even more conspicuous on a diagram having the molar ratio of $CaCO_3$ to $MgCO_3$ for its abscissa. As an obvious consequence of these results, we may formulate the second fundamental result of the tests: The solubility of a limestone is decisively influenced by its $MgCO_3$ content, even at low values of the molar ratio.

Another conspicuous feature of Figure 9 is that the solubility is an inverse exponential rather than linear function of the $MgCO_3$ content. In other words, whereas 28-hour dissolution gave concentrations up to 40 mg/l in solutions in contact with limestones containing one per cent or less $MgCO_3$, the solubility dropped to about half this value in the $MgCO_3$ range of 2 to 5 per cent, whereas higher concentrations of $MgCO_3$ entailed no further substantial decrease in solubility.

59

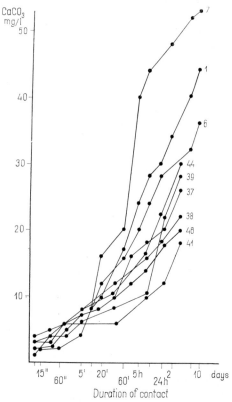

CaCO₃ mg/l

Duration of contact

Fig. 7. Rates of dissolution of various limestone types in water at atmospheric pCO_2. Numbering of samples as in *Table 7* (after GERSTENHAUER and PFEFFER 1966)

In order, to eliminate with above experiments, the influence upon solubility of the almost omnipresent other chemical components of limestones, or at least to account for it, with a view to separating unequivocally the influence upon solubility of magnesium carbonate alone, Gerstenhauer and Pfeffer (1966) have also carried out identical tests of dissolution on various mixtures of calcium and magnesium carbonate powders of analytical purity. The very noteworthy results of these tests are illustrated by *Figures 10* and *11*, Figure 10 covering the entire range of possible concentrations, and Figure 11 showing in more detail the range from 0 and 10 per cent $MgCO_3$, which includes the majority of limestones occurring in nature.

These solubility tests show unambiguously that the solubility of $CaCO_3$ or, much the same, of limestone is substantially reduced by even a minimal $MgCO_3$ content, but that further, more significant increases in $MgCO_3$ content entail much less than the proportional reduction in solubility.

Comparison of the absolute solubility values plotted in Figures 10 and 11 with those in Figures 8 and 9 reveals the interesting circumstance that the solubilities of natural limestones, both pure and those containing magnesium, are much higher than those of a calcium carbonate powder, or a mixture of calcium and magnesium carbonate powders, both of analytical purity. This somewhat unexpected result may be due to one of two causes. Either the non-carbonate contaminants in natural limestone tend to promote solubility, or the result reflects the influence of the crystallinity and texture of natural limestone.

As far as the objective assessment of karst phenomena is concerned, we urgently desire a solution to this problem. Consequently, we used GERSTENHAUER and PFEFFER's analysis data in Table 7 to compute the contents of non-carbonate contaminants in the 46 limestone samples, entering them into the appropriate column of Table 7, and also plotting them against the results of the 28-hour solubility tests (*Fig. 12*).

The considerable scatter of the points in Figure 12 reveals that the solubility of limestone does not depend primarily on the concentration of the non-carbonate constituents. Hence, any difference in solubility and other

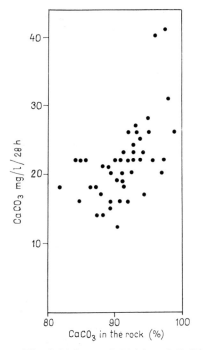

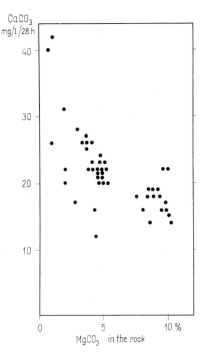

Fig. 8. 28-hour solubilities of 46 different limestone samples in water at atmospheric $p\mathrm{CO_2}$ plotted against the $\mathrm{CaCO_3}$ content (after GERSTEN-HAUER and PFEFFER 1966)

Fig. 9. 28-hour solubilities of 46 different limestone samples in water at atmospheric $p\mathrm{CO_2}$ plotted against the $\mathrm{MgCO_3}$ content (after GERSTEN-HAUER and PFEFFER 1966)

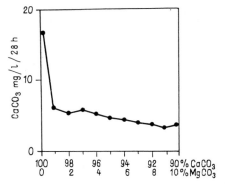

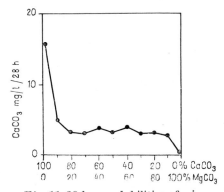

Fig. 10. 28-hour solubilities of mixtures of various proportions of $\mathrm{CaCO_3}$ and $\mathrm{MgCO_3}$ of analytical purity in room-temperature water at atmospheric $p\mathrm{CO_2}$ against mixing proportions (after GERSTEN-HAUER and PFEFFER 1966)

Fig. 11. 28-hour solubilities of mixtures of $\mathrm{CaCO_3}$ and $\mathrm{MgCO_3}$ both of analytical purity in room-temperature water at atmospheric $p\mathrm{CO_2}$ against mixing proportions (after GERSTENHAUER and PFEFFER 1966)

61

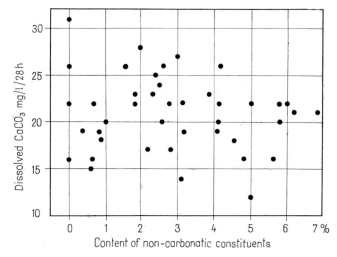

Fig. 12. 28-hour solubilities vs. the abundance of non-carbonate mineral constituents in limestones. Samples 2, 7, 11 and 30, which fall far outside the range of this diagram, have been omitted (calculated by the author from data in GERSTENHAUER and PFEFFER 1966)

specific features connected with dissolution not attributable to the Ca:Mg ratio must be ascribed to the only other possible factor, the influence of the specific features of the rock texture and crystal structure.

There is another argument for preferring this, at least for an approximate explanation of the phenomenon. GERSTENHAUER and PFEFFER's samples Nos 1, 34, 35 and 45 contain no constituent other than $CaCO_3$ and a smaller percentage of $MgCO_3$. Hence, the solubilities of these four samples should depend entirely on the Ca : Mg ratio, if the textural features are disregarded. That is, the plots for these samples should then coincide with the graph of Figure 11. The true situation is shown in contrast by *Figure 13*, plotted by the present author.

The positions of the four plots in Figure 13 can on no account be attributed to the chemical composition of the rocks, and in the present state of our knowledge the specific solubilities as illustrated can be ascribed only to the lithostructural features.

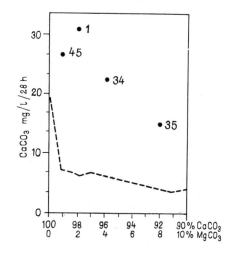

Fig. 13. 28-hour solubilities of rock samples containing no other component than $CaCO_3$ and $MgCO_3$ in room-temperature water at atmospheric pCO_2. The dashed line presents for comparison the solubilities of mixtures of components of analytical purity (calculated by the author from data in GERSTENHAUER and PFEFFER 1966)

62

2. INFLUENCE OF LIMESTONE CRYSTALLINITY AND LITHOSTRUCTURE UPON KARST CORROSION

Clearly, the results of laboratory tests cannot simply be transferred to nature, where karstification depends on an interplay of all relevant factors. But it is just as clear that the tendencies and processes recorded in the laboratory are present and active under natural conditions too. Hence, any statistical comparison between solubility values obtained in the laboratory on a given rock and the structural and textural features of the same rock may be just as useful, as it may reveal relationships equally as important objectively in controlling the dynamism of karst corrosion as the research into composition-to-solubility relationships.

Great value is therefore attached to GERSTENHAUER and PFEFFER's initiative in performing concrete laboratory tests to substantiate the previously hypothetical relationships between lithostructure and solubility.

As a first step, these authors prepared thin slides of the 46 kinds of limestone already referred to, and recorded structural and textural features under the microscope. Then, by a method of selective staining, they established the distributions of the carbonate minerals in the slides.

With respect to this latter undertaking, it should be pointed out that the chemical composition does not in itself determine the mineralogical constitution, since the magnesium content of a limestone may take three fundamental forms:

1. It is often dispersed in the calcite lattice, in which case its presence is undetectable by petrographic and crystallographic methods. It is usual to assume that the dispersion of magnesium is the result of a syngenetic incorporation into the lattice structure. We, accordingly, call the rock-forming mineral of such limestones Mg-calcite.

2. Magnesium may form grains, veinlets, etc. of dolomite mineral (as a sign of postgenetic infiltration of Mg).

3. It may be present in the form of magnesite.

In addition to recording their findings concerning the forms in which magnesium appears, Gerstenhauer and Pfeffer exposed smooth-polished surfaces of their limestone to etching by dilute hydrochloric acid and, after a certain time, recorded the tactile impression of their surfaces (very smooth, smooth, rough, very rough). Then, after further etching, they also recorded the microbiological features of the corroded surface (plane, undulating, lapies-like, with hollow depressions, pockmarked, possibly turriculated, lace-like, etc.).

The result of these studies are listed in columns II—XI of *Table 8*. Column XII contains the 28-hour solubility values, to permit direct comparison of the observed features with the recorded dissolution rates.

The data compiled in the table can be evaluated from a number of viewpoints. Whatever the approach, however, one must keep in mind that solubility is activated not only by this or that property of the rock alone, but by a complex interaction of all physical, chemical and lithological properties. Let us assume for the sake of argument that all limestones examined are exactly identical in chemical and mineralogical composition; if we could

Table 8

Dependence of solubility on mineralogical and textural features in various limestones

I	II	III	IV	V	VI	VII	VIII	IX	X	XI	XII
1.	cv	0·20—0·25 (0·25)	—	un	s	s	4	—	—	3	31
2.	p	un	0·20—0·25 (1·50)	—	s	ml	4	—	—	3	18
3.	p	un	0·05—0·10	up to 1·50	vs	g	4	2	—	—	20
4.	m	un	—	—	s	g	4	2	—	—	24
5.	mn	un	—	0·10—0·25	r	cp	—	4	2	—	26
6.	pv	un	0·25—0·40	0·05—0·06	s	s	4	2	—	2	25
7.	p	un	0·05—0·30	—	r	s	4	2	—	—	41
8.	p	un	0·05	—	vs	ml	4	3	—	3	27
9.	ma	un	—	0·10—0·25 (0·50)	vs	g	4	2	—	—	23
10.	gr	0·15—0·25	—	—	vr	s	4	2	—	—	23
11.	m	un	—	—	s	dp	4	—	3	3	22
12.	gr	0·20—0·25	—	—	vr	a	4	—	3	3	26
13.	p	un	0·15—0·20 0·50—1·50	—	s	cp	4	3	—	3	22
14.	p	un	0·25—0·50	un	r	s	4	3	—	3	19
15.	pv	un	0·05	un	s	g	4	3	—	—	18
16.	gr	0·10—0·15	—	—	vr	a	4	4	—	—	26
17.	gr	0·20—0·25 0·75—1·25	—	—	vr	ia	1	4	—	—	22
18.	p	un	0·20—0·50	—	s	s	4	2	—	—	20
19.	pv	un	0·10—0·15	0·25	vs	ml	4	3	1	3	16
20.	pv	0·50—1·50	—	—	vs	s	4	4	—	3	19
21.	gr	0·20	—	—	vr	s	4	3	—	—	16
22.	p	un	0·40—0·50	—	s	s	4	3	—	—	21
23.	pn	un	0·05	0·40—0·50	vs	g	4	3	—	—	17
24.	p	un	0·15—0·20	—	s	s	4	3	—	—	17
25.	gr	0·05—0·10	—	—	vr	g	2	4	1	—	28
26.	p	un	0·25—0·50 (1·00)	—	s	ml	4	—	—	3	22
27.	gr	0·05—0·10	—	—	vr	s	—	4	1	3	18
28.	gr	0·40—1·10	—	—	vr	a	4	—	—	3	15
29.	p	un	0·20—1·20	—	vs	ml	4	2	—	—	19
30.	gr	0·05—0·10	—	—	r	s	—	4	1	—	40
31.	p	un	0·25—0·50	—	vs	ml	4	3	—	—	23
32.	p	un	0·05—0·10 0·35—0·50	—	vs	s	4	3	—	3	16
33.	p	un	0·15—0·25	—	s	g	4	3	—	—	20
34.	gr	0·25—1·15	—	—	vr	s	4	4	—	—	22
35.	p	un	0·20—0·20	—	s	g	4	2	3	3	16
36.	m	un	—	—	s	s	4	—	3	3	21
37.	m	un	—	—	r	g	4	2	—	—	20
38.	mv	un	—	0·25	s	g	4	2	—	—	22
39.	gr	0·15—0·25	—	—	vr	a	4	2	—	2	22
40.	p	un	0·10—0·15	—	vs	ml	4	2	—	—	14
41.	m	un	—	—	s	s	4	2	—	—	12
42.	p	un	0·25—0·50 (1·50)	—	s	a	4	3	—	3	22
43.	p	un	0·25—0·30 (1·00)	—	s	a	4	2	—	-	22
44.	m	un	—	—	r	dp	—	4	1		22
45.	m	un	—	—	vs	g	4	—	—	3	26
46.	c	1·50—2·00	—	—	s	s	4	—	—	3	18

Symbols of Table 8

I — Sample number as in *Table 7*

II — Rock texture:
  m — massive (granulation at most in the form of hardly perceived minute crystal grains of a slightly different shade)
  mn — massive, with nodes or knobs of different consistency
  ma — massive, with acicular aggregates of crystals
  mv — massive, locally veined
  p — porphyry-like (a dense uniform matrix with dispersed larger individual crystal grains)
  pv — porphyry-like, locally veined
  pn — porphyry-like, with nodes or knobs of different consistency
  gr — granular
  c — coarsely crystalline
  cv — coarsely crystalline, veined

III — Typical grain size of rock matrix, diameter in mm. Figures in parentheses refer to rare, isolated occurrences

IV — Diameter (mm) of porphyric grains swimming in matrix (figures in parentheses refer to rare, isolated occurrences)

V — Diameter (mm) of grains in veins and nodes (figures in parentheses refer to rare, isolated occurrences)
  un — unknown

VI — Tactile impression of rock face etched with dilute HCl
  s — smooth
  vs — very smooth
  r — rough
  vr — very rough

VII — Microrelief produced by etching
  s — smooth (plane) surface
  g — gentle relief
  ml — micro-lapies
  cp — pitted with craters moonscape-fashion
  dp — pitted, recalling a doline landscape
  a — sharp acicular forms and ridges, like a microscopic petrified forest
  ia — isolated sharp acicular forms and ridges

VIII, IX, X and XI represent pure calcite, Mg-calcite,* dolomite and magnesite, respectively, and its concentration is represented by:
  1 — in traces only
  2 — only in the form of a few isolated crystals
  3 — only in veins and druses
  4 — dominant mineral making up most of the rock

XII — CaCO$_3$ in mg/l, dissolved over 28 hours

* Magnesium calcite is a mineral containing magnesium in a calcite lattice, inseparable mineralogically from calcite proper

5 L. Jakucs

65

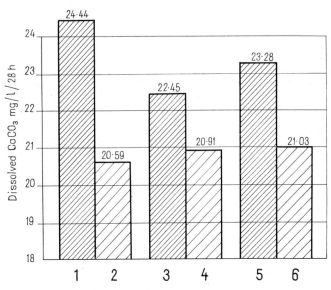

Fig. 14. Relation of limestone texture to solubility. 28-hour solubilities represent averages of individual solubilities of samples of identical behaviour (plotted by the author after data in GERSTENHAUER and PFEFFER 1966)

1 — surface formed on etching with dilute hydrochloric acid, rough or very rough to the touch; 2 — idem, smooth or very smooth; 3 — sample surface etched with dilute hydrochloric acid exhibits jagged protuberances, intricately ramified thorns, or crater- or doline-shaped pits; 4 — either no microforms exhibited, or only depressions and up-wellings of gentle relief, or possibly rudiments of lapies-like furrows; 5 — rock texture holocrystalline, coarsely crystalline, occasionally veined; 6 — rock texture either highly massive, homogeneous, or porphyry-like with crystals scattered in a massive matrix, possibly with veins, druses or small isolated aggregates of crystals

nevertheless record differences in the degree of corrosion, by elimination these would then obviously be regarded as adequate consequences of lithostructural differences, and it would be possible to quantify the influence of these latter. However, since no two limestones in nature are identical in chemical and mineralogical composition, let alone 46, we must be satisfied with statistically evidenced approximative tendencies, as derived from Table 8.

This, in contrast, is a quite attainable goal: if samples of identical structure are to be compared with another group of samples on the basis of their arithmetic mean solubilities, then clearly the greater the number of samples, the more justified we are in assuming that any difference thus found is indeed a consequence of structural differences, since the statistical comparison of large numbers of data will smooth out the marked individual differences, e.g. in chemical composition, and enhance the less dominant relationships looked for.

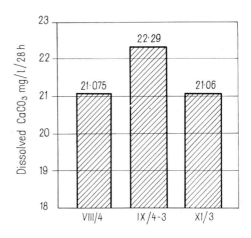

Fig. 15. Influence of solubility on the crystallinity and distribution of calcium and magnesium carbonate contents in a carbonate rock. 28-hour solubilities represent averages of solubilities of samples of identical features (plotted by the author from data in GERSTENHAUER and PFEFFER 1966)

VIII/4 — the rock is predominantly made up of pure calcite, with the $MgCO_3$ content localized largely in separate crystals and/or veins; IX/4-3 — the rock consists predominantly of Mg-calcite, that is, most of the $MgCO_3$ content of the rock is incorporated in calcite lattices; XI/3 — most of the $MgCO_3$ content of the rock is in the form of interstitial dolomite crystals and/or dolomite veins

With the above considerations in mind, we have rejected the quite unsuitable method of individual representation adopted by Gerstenhauer and Pfeffer (*loc. cit.*, diagrams VII—X) and have given the results listed in Table 8 a statistical form more expressive of objective tendencies (*Figs 14 and 15*). Adding together the individual 28-hour solubilities of rock samples grouped together on the basis of identical properties, and dividing the sum thus obtained by the number of samples in the group, we obtained the characteristic mean solubility level of each group. These were plotted as the heights of the columns in our statistical diagrams.

Even though the generalization of a conclusion of this sort as a law, and in particular the estimation of the intensity of the factor examined as related to other factors, would unquestionably require a much broader sample population, we feel that even these findings are sufficient to reveal the most important tendencies, which can be given as follows.

Solubility in a limestone is closely related to rock texture and structure. Dense limestones of uniform consistency, having the appearance of soapstone and exhibiting a conchoidal fracture, are much less soluble than holocrystalline ones (diagrams 5 and 6 of Fig. 14), presumably owing to the difference in the surfaces exposed to attack: a smooth, conchoidal fracture surface has a much smaller surface of contact with water than a jagged, crystalline one (diagrams 1 and 2 of Fig. 14). The fracture surfaces of a crystalline limestone are rougher than those of a massive one, since separation on breaking usually takes place along crystal faces, adhesion between grains being weaker than the bonds holding the crystal lattice together. During dissolution, the contact surface will further increase, since in the corrosion phase the crystal faces tend to develop minute hollows and knobs, called etching pits (diagrams 3 and 4 of Fig. 14).

Of two limestones containing equal quantities of magnesium carbonate — in the absence of other perturbing factors — that of higher crystallinity will incontestably lend itself to a more dynamic karst corrosion.

The diagrams presented in Figure 15 compare mineralogical forms of calcium and magnesium carbonate in rocks with the respective solubility

5*

levels. Statistical treatment suggests that a given amount of magnesium in the rock will retard dissolution less if it is dispersed in the calcite lattice than if forming dolomite or magnesite crystals. This will remain a tenuous hypothesis, however, until proved by many more experimental findings.

It should be pointed out again that an analysis of the influence of petro-variance upon karstification is by no means simple, since in nature several factors invariably act in concert, some with a tendency to promote, others with a tendency to retard the process of dissolution. In most cases, one or another of the factors will gain the upper hand under any specific set of local conditions, but solubility as such will, in the final analysis, always remain a complex vectorial resultant of a number of variable factors.

The problem is actually more complex than presented above, as we have not so far considered all the possible consequences of petrovariance. A review of these forms the subject of our next section.

3. INFLUENCE OF THE LITHOLOGY AND LIMESTONE STRUCTURE UPON KARST CORROSION

In the determination of corrosion dynamics, the structural and lithologic properties of the limestones play an important role. These terms include the rock's bedding, the nature of the hiatus or change in deposition giving rise to bedding planes, the fissuration of the rock, its consequent permeability and the mechanical strength of the limestone.

Unquestionably, the above features may occasionally predestine the rocks for the evolution of one or another set of forms. It was rightly remarked by MARTEL, as far back as 1908, that lapies furrows tend to be much more conspicuous on the surfaces of steeply-dipping thin-bedded limestones than on surfaces sculptured in thick-banked subhorizontal ones. We may add that laminar strongly-bedded limestones almost never exhibit "root" lapies, whereas these latter are typical microforms of dissolution in massive, poorly-bedded limestones. We shall later present abundant evidence proving this.

One of the principal structural factors controlling the qualitative aspect of karst evolution is *textural porosity*.

Dense homogeneous limestones have practically no textural porosity, and even holocrystalline ones have hardly any. This is probably due to the diagenetic compaction of calcareous mud, combined in the case of holo-crystalline limestone with a metamorphic compaction by overburden pressure and a high temperature (POLOVINKINA 1948).

On the other hand, mining under the karst water tables has resulted in an observation worthy of our attention, notably that even the densest limestones, with no apparent textural porosity to speak of, are texturally permeable to water if the pressure is sufficient. KASSAI (1948, p. 33) writes, for instance, that "In the coal basin of Esztergom, below the karst water table, the limestone invariably exhibits more than a simple humidity. Even what seems like a totally compact limestone will bleed water, the more so, the deeper we are below the level of karst water hazard — that is, the greater the hydrostatic pressure."

68

This observation, in apparent contradiction with the findings of petrographic texture studies and drying tests, is incontestably correct and unprejudiced. It has still not been decided satisfactorily, however, whether the permeability of the rock observed in this mining example is due entirely to textural porosity or to an unknown degree of invisible microscopic jointing; indeed, in most limestones, such microfissures are present almost from the last stages of diagenesis on.

The problem of rock porosity should not in any case be treated schematically. The evolution of a dense texture comparatively devoid of porosity is to some extent a function of stratigraphic age. It has been shown (CAYEUX 1935) that as a rule limestones are the denser, the greater their age. Young limestones (late Tertiary to Recent) are likely to be rather porous. For instance, the porosity of Sarmatian (late Miocene) limestone in Central Europe is usually 1 to 7 per cent, whereas that of more recent fresh-water limestones (calcareous tufa, meadow limestone) may exceed 20 per cent (PIA 1933).

* * *

Fissures and diaclases — a grid of joints in general — tend to develop primarily in massive, dense, older limestones. Owing to its compactness, the limestone is highly rigid, brittle when exposed to mechanical loads, and incapable of the slightest yielding (SCHMIDT 1953, 1957).

Even the intricate folded forms conspicuous in certain exposures of limestones must have developed by a fracturing of the rock into myriads of fragments, in their attempt to take up structural loads; consequently, the strata thus deformed are always more or less friable. If this is not the case, then their continuity is due to subsequent, post-tectonic cementation.

POLOVINKINA (1948) points out that any limestone in the earth's crust is liable to be exposed to physical loads (overburden pressure, stresses of mountain building, etc.), resulting in an intense microfissuration. Her studies revealed that the less recrystallized a limestone, the greater its degree of fissuration. This means in other words that subsequent ("annealing") recrystallization will to some extent reduce the brittleness of the rock: this should be compared with the excellent structural flexibility of calcite crystals. It is probable, incidentally, that dolomite tends to be more fissured than limestone, precisely because, in contrast with calcite, dolomite crystals are much less capable of recrystallization.

Structural fissuration is the principal factor of permeability to water in a limestone. This is why even a limestone with no textural porosity will almost invariably behave as a highly permeable deposit.

A study of the structural fissuration of several hundred limestones of various ages from different localities revealed the interesting correlation that permeability due to microfissuration in a limestone is a function, among others, of *geological age*. The largest number of fissures (10 to 36 per surface unit) are observed in Palaeozoic limestones; the numbers gradually decrease towards the present (6 to 12 for Mesozoic and 1 to 8 for Tertiary limestones). In Quaternary and Recent calcareous tufa, in contrast, structural hairline fissures are either absent or sporadic. This is to be

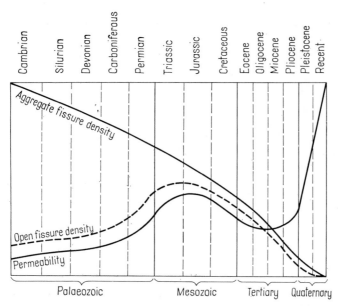

Fig. 16. Geological age plotted against permeability and open or obstructed structural fissuration in calcium carbonate rocks

expected incidentally, since a young rock can obviously not have such an eventful past of structural and other stresses as an older one.

It is also noteworthy, however, that the structural fissures of Carboniferous and older limestones tend to be cemented together quite strongly with secondary growths of calcite, which considerably reduces both their pore volume and permeability.

The interrelation between the geological age, the permeability, and the density of open and closed fissures in the limestones is illustrated in *Figure 16*.

Permeability in the limestone is one of the most fundamental prerequisites of karstification. The diagram shows that, in this respect, Quaternary limestones are most favoured: their high permeability is not due to structural fissuration, but to a high degree of textural porosity and an unconsolidated, often earthy, low-strength consistency. This is why the highest values of open-fissure network density, permeability and water storage capacity are observed in Mesozoic limestones: combined with the time required for karst evolution, this set of facts explains why the most conspicuous karst phenomena tend to occur most often in Triassic, Jurassic and Cretaceous limestones.

* * *

Another criterion of permeability in limestones is the *degree and nature of bedding* in the rock. The more pronounced the bedding of a limestone sequence, and the more numerous the bedding planes along which the rock may be separated, the better the rock will conduct water along the bedding planes. And since the bedding of limestones is, in a general way, connected with fluctuations in deposition (primarily fluctuations in pelite content), bedding-plane clefts let water pass precisely along those surfaces where the rock is most contaminated. This kind of conduction will therefore hamper dissolution; on the other hand, dissolution residues will be more abundant, facilitating the filling-up of fissures. Clearly, these circumstances are closely connected with the observation that conspicuously bedded limestones readily separable along the bedding planes are less prone to karstification than unbedded or thick-banked, homogeneous ones.

The diameters of the largest possible cavities, and the fundamental geomorphological features of the valleys and caverns formed by karst evolution, depend to a considerable extent on the mechanical strength of the limestone. Strength, in turn, is a function of bedding features and of hidden structural jointing, as well as of crystallinity and other textural features.

As a general rule, it is the completely dense, homogeneous, poorly-bedded or unbedded pure limestones with few open structural microfissures that tend to possess the highest mechanical stability. The lowest-strength limestone rocks, on the other hand, include unconsolidated calcareous tufa, and well-bedded limestones with alien matter (mainly argillaceous) along the bedding planes.

These physical properties of limestone are expediently tested by various special means (fissuration, for instance, is determined by drying a sample at 105 °C and saturating it with solutions of an intense dye, with subsequent inspection of thin slides). The detailed exposition of these methods (cf. e.g. OVCHINNIKOV 1938), however, goes beyond the scope of this book.

4. DOLOMITE CORROSION

Whereas corrosion plays a part of outstanding importance in the erosion of limestone, the corrosion of dolomite, according to the currently accepted geomorphological view, is a subordinate process (BULLA 1954/1). This finding is based in part on the facts that dolomite is less soluble both in pure water and in water containing carbonic acid than is limestone, and that the rate of karst corrosion in dolomite is therefore much slower. On the other hand, however, and this is the more decisive factor, dolomite has a tendency to disintegrate into angular fragments and powder: this process of "karstophobic" eluviation, unknown in limestone, combined with the ablation of the products of comminution, proves a dominant relief-forming factor, taking precedence over corrosive effects in dolomite areas. Hence, even though genetically it is justified to speak of the karstic corrosion of dolomite, the textbook set of karst forms will very seldom be met with in dolomite regions. This is why GRUND (1903), for one, regards dolomite reliefs as semi-karstic only.

As to the solubility of dolomite in water containing a little carbonic acid, the literature provides no mutually corroborative, clear-cut data. The references available, however, suggest that the majority of authors consider the solubility of dolomite about half that of limestone (CAYEUX 1935, TROMBE 1952, MÁNDY 1954, etc.), although others find no significant difference between the two solubilities (SCHOELLER 1956, MARKÓ 1961, MAKSIMOVICH 1963/1, etc.).

Clearly, an unequivocal stand in this matter has been much delayed by the small number of relevant experiments, and by the wide range of mineral samples examined. In fact, it appears vain to look for a single norm of solubility covering all dolomite rocks. Solubility depends fairly considerably on the chemical, mineralogical, textural and structural properties of the rock, which may vary over an even broader range than in limestone. This is confirmed by the chemical analyses of some dolomites reported in *Table 9*.

It is apparent that normal dolomite rock, made up exclusively of mineralogically pure dolomite $(CaMg(CO_3)_2)$, occurs very seldom in large masses, that is, as a monomineralic rock. Dolomite rock ("dolostone") most often contains more $CaCO_3$ than the theoretical norm (54·35 per cent $CaCO_3$ and 45·65 per cent $MgCO_3$); $MgCO_3$ is but seldom in excess (e.g. in crystals formed in the American Great Salt Lake).

In the usual cases, the excess $CaCO_3$ tends to form a calcite cement holding together the rhombohedral crystals of the double carbonate. Hence, the dissolution of an average dolomite is the result of two distinct parallel processes:

1. The dissolution of the calcite cementing together the double-salt crystals; and

2. the dissolution of the double-salt (dolomite) grains proper*.

Clearly, since the solubilities of calcite, dolomite, and magnesite all differ, in either case corrosion sooner or later results in mineralogical selection. The solubility of pure calcite (and of pure magnesite) being higher than that of the double salt, selective dissolution results in a process with characteristic end-products: the comminution of dolomite by chemical weathering, and the formation of pulverulent dolomite and dolomite debris.

This, then, leads us to a novel explanation of the comminution and structural loosening of dolomite, a topic insufficiently dealt with in the geological and physical-geographical literature. The reader will be aware that the textbook explanations (J. SZABÓ 1883, BULLA 1954/1, VADÁSZ 1955, LOUIS 1964) attribute the highly characteristic comminution and pulverulence of dolomite to the physical weathering processes of insolation and frost, combined with the extraordinary rigidity of dolomite. In Hungarian literature, moreover, the local action of hydrothermal solutions has come to be emphasized (PÁLFFY 1920/1—2, SCHERF 1922, BRUGGER 1940, L. JAKUCS 1948, 1950). Another aspect of the phenomenon, however, that dissolution too may contribute to the comminution of dolomite, in addition to the above factors, and that in this context comminution and pulverization are karst phenomena of holocrystalline dolomite, has not, as far as this author is aware, been examined at all.

* In dolomites containing excess $MgCO_3$, of course, it is the mineral magnesite that assumes the role of cement, and the process of corrosion can then be broken down into the parallel dissolutions of dolomite and magnesite. This variant, however, is fairly rare in nature.

Table 9

Chemical composition of various dolomites

Sample analysed	Percentage of sample containing								
	CaO	MgO	CO$_2$	SiO$_2$	Fe$_2$O$_3$	Al$_2$O$_3$	SO$_3$	Others	Total
Theoretical composition of pure dolomite	30·4	21·9	47·7	—	—	—	—	—	100·0
Upper Permian dolomite (Kazan age) from near *Gorki* (after SHVETSOV)	32·40	17·94	45·11	2·58	0·42	0·71	0·45	—	99·61
Lower Carboniferous dolomite from south flank of *Moscow Basin* (after SAMOLYOV and PUSTOVALYOV)	25·99	17·17	37·38	15·19	1·02	2·16	0·06	1·13	100·10
Dolomite from the *Podolian Platform* (after SMIRNOV)	35·48	14·62	44·27	2·08	1·06	1·08	—	0·98	99·57
Triassic (Lower Carnian) dolomite, *Sas Hill, Budapest, Hungary* (after BRUGGER)	29·01	20·09	44·18	5·97	0·19	0·23	0·013	0·507	100·19
Triassic (Upper Carnian) dolomite from *Nagykevély Hill, Budapest, Hungary* (after BRUGGER)	33·98	18·95	46·82	0·03	0·09	0·09	0·01	0·42	100·39
Diploporian dolomite (Ladinian, Triassic) from *Ökrös Hill, Budapest, Hungary* (after BRUGGER)	31·22	21·50	47·24	0·03	0·03	0·05	0·015	0·095	100·18

It should be pointed out that, according to my own observations and the available references, non-crystalline dolomites, with an apparently amorphous structure resembling that of massive limestones, nowhere exhibit the comminution and granulation so typical of holocrystalline dolomites. This is readily explained. Dolomites that have not undergone postgenetic recrystallization and mineralic differentiation do not, of course, lend themselves to selective dissolution by water, since the calcium and magnesium carbonates uniformly interdispersed in the rock present a uniform resistance to corrosion, just as is the case with limestones. The only difference is that, whereas the postgenetic recrystallization of limestone does not impair this uniformity of resistance, that of dolomite does.

The above considerations also provide a ready explanation for the observation that the typical corrosional features of a karst relief (lapies, dolines), so typical of limestone regions, are largely restricted in dolomite regions to those lithofacies that are either unrecrystallized or, if holocrystalline, contain $CaCO_3$ and $MgCO_3$ in a proportion not much different from the norm. In those dolomite mountains where the dolomite is saccharoidal or even marble-like (e.g. in the Buda Hills of Hungary; in the Dolomites of the Southern Tyrol; around the Binnental in Switzerland; around the Brenner in Tyrol), there are quite extensive dolomite surfaces almost entirely devoid of dolines or lapies fields, and the forms are dominated by the typical alluvial fans and other relief elements of the comminuted rock, reminiscent of a desert landscape.

All in all, then, the karstic corrosion of dolomite may result in a fundamentally different set of forms, since the process of corrosive erosion and the geomorphological character of the resulting landscape are, to a major extent, the macroformal expression of the rock's textural properties.

A phenomenon worthy of notice — obviously a consequence of the mineralogical heterogeneity of dolomites— is that the relative Mg content of a solution in contact with dolomite increases as the temperature of the solvent water increases, a phenomenon experimentally documented by MÁNDY (1954).

He compared the solubilities in CO_2-saturated water of five dolomite samples taken at different localities. After determining the solubilities at room temperature, he repeated the experiment at 40 °C, likewise using solutions saturated in CO_2. He adjusted the flow rates of the solvent stream-

Table 10

Results of dolomite dissolution from T. MÁNDY (1954)

Temperature of solution, °C	Runoff rate, litre per hour	Dissolved carbonate components of the five samples (see text) in mg/l									
		1		2		3		4		5	
		CaCO₃	MgCO₃	CaCO₃	MgCO₃	CaCO₃	MgCO₃	CaCO₃	MgCO₃	CaCO₃	MgCO₃
15	0·05	93	32	37	25	169	93	103	34	46	40
	0·2	45	17	22	16	78	40	59	19	22	20
40	0·05	23	72	30	65	40	70	38	77	31	73
	0·2	20	34	21	39	27	41	25	44	20	30

ing down the samples at both 0·05 and 0·20 litres per hour, in order to explore the influence on the dissolution of the application of the same amount of water over different periods of time. Mándy's findings are summarized in *Table 10*.

The data unequivocally prove that after cold dissolution (at 15 °C) the solution is richer in $CaCO_3$ than in $MgCO_3$. The change in flow rate affects both concentrations, but not the $CaCO_3 : MgCO_3$ ratio, which averaged over all measurements 2·07 at 0·05 l/h and 2·03 at 0·20 l/h.

As regards the results at 40 °C, on the other hand, it is seen that the concentration of Ca is less, and that of Mg more than at 15 °C: indeed, at 40 °C, Mg becomes dominant even in the absolute sense: the Ca : Mg ratio drops from about 2 to about 0·5 or 0·6, depending on the flow rate.

This temperature dependence is reflected in *Figure 17*, showing plots for the dissolution of the five samples at both temperatures, with a flow rate of 0·05 l/h.

The purport of these findings for the karstic corrosion of dolomite confirms the earlier deductive conclusion that cold phreatic waters dissolve first and foremost the calcite cementing the dolomite grains; the dolomite grains proper are dissolved to a much smaller extent. The dolomite debris resulting from corrosion is therefore invariably closer in composition to the norm of pure dolomite than is the parent rock. Mándy's findings verify this experimentally.

The experiments proving the considerably increased aggressivity of water at 40 °C towards the dolomite compound, together with a reduced calcite aggressivity, imply that hot water (e.g. a thermal spring) does not give rise to selective dissolution and hence to comminution, since the rate of dissolution of the double carbonate crystals is higher than that of the calcite cementing them.

This conclusion might appear to contradict the findings of some Hungarian research into hydrothermally induced pulverization in dolomites (SCHERF 1922, L. JAKUCS 1950). In reality, however, there is no such contradiction, because if the hydrothermal solutions exerted merely the

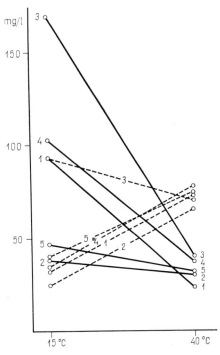

Fig. 17. Solubility rates of various dolomites (after MÁNDY, 1954) under a dripping of 0·05 litre per hour of water saturated at atmospheric pCO_2 at 15 and 40 °C. Abundances in the solution are shown by full lines for $CaCO_3$ and dashed lines for $MgCO_3$

Sampling localities: 1 — Veszprém, Séd Valley, Balaton Highland; 2 — Tatabánya, Quarry, Gerecse Hills; 3 — Budapest, Gellért Hill; 4 — Budapest, Rózsadomb; 5 — Vác, Naszály Hill

pure dissolving action of hot water, there would be no reason for dolomite to be pulverized next to a hot spring. Natural thermal waters, however, also attack the rock via a number of other chemical agents, including strong acids (sulphuric acid in particular), ascending from great depth, and other compounds that selectively react with the calcite content of the rock.

We have already considered the exchange reactions involving $CaCO_3$ and the fairly widespread sulphuric acid and iron sulphate [eqs (7) and (15)]. If the calcite cementing the dolomite crystals is converted by these agents into gypsum or siderite, then the rock will certainly fall apart immediately.

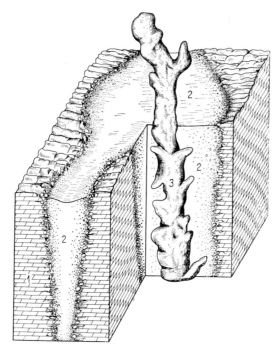

Fig. 18. Hydrothermally induced pulverization in dolomite accompanying a silicified former hot-spring funnel from the Csiki Hills, Budaörs, near Budapest

1 — fresh dolomite; 2 — pulverized dolomite; 3 — silicified spring funnel raised above the surface by selective erosion

On the other hand, it was shown some time ago (L. JAKUCS 1950) that the pulverization of dolomite, almost an obligatory accompaniment to hot springs (recent and ancient) (e.g. in the Buda Hills), is due to the fact that, in the zone warmed up by contact with the surging hot water, the pore solutions will deposit aragonite and possibly also anhydrite in the rock texture; the conversion of these minerals to calcite and gypsum, stable at the mean ambient temperature after cessation of the hydrothermal activity, will result in a volume increase. This swelling entails a loosening of the entire rock body.

The pulverized loosened dolomite may thus be a product of various processes. If it is restricted in space to a narrow zone about a hot spring (*Fig. 18*), it is logical to ascribe it to the chemical and mineralogical factors just described, whereas a more areal occurrence (e.g. in the Dolomites of the

South Tyrol) entails the dominance of selective karst corrosion, discussed farther above. The loosening of the rock structure can thus be identified as to origin in almost every case simply by studying the geometry of the phenomenon.

BRUGGER's (1940) interesting observations concerning the in situ pulverization of dolomite next to an entirely fresh dolomite rock, and the chemical and mineralogical differences between the two, are in full agreement with the above considerations concerning the selective dissolution behaviour of dolomite. After a very painstaking study, Brugger concluded that the contents of Fe_2O_3, SiO_2 as well as $CaCO_3$ in the pulverized dolomites of hot-spring zones are higher than those in the parent rock. Brugger could find no explanation for this observation, but the present state of knowledge does permit this.

Selective dissolution of the double-carbonate crystals of the rock by hot hydrothermal water affects the comparative enrichment of $CaCO_3$ in the thermal corrosion zone. This dissolution does not yet result directly in pulverization. It is the iron sulphate content of the water infiltrating the rock that brings about a certain degree of sideritization in the texture (as proved by the increased iron content) and acts as a pulverizer. Incidentally, the slightly raised SiO_2 content is also an indicator of hydrothermal origin.

To revert to the original problem — the normal areally extensive karst corrosion of dolomite and the resulting comminution — it is necessary to point out another connexion. Reports by H. LEHMANN (1948, 1954/2, 1955, 1960), BULLA (1954/2), RENAULT (1959), SAINT-OURS (1959) and WHITE (1962), etc. indicate that weathering by comminution, so typical of the erosion of dolomite reliefs in the temperate zone and the concomitant formation of alluvial fans in the foothills, is absent from the tropical zones, especially those regions with two rainy seasons. In these zones, even holocrystalline dolomites exhibit a set of forms similar to the corrosive karst forms of a limestone relief. That this is a regular phenomenon is verified by some Hungarian examples, as the dolomite-karst reliefs underlying the bauxite deposits of Transdanubia, sculpted by corrosive erosion under the tropical climate of the Cretaceous, exhibit the same karst forms as the adjacent limestones (VADÁSZ 1951/1, 1955, 1957, P. Z. SZABÓ 1956, 1964, 1968).

The comminution of dolomite has earlier been attributed in geomorphology to frost action, with the traditional, obvious, but rather shallow argument that as there is no frost in the tropical zone there is no dolomite comminution either. It must now be recognized, however, that there is another factor, by no means insignificant in comparison with frost action, in the selective corrosion of dolomite: its mechanism of action is strongly temperature-dependent. It therefore requires no particular courage to present as a new principle the statement that the absence of dolomite comminution in tropical regions, combined with the dominance of karst forms typical of limestone regions, is attributable not only to the absence of frost action, but also to the characteristic aggressivity of warm rains towards dolomite, a fact recognized some time ago.

It is still too early to try to assess the comparative intensities of the factors involved. It is to be hoped, however, that suitably oriented field studies will soon permit them to be ascertained.

5. DISSOLUTION OF GYPSUM AND ROCK SALT

In addition to the limestones and dolomites already discussed, the earth's solid crust also contains other rocks soluble in water, which exhibit similar corrosional (karst) phenomena. In general, any monomineralic rock deposited from aqueous solution is capable of total, residueless dissolution in water.

This group is known to contain deposits whose rates of dissolution are exceedingly low (e.g. silica gel): accordingly, their forms of erosion do not reflect the phenomena of corrosion. In some others, dissolution is much more rapid, and may therefore become one of the controlling factors of the relief. In this second group, rock salt should be mentioned first, gypsum and anhydrite second.

The dissolution of rock salt and gypsum in water are much simpler processes than the carbonate dissolution of limestone, as the dynamism depends merely on the solubility coefficient of the substance in question, the area of the interface between solvent and solid phase, the duration of contact, and the temperature of the system. Carbonic acid, the complicating factor in the dissolution of limestone, is not involved.

The solubility product of NaCl (rock salt) is particularly high, and depends comparatively little on temperature. It may be stated as a fair approximation that three parts of water (by weight) dissolve one part of NaCl.

The case of calcium sulphate is not quite so simple and clear, mainly because it is necessary to make a distinction between gypsum, which contains two molecules of combined water ($CaSO_4 \cdot 2H_2O$), and anhydrite, which contains none. Gypsum is more soluble than anhydrite, but both are far less soluble than rock salt and much more soluble than limestone. Expressed numerically, gypsum is 183 times, and rock salt more than 25,000 times more soluble than calcite in distilled water at 20 °C. The exact figures are listed in *Table 11*. It is apparent from the table that, in the range most widespread in nature, 0 to 20 °C, a temperature drop in the

Table 11

Temperature dependence of solubility and recrystallization of calcium sulphate minerals

	Dissolution in pure water		Nature of phase precipitated		
Temperature °C	Anhydrite $CaSO_4$ g/l	Gypsum $CaSO_4 \cdot 2H_2O$ g/l	from single-component solution	from saturated NaCl solution	from normal sea water
0	1·756	2·221	gypsum	gypsum	gypsum
10	1·926	2·436	gypsum	gypsum	gypsum
18	2·016	2·550	gypsum	gypsum	gypsum
25	2·085	2·637	gypsum	gypsum	anhydrite
30	2·095	2·650	gypsum	gypsum	anhydrite
35	2·105	2·662	gypsum	anhydrite	anhydrite
40	2·108	2·666	gypsum	anhydrite	anhydrite
45	2·1000	—	gypsum	anhydrite	anhydrite
55	2·083	2·634	gypsum	anhydrite	anhydrite
65	2·075	—	anhydrite	anhydrite	anhydrite
75	1·88	2·38	anhydrite	anhydrite	anhydrite
100	1·69	2·14	anhydrite	anhydrite	anhydrite

saturated solution will precipitate a comparatively large quantity of calcium sulphate. For instance, a temperature reduction from 10 to 0 °C will precipitate out about 0·2 g/l of gypsum: that is, even one degree of cooling will yield about 20 mg/l.

TROMBE (1952) is thus probably right in calling attention to this aspect of the formation of gypsum together with ice stalactites in ice caves. He states that, in the Devaux cave, situated at an altitude of 2840 m, and also in the Esparros Sinkhole in the Pyrénées, subterranean ice formations are accompanied by substantial amounts of gypsum of Recent crystallization. TROMBE ascribes these formations to the calcium sulphate supersaturation from a substantially cooler solution.

Solution behaviour as a function of temperature is presented for both gypsum and anhydrite in *Figure 19*.

Table 11 further reveals that the mineralogical form of the precipitate (either gypsum or anhydrite) is substantially influenced by the other salts present in solution: anhydrite is formed from a single-component solution only above 63·5 °C, whereas normal sea-water precipitates anhydrite even at 25 °C. Indeed, in brines more concentrated than sea-water, the temperature of changeover from gypsum to anhydrite is even further reduced.

This is, incidentally, why the seas tend most often to deposit anhydrite rather than gypsum: even under conditions favourable for hydration, these primary layers change into gypsum only later, by subsequent absorption of water.

The transformation of anhydrite into gypsum by the uptake of water requires additional space, however, as the process is accompanied by a substantial swelling. One cm³ of anhydrite gives rise to 1·577 cm³ gypsum, a swelling of about 36·5 per cent (BIESE 1931). In terms of linear expansion this means that each centimetre of an anhydrite column expands to 1·164 cm.

In nature, anhydrite will swell by hydration only if the stresses generated by the process can be released by the displacement of the overburden. Even the pressure of a gypsum deposit 4 to 5 m thick is sufficient to forestall hydration. This is why anhydrite deposits of considerable thickness (e.g. at Stassfurt, in the Harz or Kyffhäuser mountains, etc.) remain as anhydrite over

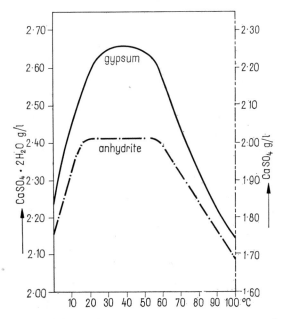

Fig. 19. Solubilities in pure water of gypsum and anhydrite plotted against temperature

Photo 1. "Forest Smithy" ("Waldschmiede") grotto due to gypsum swelling, near Walkenried on the southern rim of the Harz Mountains (GDR). The photo shows clearly that the layer transformed into gypsum by wetting, and forming a half-collapsed bubble, is just a few tens of centimetres thick, as the intake of crystal water by anhydrite is prevented by overburden pressure at greater depths. Of several such grottoes known in the Harz Mountains, this one was the largest (8 m long, 4 m wide and 2 m high). Unfortunately, according to REINBOTH (1967) the arch of the grotto has been seriously damaged by hikers, so that today it presents a rather depressing sight

very long periods of geological time; gypsum is formed only at the top of the deposit, along faults, and in the linings of erosional caverns within the deposit proper (*Photo 1*).

This is precisely the *fundamental difference between the corrosive erosion of a limestone and a gypsum karst*. In a limestone karst, any small fissure in the rock has the potential of widening, in time, into a spacious passage, and this potential is realized in a large number of cases during the development of the karst, whereas in a gypsum karst no deep passage for water can form in this way, since we have just seen that only the top few metres really consist of gypsum, the rest of the deposit below being anhydrite throughout.

FULDA (1912) was the first to point out that even if joints or fissures traversing the gypsum cap rock and penetrating into the anhydrite may develop for one reason or another, these will close up in a very short time, owing to the swelling resulting from conversion of the anhydrite into gypsum by the water seeping down the fissures.

In contrast to limestone, then, corrosive karstification does not involve the entire mass of anhydrite lying above the baselevel of erosion, but only a few metres thick gypsum layer, coating the anhydrite deposit, the central anhydrite core remaining unaffected. Exceptions, if any, are restricted to fissures and cavities so wide that no swelling can close them up. Such exceptions include structural or non-structural fissure caverns which, under suitable hydrological and environmental conditions, may unite the development potentials, as well as the initial stages, of both corrosional and erosional gypsum caves.

If the circumstances just discussed were to be disregarded, no realistic interpretation of the intensity of karst dynamism due to the processes of erosion of anhydrite and gypsum could be achieved, nor could a morphogenetic analysis of gypsum karsts be provided. For one thing, it would be incomprehensible why the development of gypsum karsts, as reflected by their set of relief forms, does not attain in any region or climatic zone that of the limestone karsts exposed to similar conditions, although the solubility of gypsum exceeds that of limestone almost 200 times.

6. KARST CORROSION OF POLYMINERAL ROCKS

Our interpretation of corrosion phenomena above was concerned exclusively with *chemically monogenous sedimentary deposits.* This has been relevant since even karsts formed from sediments contain little or no mineral substance of extraneous, primarily detrital, origin.

Of course, polymineral rocks too are soluble to some extent, but this does not play a decisive role in controlling the erosion of the rock. There are two reasons for this.

Firstly, the individual grains of polymineral rocks (whether igneous or sedimentary in origin) have different solubilities, and thus any dissolution is selective. We have learned from the selective dissolution of dolomite, however, that the evolution of the corrosion forms observed in limestones is hampered and repressed by the mass of debris resulting from the falling-apart of the rock from textural reasons.

Secondly — and in most polymineral rocks, more significantly — the chemical decomposition of one or other, or possibly a combination of the mineral constituents of the rock may proceed faster than the process of dissolution; in this case, the accumulating insoluble residues of weathering act as an obstacle to corrosion. Their immediate removal would not accelerate the process either, as in a relief underlain by such rocks the influence of slower dissolution is insignificant compared with the much faster chemical weathering, which gives rise to an entirely different set of forms.

Thus, the reason for not mentioning the dissolution, for example, of granite, andesite or clays in rainwater and ground water does not imply the absence of the phenomena of dissolution, but that *de facto* dissolution is subordinate, as a rule, in relief forms to the other, more aggressive and dynamic tendencies of weathering. But as the trained ear of a music lover will pick out the note of the faintest instrument from the fortissimo flood of sound of a full symphonic orchestra, so must we recognize and purposefully explore all intrinsic factors affecting the evolution of relief forms.

Of course, the dissolution effects are the harder to recognize, the more dominant the weathering process, whose intensity depends far more than corrosion on factors of climatic zonality. Thus, even in granite, held to be the most typically weathering rock, a suitable combination of extrinsic conditions in the absence of all the climatic prerequisites of chemical weathering will permit corrosive forms to assert themselves.

As an illustration, let us refer to RASMUSSON (1959), who described limestone-like forms of corrosion in the Fichtel Mountains granite (FRG), or to BULLA (1954/1), who discussed in detail lapies-like forms indicative of dissolution phenomena in granite. Bulla mentions, for example, that, as a result of dissolution, depressions and basins of various sizes develop on a bare granite surface; rain-water will accumulate and stagnate in these. Their diameter and depth may attain one metre; they may be bounded by vertical and even overhanging slopes. Such granite basins on the tops and slopes of smooth-surfaced granite domes in the Diamond Mountains near Seoul are locally called the "angels' ointment jars". Shallow basalt dolines in Transdanubia (Hungary) are probably of the same origin. In South Korea, the corrosion of granite has even resulted in some small caves. According to MAUFE, there are corrosion caves in the granite of the South African Matapo Hills, due to dissolution by the humic acids produced by roots reaching down into vertical rock fissures (cf. in this respect TÓTH 1931, MORTENSEN 1949 and LAUTENSACH 1945, 1950).

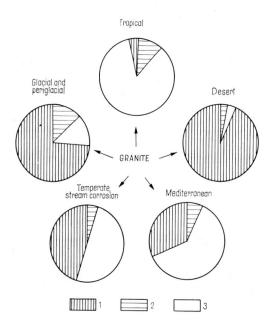

Fig. 20. Contribution to granite erosion of aqueous corrosion in various zones of climatic morphology

1 — physical weathering (insolation, frost); 2 — dissolution; 3 — chemical weathering

After a critical listing of literature references and their comparison with our own observations, we composed diagrams showing the percentage contributions of various agencies to the erosion of granite in the different climatic zones. The results are shown in *Figure 20*.

Some of the polymineral rocks are, of course, far more amenable to dissolution than granite, such as those in which the end-products of a weathering cycle (e.g. sand grains) are cemented by a soluble mineral, say calcite. These rocks will usually undergo selective dissolution, in almost the same way as does dolomite. This group of deposits includes sandstones with calcareous cement and loess.

In a sandstone, corrosion attacks the calcareous cement holding the quartz grains to-

82

Fig. 21. Ordnance map of the north-west part of the loess plateau at Titel (near confluence of rivers Danube and Tisza). On the plateau, sharply outlined by erosion scarps, a large number of loess dolines are apparent

gether. The advance of corrosion is indicated by the comminution of the rock: its falling-apart into sand. The phenomenon does not usually attain an intensity comparable with the corrosion of dolomite, however, because calcareous sandstones usually possess less free porosity, and thus offer less surface to attack by corrosion, than do holocrystalline dolomites.

To recognize the validity of this, one should bear in mind that sandstone diagenesis is effected by calcareous solutions pervading unconsolidated layers of sand, the precipitated calcite in most cases completely filling the interstices of the grains, eliminating all porosity. In dolomite, on the other hand, diagenesis takes a different course. Most dolomites were limestones to start with, and were dolomitized post-depositionally according to eq. (18) by magnesium solutions permeating the deposits. As we have seen, however, the emplacement of magnesium in limestone entails a reduction in volume, the shrinkage cracks between the dolomite crystals (mostly rhombohedral) being only partly filled with the calcium carbonate remaining after reaction, and playing the role of a mortar. Hence, in dolomite, corrosion may penetrate deep into the texture; that is, a rock body may be karstified three-dimensionally to some depth. In sandstone this is impossible: corrosion will be areal (two-dimensional), that is, much slower compared with the dynamics of dolomite corrosion.

Loess corrosion provides another example of selective dissolution; as it is taken into the rock, calcium carbonate dissolved during passage through surface layers is transferred deeper into the ground-water zone, where it is often precipitated to form the so-called "loess dolls". In thick loess deposits where the water table is deep down, and all water over long periods filters downward, considerable leaching of calcium carbonate from the surface layers may occur; this is accompanied by the near-surface compaction of the loess, deprived of its calcareous skeleton, and loam formation. In our view, this is the explanation for the classic loess dolines on the loess plateaux in China and near Titel (Yugoslavia) (*Fig. 21*).

The above emphasis is required because our opinion differs from the textbook schemes. According to BULLA (cf. Vol. II of his General physical geography, 1954/1, pp. 467—468), "there is a direct connexion between the calcium carbonate content of loess and the karst forms (loess dolines, cavities, loess sinkholes) developed in it, in the sense that the precipitations seeping into a loess dissolve the calcium carbonate linings of loess particles, thus widening the capillaries. The vertical clefts thus formed then gradually coalesce. After the collapse of the walls separating the vertical fissures, the domes covering larger and wider cavities can not stand up to the load; they collapse into themselves and remain drainageless saucer-shaped depressions, loess dolines of various sizes.

Our observations suggest that the process described by Bulla mainly refers to loess sinkholes and canyons, and the formation of loess dolines is not due to the collapse of cavities but to pedogenetic processes accompanying decalcification by corrosion as described above; the pedogenetic processes of clay formation, changing the consistency of the deposit, result in local compaction, accompanied by what might be termed the phenomena of micro-solifluxion. In the course of our field studies with S. LEEL-ŐSSY, concerning the loess dolines about Tinnye and Zsámbék (Hungary) we invariably observed more clayey, compact, more leached loesses in the dolines than farther away. Loess corrosion still presents many unsolved problems but discussion of these lies beyond the scope of this book.

EPEIROGENIC MOVEMENTS AS FACTORS OF KARSTIFICATION

We have so far studied the process of karst corrosion from the aspect of the dissolution potential of water and of the solubility of the rock. Karst erosion is controlled by a number of other essential factors too, however, serving both qualitatively and quantitatively as fundamental criteria of the process reflected in the resulting set of forms. One of the most important of these factors is the *specific structural condition* of the rock body: this means that we must investigate the local features conducive to or repressive of karstification; these features stem from post-diagenetic dislocations resulting in the macrotectonic structure of a rock suitable for karstification particularly connected with its petrographic nature.

It is not our task, of course, to present the relevant concepts, processes and consequences of geomechanics: these are satisfactorily treated in the excellent works of BILLINGS (1942), SCHMIDT (1957) and KETTNER (1959). Some of the fundamental problems are of such immediate karst genetical relevance, however, that we cannot avoid touching upon them. It must be pointed out, among others, that a pack of strata may, during its epeirogenic and orogenic deformation in the earth's crust, be exposed to the fundamental types of influences shown in *Figure 22*; these will be functions of its consistency, its temperature, the absolute pressure of the reaction space, the axial stress, and their duration.

The reaction may be of two types: folding or faulting, or possibly a combination of the two in the same or in different time. Factors imparting a predisposition towards folding (the development of folded forms) include plasticity of the rock, high temperature, a comparatively strong geostatic pressure and a comparatively weak axial stress, and a long duration of both. In contrast, faulting is promoted by the rigidity of the rock, low temperature, low geostatic pressure in the deformation space, and a short paroxysm of strong axial stress.

The overall rigidity of the rock may depend not only on its composition, but also to a certain extent on the nature and degree of its bedding: a thick-bedded limestone, for instance, may be more brittle under dynamic stresses than a slaty-bedded limestone, otherwise of identical composition, whose bedding planes may serve as slip planes, thereby increasing the overall plasticity of the pack of strata.

Depending on the vectorial resultant of all these factors, the crustal stress situations outlined in Figure 22 may give rise to the fundamental types of deformation presented in *Figure 23*.

Of course, any dislocation taking place above the local base-level of erosion has a tendency to promote karstification, as surface contact between

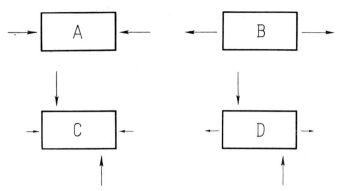

Fig. 22. Fundamental types of mechanical stress acting on a rock
A — linear compression; B — linear extension; C — shear plus
lateral compression; D — shear plus lateral extension

rock and water increases. Even in the situations A/II, C/I and C/III (in Fig. 23) involving compression, the closed fault planes will open up the rock to allow the passage of water. This is a separate process from water migration through the innumerable syngenetic hairline fissures developed in the rigid rock without displacement during times of intense stress, which accompany the plane of visible displacement in a block-faulted mountain.

The zones of preferred fissuration in folded forms due to tangential stresses are illustrated without commentary and are self-evident in *Figure 24*.

Those dislocations derived from tensile stresses in the crust most often result in broad gaping fissures. These clefts may be several metres wide, several hundred metres long, and often arranged in a grid pattern of intersecting subparallel sets; they tend to give rise to very complicated, labyrinthine fissure caverns, independent of all previous karstification, but they represent a substantial influence on the post-tectonic stage of karst evolution.

An idea of the extent and grid density of open fissures accessible to man within a given rock mass is given in *Figure 25*; this is the ground plan, bearing witness to a monumental mapping effort, of the Optimisticheskaya Peshchera (Optimists' Cavern) in the Upper Tortonian (Miocene) anhydrite and gypsum karst of the Podolian Platform along the Seret River (Soviet Union).

It is worth pointing out that this is the longest known gypsum cavern on earth; as surveyed up to 1974, the aggregate length of its passages, about 2 m wide and 2·7 m high on average, is 109 km (SAVCHIN 1974 after DUBLYANSKY 1966). The passages have developed in a horizontal deposit of anhydrite, not more than 15 to 25 m thick, largely transformed to gypsum by now, in an area of not more than 2·3 square kilometres.

Several other extensive gypsum caverns are also situated on the Podolian platform. The so-called Ozernaya Peshchera (Lake Cavern), according to a survey between 1966 and 1973 by the "Cyklop" Speleological Club of Lvov,

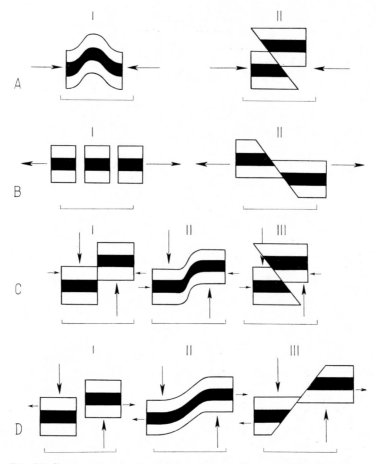

Fig. 23. Compressive and extension deformations resulting in joints
and diaclases: fundamental types

A/I — compression by folding (plastic deformation); A/II — compression by reverse faulting (brittle deformation); B/I — extension
by vertical faulting (formation of chasms: brittle deformation);
B/II — extension by normal faulting (brittle deformation); C/I —
vertical, unopened fault caused by shear plus lateral compression, with no change in the horizontal extent of the crustal segment
involved (brittle deformation); C/II — double flexure caused by
shear plus lateral compression (plastic deformation); C/III — reverse faulting caused by shear plus lateral compression, resulting
in shortening of the crustal segment involved (brittle deformation);
D/I — formation of chasm involving extension of crustal segment
involved under shear plus lateral extension (brittle deformation);
D/II — double flexure with thinning of middle limb under shear
plus lateral extension (plastic deformation); D/III — normal fault
caused by shear plus lateral extension (brittle deformation)

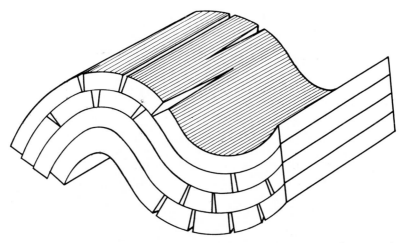

Fig. 24. Genetic interpretation of diaclases on an anticlinal ridge and in a synclinal trough, parallel to the fold axis (after TRIMMEL 1950)

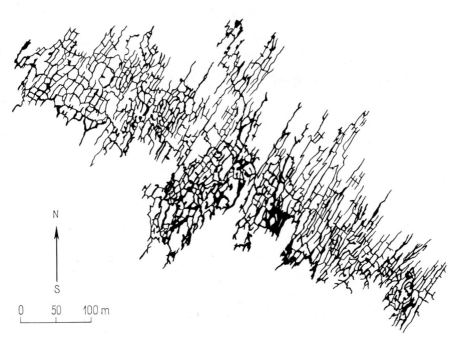

N

↑

|

S

0   50   100 m

Fig. 25. Ground plan reflecting a structurally controlled speleogenesis on a complicated fault pattern: Kristalnaya Peshchera (Crystal cavern; after DUBLYANSKY 1963)

Photo 2. Fault-plane striation indicative of a vertical fault-block displacement on a wall of a cavity of structural origin in the Baradla Cavern at Aggtelek, Hungary

is 103 km long. This cavern is likewise a labyrinthine array of pseudostructural fissures.

The most important distinctive feature of fissure caverns is the presence of smooth plane-sided walls, and also the great height and length of the passages as compared to their usually uniform narrow width. The cross-sections of the passages are usually of the types shown in *Figure 26*.

If the cavern is indeed of tectonic origin, with passages formed by orogenic crustal deformations, then at the points marked by X in the cross-sections one is likely to find fault breccias and other traces of stress reaction, whereas the side walls often exhibit parallel striations (cf. *Photo 2*). These features are never observed in pseudotectonic (or non-tectonic) fissure cavities.

90

Pseudotectonic cavities may be formed in various ways, for instance by surface rockslides, by the formation of desiccation or shrinkage cracks, by the collapse of cavities of a different origin, etc. Comparatively frequent occurrences include the type of cavity formed by huge blocks of rock falling down an undercut high steep slope and leaning against it (A in *Fig. 27*), and the displacement of a block of rock by plastic deformation of the underlying beds under overburden pressure (B in *Fig. 27*).

As pointed out by SZÉKELY (1953), this was the origin of the largest non-karstic cavern of Hungary, the 139 m long Csörgőlyuk in the Mátra Hills. According to Székely, the cavern was preformed by a NE-SW structural line. The

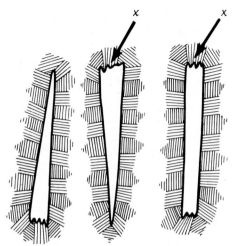

Fig. 26. Most frequent profile types of passages in structurally controlled caverns (there is usually a mylonitic breccia at the point marked *x*)

fissures were opened by the slow spasmodic sliding of the rock slab on and in the underlying rhyolite tuff, rendered plastic by saturation with water and by other phenomena.

Of course, both tectonic and pseudotectonic fissure caverns may form in any kind of rock, but they do not usually control the subsequent nature of erosion of the rock mass except in limestones, because it is in limestone,

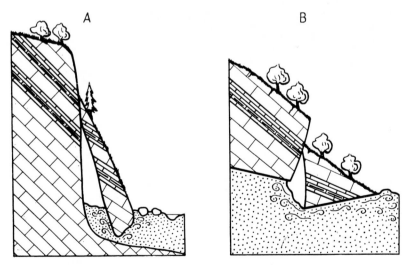

Fig. 27. The most frequent modes of formation of pseudostructural fissure caves

Photo 3. Furrowed masses of rock salt indicative of intense surface corrosion by precipitation (Parajd, Transylvania)

owing to the specific petrophysical nature of that rock, that fissures thus formed may persist longest; so long indeed, that their widening via slow karst corrosion by the waters gaining access to them may keep pace with the natural processes of cavity destruction. Limestones do not incorporate those insoluble residues that sooner or later fill up the tectonic fissures in polymineral rocks.

Even among monomineral rocks soluble without a solid residue, limestone stands out by virtue of its high strength. Gypsum caverns, for instance, may not be long-lived in the geological sense, since gypsum — being much more plastic than limestone — sooner or later fills its own cavities by plastic deformation, unless strong secondary processes of reaming (erosion or corrosion by running water, for example) take a hand in counteracting these destructive tendencies. For precisely these reasons, in rock salt, well-known to be more plastic even than gypsum, open structural fissures do not develop in the first place; even if some open fissures are formed, they are closed up very quickly. This is why all karst corrosion is superficial in rock salt, where the interior of the salt mass is inaccessible to dissolution processes. Hence even the salt karsts exhibiting the best developed forms of surface corrosion lack caves (*Photo 3*).

All in all, it is for the karst evolution of limestone with its high strength that epeirogenic movements are of the greatest significance: its influence consists in the tectonic preformation of certain zones or lines (or planes, when their continuation in the rock body is also taken into account); these are preferred by karstification, which may be rendered more intense and more efficient in sculpturing its own particular sets of forms along these lines and planes.

Tectonic preformation, however, is also a precondition of hydrothermal karstification, since deep-reaching faults are required to let thermal waters rise to the surface. This is why hydrothermal karst forms, particularly abundant in Hungary, are invariably localized along main structural lines, with their centres unequivocally pinpointing the intersections of crossing faults with each other and with the relief.

This is illustrated by the map in *Figure 28*, showing the dolomite occurrences in the hills around Budaörs near Budapest, with the comminuted dolomite facies, and especially those rendered pulverized by fossil hydrothermal effects, as well as the main faults and fissures recorded by a detailed mapping of the area (L. JAKUCS 1950).

When hot water surges along spacious open passages, a secondary sculpture and/or widening of fissures by hydrothermal corrosion often takes place. The resulting form is called a hot-spring cavern.

In Hungary, in the Buda Hills in particular, there are a fair number of tectonic fissure caves widened by the peculiar subsequent action of thermal waters. The Ferenchegy, Szemlőhegy, Mátyáshegy, Pálvölgy, etc. caves were largely sculptured in this way (cf. *Fig. 29*). The chessboard pattern of their ground plan coincides with the fault pattern that gave rise to the present checkerboard-type, block-faulted aspect of the hills (BORBÁS 1934, KEREKES 1941, etc.).

If a tectonic (fault) fissure is further sculptured by secondary corrosion (possibly hydrothermal), or erosion, the cross-sections of the passages often

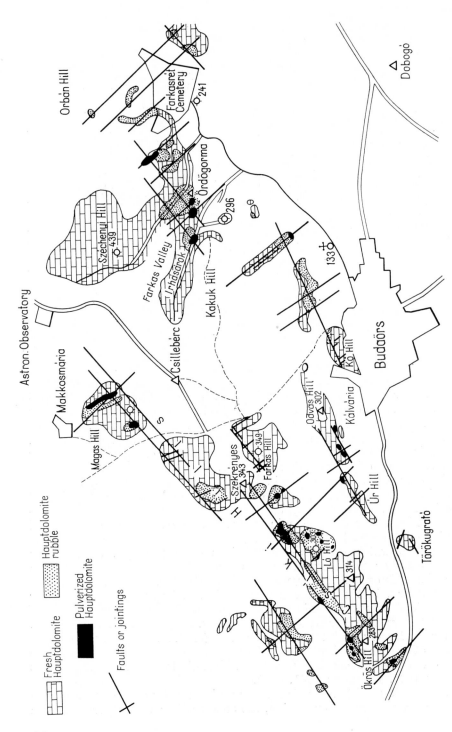

Fig. 28. Relationship between dolomite pulverization and structure in the Budaörs Hills of Hungary (mapped by the author)

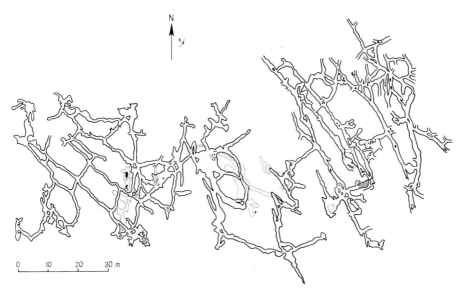

Fig. 29. Grid-pattern ground plan indicative of strong structural control of the principal passages of the Ferenc Hill Cave, Budapest, converted into a hot-spring cave in a secondary stage of speleogenesis

reveal this fact by conspicuous bulges. If the secondary agency acts over the entire cross-section (the passage being entirely filled with water), the cross-section shown as A in *Figure 30* will develop, whereas B is indicative of the action of a stream with a free surface.

If the tectonic deformation results in closed and hidden fissures rather than open and gaping ones, the water moving in the rock will seek these out; excavation, if any, will be due exclusively to the action of water. The cross-sections and ground plans of the caverns thus formed nevertheless make abundantly clear the tectonic preformation of the system.

A photograph of a tectonically preformed cave passage excavated by water is given in *Photo 4*.

It emerges even from the above considerations that epeirovariance is indispensable when accounting for all aspects of karst corrosion. It is all the more remarkable that this circumstance should have been ignored for so long in form analyses by the classic authors.

Treatises on genetic connexions between tectonic structure and karst forms are restricted to the last few decades (NIKOLAEV 1946, TRIMMEL 1956, etc.). In today's karst morphologic analyses, however, the hydrographic and morphologic consequences of tectonic preformation are almost invariably given the proper attention. A noteworthy and instructive example of this is the set of genetic cavern maps (*Fig. 31*) prepared by PASA (1961) to illustrate the evolution of the Italian Rana karst cavern; others are provided by the latest tectospeleological analyses of Soviet workers (SOKOLOV 1962, BACHINSKY et al. 1964, KUZNETSOVA 1965, SHCHEPETOV et al. 1965, TATARINOV 1965, DUBLYANSKY 1966, etc.) who, by a statistical

95

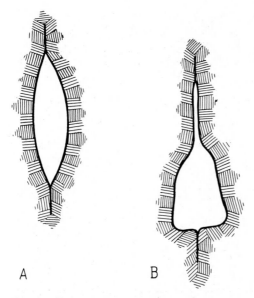

A   B

Fig. 30. Types of cross-sections of cave passages structurally preformed but sculptured by water

A — section indicating sculpture largely by corrosion, with full inundation in the phase of active evacuation; B — section indicating sculpture largely by erosion, with at any rate the presence of an open water surface

analysis of data derived from surveys of numerous subterranean systems, have prepared orientation diagrams of the passages of many karst caverns in the Soviet Union. Two of these, relating to the Bear Cave discovered in 1963 in a rock cliff on the right bank of the Kizel River (Perm Region), and to the Maksimovich Cavern of the Southern Urals (Bashkiria) are shown here in *Figures 32* and *33*, respectively.

Evidently, the immeasurable significance of tectonic preformation for karst corrosion finds expression not only in subsurface karstification, but also in surface forms: indeed, doubly so, since the tectonic structure of a karst relief is reflected not only in the areal distribution of macroscopic karst forms, but also in the intrinsic evolutionary features of the individual forms.

This relationship may occasionally have a very tight causal dependence, as for instance in the case of the *poljes* on the Dinaric Karst, where, in agreement with Cvijić (1895) and Grund (1903), the primary tectonic origin of these macroforms must be conceded in most cases. This is proved convincingly by a general map of the principal poljes (*Fig. 34*), whose major axes are almost invariably parallel to the structural and/or orographic trends of the mountains.

Poljes, however, are not in the main forms of karst origin, but decidedly structural, tectonic, orogenic ones: drainageless basins often due to rift faulting and other intercolline, sometimes folded, structures, whose connexion with karst erosion is restricted to survival and continued evolution and cannot be traced to its origin. Clearly then they offer no satisfactory proof as to the tectonic control of the areal distribution of true karst forms.

As regards the corrosional karst forms of the relief, tectonic preformation is most evident in the arrangement and geomorphic features of *dolines* and *lapies*. In almost all Central European karst regions, for instance, one observes the arrangement of dolines along certain lines ("doline strings" or "sinkhole rows"). These alignments of karst forms are invariably parallel either to the preferential structural trends of the mountains, or to the axes of ancient valleys in the karst planina, most often in the sense that the dolines will line up along the axis of a valley that has been long inactive. However, since these valleys themselves reflect a structural orientation

Photo 4. Entry of Zuberec Cave (Béla Tatra): the section of the passage at once reveals a complex interaction of structural preformation and sculpture by water (after Kunsky 1957)

(most conspicuous in the embryonic phases of valley sculpture), we have in this case an indirect structural control over karst forms.

Incidentally, karst valleys regressed to an inactive state will, if elevated for prolonged periods above the local baselevel of erosion (that is, the karst water table), invariably develop strings of dolines, which are entirely natural since the accumulated sediments will tend to promote the biological and pedological conditions (indeed, sometimes even the primary hydrological conditions) of karst corrosion to a greater extent on the valley bottoms than on the flanks or the divides between them. Some fine examples of this are provided by the strings of sinkholes in the Mecsek and Bükk Hills and in the North Borsod Karst, all in Hungary, but a similar effect is also apparent in the South Slovakian karst regions (Szilice, Konyár and

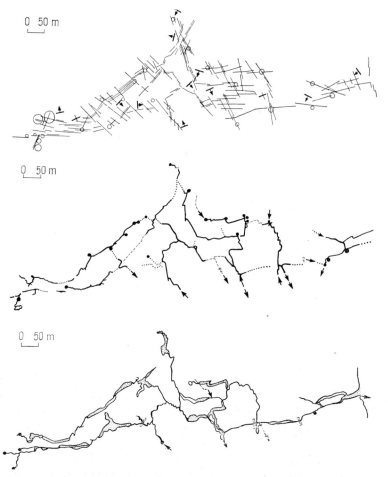

Fig. 31. Three-phase speleogenetic map of the Italian Rana karst cavern (by PASA 1961, who attributes the cavern's origin to primary structural preformation)

Pelsőc plateaux), in the Moravian Karst and in the karstic surfaces of the Dinarids; we too have made similar observations in the karst planinas of the Crimean Peninsula (Chatyr Dagh).

Photo 5 shows part of the Čepovani Valley in Slovenia, where the initial stage of evolution of a doline string along the valley axis is readily perceived.

It should be pointed out in this context that, after a prolonged period of karst sculpture, the series of dolines may grow so wide and deep, or so dissected by another generation of juvenile dolines, as to repress entirely the original geomorphic features of the primary, erosional valley. In any given karst planina, such old strings of dolines may coexist with younger ones. In such cases the younger string is usually in a lateral, suspended,

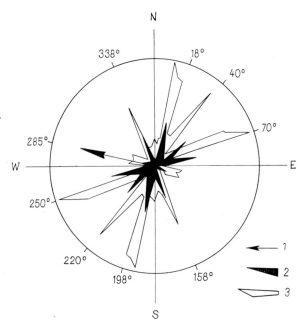

Fig. 32. Comparative orientation diagram of cavern passages and fissures in the Bear Cave of the Perm district, USSR (after KUZNETSOVA 1965)

1 — dip and strike of strata; 2 — orientation and abundance of fissures; 3 — orientation, length and width of cave passages. (The length of each arrow is proportional to the magnitude of the parameter it represents.)

Photo 5. Cepovani Valley near Idrija in Slovenia. Incipient aligned doline formation is visible along the valley axis

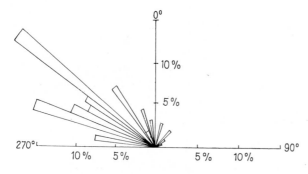

Fig. 33. Histogram of passage orientations expressive of a strong structural control in the Maksimovich Cavern of the Southern Urals (Bashkirian SSR), as percentages of the total length of passages (after SHCHEPETOV et al. 1965)

subsequent situation with respect to the older one, which suggests that the side valley may have retained its linear above-surface watercourse for quite some time after the drying out of the main valley and the commencement of its dissection by karst corrosion. We shall return to this problem later on.

The relationships just discussed are often reflected in a remarkable way in karst regions of folded structure, where dolines are aligned at times

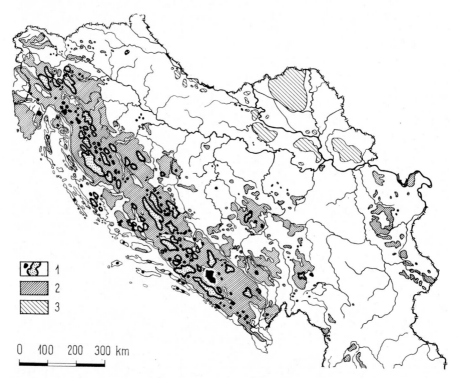

Fig. 34. Distribution of poljes of karst origin in Yugoslavia (after SERKO and MICHLER 1953). 1 — small and large poljes; 2 — karstic limestone; 3 — other formations showing karst forms among other forms, largely loess

100

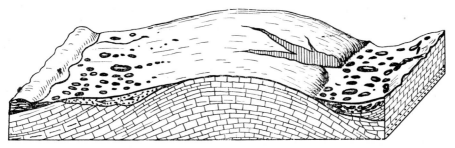

Fig. 35. Localization of karst dolines on anticlinal limbs in the karst region of the Perm district of the USSR (after MAKSIMOVICH 1965)

Photo 6. Giant lapies furrows as opposed to stratification, preformed by structural jointing, near Podgora in Dalmatia

along the syncline axis, at times along the watershed on the anticline. The latter is the more frequent case, as an immediate consequence of a fan-shaped arrangement of tension cracks such as shown in Figure 24. However, especially in flat folds where the stress on the anticline was not excessive, it happens that the concerted attack of waters accumulating along the axis of the syncline or on the gentle anticlinal flanks will gain the upper hand. One contributing factor may be that the dynamism of karst erosion is reduced on flanks and divides laid bare by sheetwash and mass wasting. In such cases, dolines will form along the synclinal axis. One fine example in point, relating to the Perm Region of the Soviet Union, is presented by MAKSIMOVICH (1965) in *Figure 35*.

Fissures and joints in the rock and other evidence of tectonic stress are rendered highly conspicuous morphologically in lapies fields, especially those of the furrow type, where the orientation of the developing karst furrow invariably depends both on the slope and the bedding, and also on the macrostructural elements (*Photo 6*). Moreover, the localization of other karst phenomena such as springs, sinkholes, etc. can most often be ascribed primarily to structural factors, as has been emphasized (indeed, perhaps occasionally overemphasized) by SCHMIDT (1944, 1957).

Since the origin of karst forms is, in the final analysis, a complex resultant of many effects, and we should like, by the proportions of the chapters in this book, to reflect the proportions in which the individual factors contribute to karst evolution, we shall not go into more detail here concerning the role of structural preformation in promoting karstification.

CLIMATIC CONTROL OF KARSTIFICATION AND THE GEOMORPHOLOGICAL CONSEQUENCES OF CLIMATIC VARIANCE

In the classical period of karst morphology, linked with the names of Eckert, Cvijić, Grund, Krebs, Katzer, Martel, Penck, etc. who essentially performed a deductive analysis of the karst phenomena and processes of the temperate zone, an azonal view of karst evolution came to be developed; this generalized the system of formal and essential karst categories characteristic of Central and Southern Europe to the entire globe. That is, geomorphologists regarded the forms of the Dinaric Karst, the French La Causses, and so on, to provide the criteria of a karst anywhere in the world and in most cases considered limestone regions where these features could not be described as non-karstic.

This notion is reflected in DUDICH's (1932) and KADIĆ's (1936) definitions of the karst, cited earlier in this book; or in the work of CHOLNOKY (1928, 1932/2, etc.); indeed, up to the fifties, this was the view that dominated the thinking of almost all authors. Geomorphologists admitted only quantitative, but not qualitative differences between the processes of karstification in the various climatic zones. Hence, any early description that assigned the term karstification to radically different processes of limestone erosion (e.g. DANES 1914, 1916, H. LEHMANN 1936, MEYERHOFF 1938) was doomed to be overlooked.

It was the Soviet school of geomorphology, in developing the teachings of DOKUCHAEV 1883 (MAKSIMOVICH 1947, APRODOV 1948, GVOZDETSKY 1947, 1950), that first emphasized broadening the concept of karstification by incorporating certain criteria of climate zonality. Thus, in addition to normal karstification and the related set of classic karst forms, Maksimovich and other scientists already distinguished the *thermokarst* (frost karst) of frozen climes and tundra regions, and gave descriptions of both the mechanism of the process and its quite characteristic formal consequences (cf. also BOTS' paper of 1957).

This was soon followed by pioneering publications concerning the special forms of *mountain karsts* (RATHJENS 1951, 1954/2); and also by the first papers of H. LEHMANN (1948) and BÜDEL (1951), placing in the foreground of interest the characteristic formal consequences of *tropical karstification*, as highlighted by a genetically oriented system.

Subsequently, the international karst literature of the fifties and sixties saw a sudden proliferation of studies into climatic karst morphology, with substantial advances especially in the knowledge of tropical karst processes and phenomena. Treatises of a general, pragmatic nature were published, as well as new regional geographies of land forms.

In the first group, the works of H. LEHMANN (1954/1, 1956, 1960), WISSMANN (1954), KOSACK (1952), CORBEL (1954/1, 1955, 1959, 1961/2), P. Z. SZABÓ (1957), GVOZDETSKY (1958), KLIMASZEWSKI (1958), BIROT (1959), RENAULT (1959), BÜDEL (1963), GERSTENHAUER and SWEETING (1960) were the most important, whereas of the land form descriptions of lasting value one should cite the publications of H. LEHMANN (1954/2, 1955), CRAMER (1955), GLENNIE (1956), WISSMANN (1957), GVOZDETSKY (1959), KUKLA (1958), SAINT-OURS (1959), SUNARTADIRDJA and LEHMANN (1960), GER-STENHAUER (1960, 1966), WHITE (1962), SMITH (1963), DOUGLAS (1964), MAKSIMOVICH (1964/1), VERSTAPPEN (1964), CHIKISHEV (1965) and ROSE (1966). Still, however numerous the publications, both general and regional, concerned with the morphological consequences of climatic variance in its influence upon karstification, we must recognize that, especially concerning the dynamic range of karstification in different climatic zones, no consensus exists even today. Some authors still adhere to concepts concerning the mechanism of karst corrosion inherited from the classic school of karst morphology, which are in irreconcilable antithesis with the ever more abundant facts of observation.

According to the traditional textbook schemes of karst corrosion, the absorption of carbon dioxide in water, and hence the corrosive potential of water, varies inversely as the temperature (cf. Table 3). Hence, in polar or any other cold regions (e.g. in high mountains), its dissolution potential should exceed that of the warmer waters in hotter climates. In contrast, karst forms actually observed in tropical karst regions indicate almost invariably a state of denudation several times further advanced than in the cold zones.

A clear assessment of the problem was further complicated by the findings of the renowned French karst scientist CORBEL, who published data concerning the chemical composition of waters draining off the karsts of various climatic regions; although strictly correct statements of facts, these data were exceedingly well suited for further exacerbating this controversy. CORBEL showed (1954/1—2, 1955, 1959) that the waters of rivers draining karst surfaces under cold climates remove about ten times as much dissolved calcium carbonate as the rivers in limestone areas of warm climates. From these findings he then proceeded to draw the conclusion that karstification proceeds much faster in a cold than in a warm climate.

In a study of rates of denudation, Corbel compared the results of systematic daily measurements on the rivers Kissimmee in Florida and Tanana in Alaska with one another and with data for rivers of other regions, and published the rates of denudation presented in *Table 12*.

After our discussion of karst corrosion in the chapters analysing the dissolution of limestone, it is not difficult to recognize that, although the factual material calculated from the water composition and discharge data apparently confirm Corbel's ideas, the presentation of the problem in this form has led the French scientist to one of the most typical fallacies of geomorphology. This is a tragically typical example of how a one-sided approach in science will lead to grave errors. Furthermore, if this approach sets out not from laboratory work, but from an attempt to collect evidence

104

Table 12

Comparison of erosion rates on limestone surfaces, according to CORBEL (1954)

Locality studied	Rate of erosion in m^3/year/km^2 or mm per mile per year
Mountains with 2000 to 4000 mm of annual precipitation	
cold zone: North Norway, British Columbia	450
warm zone: Rio Usumacinta	45
Hills and plains with 1000 to 1600 mm of annual pre-cipitation	
cold zone: Quebec, West Scotland	160
warm zone: Rio Champoton, Yucatan	16
Kissimmee, Florida	5
Plains with 300 to 500 mm of annual precipitation	
cold zone: Tanana, Alaska	40
Inner Lapland	40
warm zone: Chélif, near Orleansville	4
Plains with less than 200 mm of annual precipitation	
cold zone: Lower Mackenzie	14
warm zone: Rio Grande near Acacia	1·4

to support a part-truth derived from speculation, the author in question is certainly liable to self-deception.

In his fundamental considerations, Corbel appears to have neglected some very important circumstances:

1. the concentration of carbonic acid in a water, and hence its dissolution potential, does not depend exclusively on the CO_2 content and temperature of the precipitation and of the free atmosphere in contact with it;

2. the soil cover of a karst surface, thriving with plant associations and rich in decaying organic matter, plays a much more important role than the atmospheric CO_2 factor, for the soil atmosphere, which contacts the infiltrating waters over a large surface, may have a CO_2 content exceeding that of the atmosphere by several hundred times;

3. the composition of this soil atmosphere itself may exhibit decisive differences depending on the climatic zonality;

4. even within one and the same soil, the CO_2 content of the soil atmosphere varies considerably, primarily under the influence of the temperature fluctuations which also control the life rhythms of the soil bio-organisms;

5. according to the French worker TROMBE (1951/1—2, 1952), the rendzina soils covering the French karsts, for instance, contain a soil gas with up to 10 per cent CO_2 in the summer, but no CO_2 at all in the winter, just as there is practically no CO_2 in the meagre soils without vegetation on high mountains and in the polar and subpolar climatic zones;

6. in the humus-rich, fast-maturing soils with intense dynamism in the tropical regions, the CO_2 concentrations are several times higher even than the summer concentrations of the soils in the temperate zones; and finally,

7. limestone corrosion is wrought not only by the carbonic acid content of water, but just as effectively by other organic and inorganic acids and

other compounds, while the concentrations and intensities of these latter are likewise enhanced by heat and abundant rainfall.

If Corbel had taken the above factors into account, he would presumably have formulated findings of a quite different orientation concerning the degree of intensity and climatic zonality of the corrosional wasting of limestone: findings in harmony with the modern theories of dissolution, as well as with the unequivocal evidence of geographic form analysis, both of which reveal that tropical karstification is not less intense by a factor of ten than karstification in a cold climate, but, on the contrary, is a more effective and faster process of erosion by a factor of at least ten.

If Corbel had not viewed the chemical composition of water flowing off karsts of diverse climates in a mechanical way, and out of the context of the environmental factors, he would have recognized that his data do not prove what he intended them to. He neglected the fact that one factor governing limestone solubility is that fraction of the infiltrating precipitation finally absorbed from the soil by the vegetation and recycled by evapotranspiration into the atmosphere, and he ignored that fraction by linear drainage owing to direct respiration and evaporation by the soil proper. Now these fractions of the water involved become the more important, the hotter and rainier the climate, since the regional drainage coefficient depends primarily on the climate of the region, as well as on the relief and the petrovariance factor.

Corbel himself writes that, whereas 100 per cent of the 450 mm annual precipitation falling onto the cold drainage area of the Tanana in Alaska is drained by the river, of the 1200 mm falling onto the warm drainage area of the Kissimmee in Florida only the equivalent of 175 mm (14·58 per cent) is drained by that river.

This 14·58 per cent of the total precipitation available for linear drainage will — as we have seen — wash 5 m^3 of dissolved limestone off each sq. km of the drainage area. So far so good; but if the total precipitation were collected in the Kissimmee River bed, this would mean that the amount of calcium carbonate dissolved by corrosion and removed per sq. km would amount to $5 \times 7 = 35$ m^3/year, not so far behind the 39·9 m^3/km^2 for the drainage area of the Tanana! And this calculation is justified, unless we believe the naive concept, unstated but applied by Corbel, that the dissolution potential of rain-water is decided by the percentage ultimately drained into the rivers.

The Corbel pseudo-truth, however, also has other weaknesses. Corbel does not allow for the reversibility of hydrocarbonate dissolution of limestone; that is, the equilibrium of the solution is highly sensitive to any slight change in the surroundings. Thus, the water of a river subject to the typical softening influences so evokingly described by Corbel could not retain its hardness even if it were fed at its source with the hardest possible waters. Corbel himself writes that "in the reaches of the Kissimmee, the surface overgrown with dense grass is dissected by a net of open water surfaces and meandering river branches, and the water in the river is very warm. The daily mean temperature seldom sinks below 20 °C, and over three months stays close to 30 °C".

106

All this, then, of necessity entails the rapid escape of CO_2 from the solution, and a considerable softening of the water by precipitation of calcium carbonate. Under such conditions the chemical composition of a river water says nothing about the intensity of karstification in the remote drainage area. This is particularly so in tropical regions, where the degree of carbonic acid aggressivity of all waters infiltrating into the soil, and thus available for calcium carbonate dissolution (and hence the rate of corrosion proper) is determined by a soil atmosphere with a high partial pressure of CO_2, whereas the dissolved CO_2 content of the waters of the surface rivers is restricted within very narrow limits by extremely unfavourable conditions for the absorption of the gas. Let us recall one of our earlier findings, that in both the infiltration zone and the linear-drainage reaches, the dissolved gas content of a water depends on the local conditions of temperature and partial pressure, and the equilibrium of diffusion or absorption, whichever the case may be, and equilibrates the sooner (the interface area being equal), the higher the temperature where the reaction takes place.

It is quite obvious, incidentally, that the streams draining the bare, cold karsts of polar regions or high mountains hardly differ in composition from the waters circulating in the fissure network of the rock or flowing out of its springs, since there are practically no differences in either temperature or partial pressure of CO_2 between the air spaces in contact with the infiltration zone and the linear-drainage reaches. Hence, the amount of calcium carbonate removed in the streams flowing off a cold karst do indeed serve as a measure of denudation.

However, the more the chemical equilibrium of the infiltrating precipitations is affected by the soil atmosphere and by the concentration of CO_2 — largely of biogenetic origin — accumulated in it (that is, the hotter the climate), the wider the discrepancy between the rates of dissolution and removal; the limit is attained in most contemporary tropical karsts, where the removal of calcium carbonate in river waters is virtually insignificant compared with the effective rate of wear by karst processes.

Our debate with Corbel has thus led us to the formulation (as a by-product, so to speak) of one of the most fundamental theses of karst morphology: cold karsts evolve towards leached skeletal karsts, whereas, owing to the precipitation (either at deeper levels or almost in situ) of the calcium carbonate dissolved at higher levels, the karsts in hot climates develop into massive karsts, with calcium carbonate transport largely vertical, and the horizontal component severely limited.

This is why polar karsts exhibit no deposits of calcareous tufa, and their caverns are so poor in dripstones (TELL 1962, ROHDENBURG and MEYER 1963); it is also, on the other hand, the reason for the extremely intense surface and underground deposition of calcareous tufa and dripstones in tropical karsts, a phenomenon we shall return to later.

It is self-evident that temperate-zone karsts are intermediate in this respect, not only as regards geographical latitude, but also climato-genetically, between the process intensities and the qualitative peculiarities of tropical and polar karsts.

All this is accessible to logical comprehension, however, only after thorough exploration of the complex process of corrosion and assessment of all its controlling factors. It is thus natural that CORBEL, who disregarded almost all the decisive facts and factors, should have arrived at a misleading conclusion, by what can hardly be called a scientific process.

We would not have spent so much space on a critical reappraisal of Corbel's efforts, worthy of a better fate, were it not that his teachings have had such a profound influence on the views of so many workers. In fact, his publications have misled even quite outstanding specialists of the field. KÉZ, for one, became a zealous advocate of faster karstification in colder climes, urging in the concluding statement of his paper of 1959 that Corbel's views should be paid proper attention in the interpretation of the evolution of Hungarian caverns.

Corbel's activity in the field of climatic morphology has had also some highly positive consequences, however. We have in mind here the profound shock that his conclusions gave to a number of workers. These immediately passed to a counter-attack, starting on their "anti-Corbel" work, which necessitated first of all, the collection of a host of new observational data.

We are perhaps not far wrong in assuming that some of the most valuable publications in climatic karst morphology (already cited above), written in the late fifties and in the sixties, were due to such a motivation. In the Hungarian literature, the problem is reviewed with much intuition in BALÁZS' paper (1963/1), but it seems that the international literature still lacks the expression of a truly general contrary opinion, probably because of the difficulties of collecting the necessary data, an effort requiring enormous work and expense. Let us not forget that Corbel started the collection of his 8000 (!) data on the Tanana and Kissimmee rivers as far back as 1930; the mere volume of his data makes it fitting that he be refuted by more than just one's belief in the correctness of one's own views.

Even if the scientific information resulting from two decades of international climatic karst research may be insufficient to give a fitting rebuttal to Corbel's teachings, it is surely copious enough to let us make a first attempt at estimating the relative intensities of karst corrosion, and within this, the percentage contributions of the individual karstification agencies in the various typical climatic zones of karst morphology.

Let us emphasize once more that we regard this attempt as merely a first approximation, in need of refinement in a number of details; this may be expected from the calculations and deliberations of other authors, and from new, as yet unpublished data, which might give rise to novel viewpoints. We feel, however, that the fundamental tenets of our calculations and conclusions are not so far wrong (even in their present state) or that their presentation as a basis for discussion might put in jeopardy any of our potential achievements.

We start from the fact that the ranges of karst corrosion dynamism in limestone permit five distinct well-defined climatic zones; although these may not coincide absolutely with the classical zones of climatic geomorphology (DOKUCHAEV 1883, PENCK 1913, BÜDEL 1948, 1963, BULLA

1954/1—2, H. LEHMANN 1954/1, 1956, LOUIS 1964, etc.) they are readily distinguishable on the basis of both the intensity of karstification and its formal consequences, the differences being demonstrably climatogenic. These zones are as follows:

1. *Mountain and periglacial regions*, including the frost karsts of the polar and subpolar zones, the tjäle and the tundra zones, and the zones above the forest line in high mountains;

2. the *temperate zone* including grasslands;

3. the *Mediterranean*, including semidesert steppes;

4. the *desert zone*; and finally

5. the *tropical region of karst morphology*, which in the present context is meant to include the savannah zone and the zone of monsoon rains.

Of course, any one of the above five groups could be further divided, but the assessment of the degree of intensity of karstification required by a finer subdivision would not be justified by the volume of data at present available.

The approximate percentage representation of the relative intensities of karstification in the above zones, based on calculations from several approaches, is as follows: periglacial and high-mountain regions, 6 per cent; temperate region, 9 per cent; Mediterranean, 12 per cent; desert regions, 1 per cent; and tropical regions, 72 per cent. That is, the intensity of tropical karstification is about 71 times that of desert karstification, 6 times that of Mediterranean karstification, 8 times that of temperate karstification, and about 12 times that of high-mountain karstification. The Mediterranean karst processes are thus about one and a half times as intense as the temperate ones, and twice as intense as the subnival and subpolar ones.

Even within this dynamic range of the relative intensities of karst denudation, however, there are marked differences in the contributions of the individual agencies, as expressed numerically in *Table 13*.

Table 13

Contribution (in per cent) of the individual genetic agencies of karst corrosion to karst modelling in five climatic zones

	High-mountain and periglacial	Temperate, running water	Mediterranean	Desert	Tropical
Atmospheric CO_2	45	7	4	30	0·5
CO_2 of inorganic origin	5	9	8	15	2·5
Biogenic CO_2	30	54	55	0	50
Inorganic acids	5	5	8	55	4
Organic acids	15	25	25	0	43
Total	100	100	100	100	100

Figure 36 presents the comparative intensities of karst corrosion within the individual climatic facies zones, and the percentage contributions of the individual agencies. These figures reveal clearly all the substantial

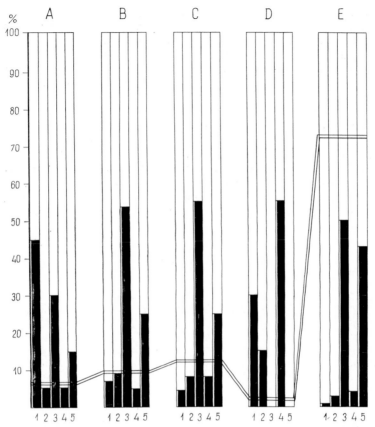

Fig. 36. Relative intensities of karst corrosion and percentage contributions by various agencies in the fundamental climatic zones of karst morphology

Double line indicates the relative percentage intensity of corrosive karst erosion in the various climatic zones; column A — high-mountain and periglacial (6%); B — temperate, by running water (9%); C — Mediterranean (12%); D — desert (1%); E — tropical (72%)

Agencies of karst corrosion:

1 — CO_2 fraction of atmospheric origin; 2 — idem, due to inorganic pedogenic processes (e.g. weathering); 3 — idem, due to biogenic processes of pedogenesis; 4 — contribution of other inorganic acids; 5 — contribution of organic acids (humic, huminic, and root acids)

features justifying the special significance of the decisive and characteristic qualitative features distinguishing the dissolution processes of the individual climatic zones, over and above the quantitative differences.

Close study of Figure 36 shows that the columns making up the histograms A to E are comparable only within each individual group. Any comparison with a neighbouring group is at best relative, and says nothing about absolute intensities; a 50 per cent contribution of the biogenic CO_2

factor, for instance, means an incomparably higher pCO_2 level in the high-intensity tropical karst than in the temperate zone, the ratio of the dynamic factors of total corrosion of the two zones being 72:9.

In order to permit comparison of absolute intensities for the various agencies contributing to karst corrosion, we have therefore calculated the absolute magnitudes of these agencies by examining, for instance, the quantitative contribution corresponding to the 45 per cent atmospheric CO_2 factor of the periglacial zone, and so on for the remaining percentages. This calculation required the calculation of 45 per cent of the 6 per cent dynamic factor of the periglacial zone, and then in a similar manner of the characteristic values for the remaining climatic zones. The quantitative parameters thus obtained, listed in *Table 14*, can be compared realistically and very instructively in the horizontal sense too. (The last column of this table gives the sum for any individual factor over all the climatic zones, thereby expressing the intensity of the factor in a planetary context.)

Table 14

Absolute intensities of the agencies of karst corrosion in five climatic zones, expressed as percentages of the average dissolution intensities of these zones (in per cent)

	High-mountain and periglacial	Temperate, running water	Mediter-ranean	Desert	Tropical	World-wide contribution of factor
Atmospheric CO_2	2·70	0·63	0·48	0·30	0·36	4·47
CO_2 of inorganic origin	0·30	0·81	0·96	0·15	1·80	4·02
Biogenic CO_2	1·80	4·86	6·60	0·00	36·00	49·26
Inorganic acids	0·30	0·45	0·96	0·55	2·88	5·14
Organic acids	0·90	2·25	3·00	0·00	30·96	37·11
Total	6·00	9·00	12·00	1·00	72·00	100·00

If Table 14 is used to construct the complex diagram of the causal components of dissolution, in their subdivision according to climatic facies, we obtain a representation of the undistorted intensities of these effects in nature, which will immediately be of direct use in assessing karst morphological problems (*Fig. 37*). The individual curves of this figure are highly instructive, and so also is their comparison. We discuss in more detail below the objective tendencies reflected by this extremely important diagram.

One immediately obvious feature is that the behaviour of the atmospheric CO_2 fraction (curve 1) is opposed to that of all the other factors: whereas all these latter rise steeply as the temperature and total precipitation increase, the former curve falls.

This tendency is only to be expected, however, as it merely expresses the Henry-Dalton law of gas absorption (discussed earlier above), i.e. the fact that cold water will absorb more gas than warm water. (It was on this basis, and unfortunately this basis alone, that Corbel formulated his generalizations.)

The Henry-Dalton law, however, cannot in itself explain the substantial differences between the successive steps of this falling line, as the

111

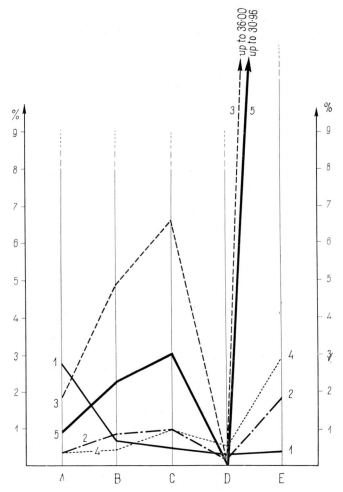

Fig. 37. Absolute intensities of the individual agencies of karst corrosion. Lettering and numbering as in Fig. 36

temperature difference between climatic zones A and B, for instance, is not great enough to justify such a steep drop, especially if we also consider the further course of the graph; there are sizeable temperature differences between B and E, too, but these are not accompanied by anything like proportionate differences in the activity of atmospheric CO_2 gas.

This phenomenon may in all probability be ascribed to the fact that in A most of the precipitation is in the form of snow and drizzle (both favourable for gas absorption); snow in particular lies on the ground for prolonged periods, in contact with the atmosphere all the time. This is probably the only climatic zone where the durable long-term equilibrium of calcium hydrocarbonate in solution develops as early as in the infiltration zone, as a function of the atmospheric pCO_2, and thus the total amount of CO_2 absorbed from the atmosphere is determined not only by the simple physical absorption of the gas, but also by the chemical gas demand of the hydrocarbonate dissolution reaction.

Another, not so conspicuous, but recognizable feature of curve 1 is that in the case E (in the tropics) the total concentration of atmospheric CO_2 in the water is slightly higher than for D. Since this cannot be due to a lower temperature than in case E, this phenomenon must be a reflection of the higher overall CO_2 level of the tropical atmosphere.

Clearly atmospheric CO_2, compared with the other factors of dissolution, does not play a significant role in karst corrosion, apart from mountain and periglacial (subpolar) climates, and its presence and influence are negligible beside the other components of corrosion, whose intensities are several times higher (with E, for instance, the biogenic factor is exactly 100 times more effective than the atmospheric!).

As regards the other diagrams in Figure 37, Nos 2 and 4 (the CO_2 fraction due to inorganic processes in the soil, and other inorganic compounds, mainly acids) indicate a slow and almost proportional increase of these factors as the temperature increases and the precipitation becomes more abundant. This is understandable inasmuch as higher temperatures as a rule accelerate inorganic reactions of weathering, while moisture, the medium of ionic reactions in the soil, makes all these reactions possible. As a result, these two factors are 2 to 10 times more efficient as agencies of limestone dissolution in the tropical zone than in any other zone and, except for the polar zone, slightly more efficient as a rule than atmospheric CO_2. Nevertheless, their contribution to corrosion dynamics taken as a whole is not too significant.

It should be pointed out even at this juncture that, in the climatic zone D (desert), almost all the corrosion factors are greatly reduced. The sole reason for this is the scarcity of water, which almost totally eliminates the biogenic contribution, while it also reduces substantially the biogenic intensities of the other chemical processes. Karst corrosion in the D zone is thus restricted to a little CO_2 of atmospheric origin, acting largely via the intermediary of dew, and to the low-intensity mineralic reactions of "desert weathering", with their almost immeasurably small results.

The evidence provided by curves 3 and 5 may be somewhat unexpected. These express the contributions to karst corrosion of the biogenic CO_2 fraction in the soil and of the organic soil acids. Both factors are convincingly shown to be extremely sensitive to climate; further, they are the principal carriers of karst corrosion to the major part of the earth's surface. Their role is important even in the cold and largely barren A-type karsts, in the presence of even the most modest growth of lichen on a rock face, or of the weakest soil bacterium. In the temperate and Mediterranean karst processes, on the other hand, they acquire decisive importance; and as the biomass on the ground surface (especially the vegetal cover) grows denser and denser and its seasonal biological cycle is smoothed out, so their denudative efficiency progressively increases. This is why in areal karst corrosion in a tropical region, all other factors of karst corrosion are practically negligible in comparison.

The vast mass of data in the international geomorphological literature indicates almost unambiguously that the geomorphological activity of tropical corrosion — especially through these last two factors, biogenic CO_2 and organic soil acids — can find expression not only in limestone regions, but also in regions of reliefs sculptured in other rocks, such as granite, andesite, etc., and may occasionally turn up as a dominant component, in the sculpture of even such macro- and microforms as are usually due essentially to weathering and linear and areal erosion.

Curves 3 and 5 in Figure 37 may perhaps shed light upon another interesting relationship. From a comparison of the sections between A and C, it is seen that the biogenic CO_2 increases at a faster rate towards C than do the organic soil acids. This initial tendency does not continue into E, however, as the difference between the values of the two factors (36·00 and 30·96) is much less significant compared with their absolute values. In other words, whereas in the Mediterranean zone, for instance, the intensity of corrosion by biogenic CO_2 is almost twice that by organic acids, in tropical regions this ratio is almost unity.

On looking into the causes of this phenomenon, it seems as if, under favourable conditions, the corrosion capacity of organic acids would catch up with the maximum accumulation of biogenic CO_2 in the soil; this accumulation can obviously not grow unlimitedly, for one thing it is restricted by soil respiration, and for another, an excessive CO_2 concentration in the soil biotope will retard precisely those biogenic processes that produce CO_2. A rigorous discussion of this problem would be very difficult as yet, however, in the absence of any tropical research aimed directly

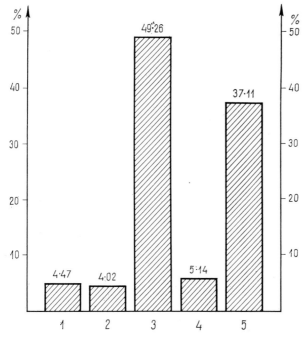

Fig. 38. World-wide distribution of the main agencies of corrosion contributing to the karst erosion of limestones

Agencies of karst corrosion:

1 — CO_2 fraction of atmospheric origin; 2 — idem, due to inorganic pedogenic processes (e.g. weathering); 3 — idem, due to biogenic processes of pedogenesis; 4 — contribution of other inorganic acids; 5 — contribution of organic acids (humic, huminic, and root acids)

114

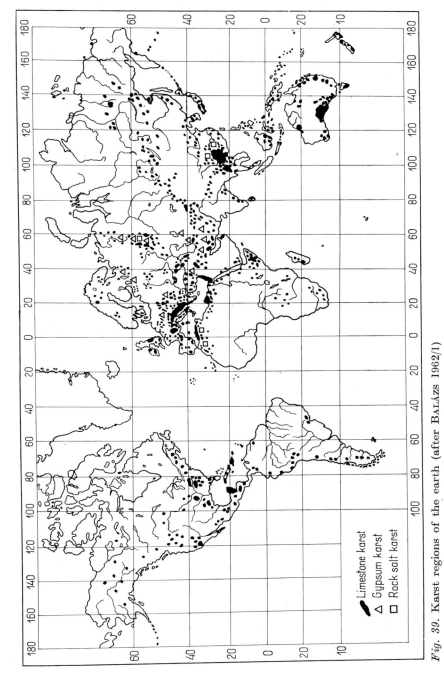

Fig. 39. Karst regions of the earth (after BALÁZS 1962/1)
The distribution of the spots all over the globe reflects joint control by petrovariance (mainly along orogenic belts) and favourable factors of climatic zonality

Limestone karst
△ Gypsum karst
□ Rock salt karst

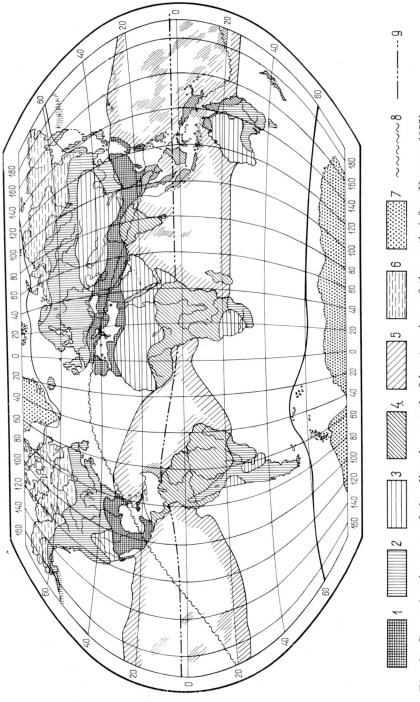

Fig. 40. Comprehensive map of the climatic control of karst regions of the earth (after KOSACK 1952)

1 — high-karst regions; 2 — covered karsts of the temperate zones; 3 — pseudo-karsts of arid regions; 4 — tropical karsts (under favourable lithological conditions); 5 — forms of dissolution on Recent corallian limestones; 6 — regions of permafrost; 7 — polar regions; 8 — axis of maximum abundance of karsts; 9 — axis of Recent regions of coral growth

at this problem. Still, we expect that appropriate future research will put this relationship in an entirely new light.

In order to illustrate the absolute planetary intensities of the principal factors of karst corrosion and limestone erosion, we have plotted the figures in the last column of Table 14 in the form of a histogram (*Fig. 38*).

On the basis of this figure we may now formulate with confidence the most important result of our considerations: the karst corrosion of limestone rocks in nature is in a genetic sense essentially a reflection in the sculpture of the forms in the soluble bedrock of the biological and chemical phenomena of evolution of the soil covering the rock.

In the above light, the zonal distribution of karst as presented by KOSACK (1952), GVOZDETSKY (1958) and BALÁZS (1962/1) is self-evident and requires no further explanation (see *Figures 39* and *40*).

1. KARSTIFICATION IN THE GLACIAL AND PERIGLACIAL REGIONS OF GEOMORPHOLOGY

In the karst morphological literature, data on karst phenomena in the glacial morphological region are extremely scarce. This is in all probability due to two circumstances: in the polar and mountainous regions covered with snow and ice and in the zone of permafrost soils there is hardly any superficial or near-surface aqueous dissolution to speak of; and further, even the corrosional karst forms that might develop are effaced almost without a trace by other, very intense erosion processes, characteristic of this climatic region. The region may be thought of as being karstophobic in both the functional and formal sense, the primary example being glacial erosion. Beyond this, however, in the true glacial zones, the rock surface proper is most often inaccessible to study, being covered in the inland ice regions in particular (in the interior of Greenland and in Antarctica) by a thick ice, with the exception of some insignificant surface outcrops (nunataks).

It must nevertheless be assumed that under the level of permafrost (which in some cases means several hundred metres beneath the local base-level of erosion), water flows in the fissures of the calcareous rocks, and also effects dissolution. Indeed, this effect may occasionally result in very hard waters, as the water at this depth flows under a considerable hydrostatic pressure ("confined karst aquifer"). Moreover, since all solutions are frozen at the higher levels, virtually no processes of oxidation and decomposition may take place there, whereas at these deeper levels the reactions of organic and mineral decomposition can run their course free from the inhibition of frost. The necessary oxygen is provided by the melting ground ice originally formed from snow. Moreover, the karst water confined by the practically impermeable barrier of frozen ground or rock has no chance at all to lose CO_2 by evaporation: hence, at this level, the CO_2 content of water, and its dissolution potential with respect to limestone, may attain quite significant values locally.

It is very probably due to the above circumstances that some of the waters surging from beneath a thick permafrost zone are so highly satu-

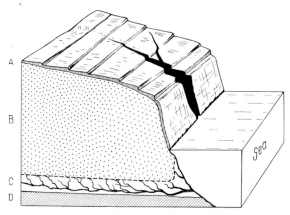

rated in hydrocarbonates, as in Svalbard (Spitsbergen), the North Canadian region of Mackenzie and around Kotzebue in Northern Alaska (CORBEL 1952/2, 1954/1, 1959). Notwithstanding all this, it makes no sense to speak of karstification as reflected in relief forms in the polar regions.

The corrosional cavern-forming activity of waters in stratiform aquifers is not significant either, since even though these waters are high in calcium hydrocarbonate, their quantity is small and their continual recharge is not assured. This is also reflected by the lack of karst springs in these regions (*Fig. 41*).

Fig. 41. Diagram of a polar karst (Victoria Land in Canada, or Svalbard Islands; after CORBEL). The slopes of the surface reflect the tabular structure of the limestone (in the form of low steps), a subdued formation of lapies and irregularities due to solifluxion. The sparse intermittent streams soon cut deep and narrow gorges into the limestone whose structure is loosened up by freeze-and-thaw. These gorges are often filled with the detritus of rubble glaciers. There is practically no karstification of the kind resulting in the conventional set of karst forms
A — topsoil, thawing out in the summer to a depth of about 50 cm only (with slow seepage of water in it); B — permafrost ground; C — limestone zone beneath the permafrost, where a slow confined flow of karst water is possible; D — impermeable bedrock

It should be pointed out that the caverns described by MUNCK (1963) in Greenland, and the formation of a cavern under a valley glacier (HORN 1935), in no way contradict the above statements, since these caverns are already in the freeze-and-thaw zone, and moreover involve an entirely different mechanism of evaluation, inoperative in the glacial region.

Whereas it makes little sense to speak of karstification in regions covered with ice and snow all the year round (indeed, as far as the intensity of karst dynamism is concerned, these regions best resemble the karst corrosion features of the deep desert), the subarctic and mountainous tundras of the *periglacial morphological region* may boast a number of interesting true and pseudo-karst forms.

This fact is made obvious merely by the volume of literature concerned with these phenomena: to mention only the most important, these include treatises by AGADZHANOV (1947), BALÁZS (1962/2), BARANOV (1940), BAUER (1953, 1958), BOTS (1957), CHIKISHEV (1965), CORBEL (1952/2, 1954/1, 1957, 1959), DOBROVOLSKY (1965), GVOZDETSKY (1958, 1961), HORN (1935, 1939, 1947), KACHURIN (1940), H. LEHMANN (1954/1, 1956, 1960), LINDBERG (1956), MAKSIMOVICH (1947), MUNCK (1963), PARMUZIN (1954), RASMUSSON (1958), RATHJENS (1951, 1954/2), ROHDENBURG and MEYER (1963), SCHAUENBERGER (1951), GERSTENHAUER and SWEETING (1960), SOKOLOV (1962), TELL (1961, 1962), and TROLL (1944/1). These publications give many-sided analyses of the agencies and processes involved, and are also concerned with descriptions of forms; however, it would seem as if — regarding the interpretations of the forms in particular — no definite answers had been arrived at in respect of some of the problems.

From the karst morphogenetic viewpoint too, it is reasonable to divide the periglacial morphological region into two subregions: the subarctic tundra and the periglacial subregion in the mountains. In these two subregions, karst corrosion operates at different rates of efficiency; this results in different formal manifestations of the processes, mainly because there are also substantial differences in other relief-forming factors, much more intense than the karst process, and exerting upon it a repressive influence (frost comminution, solifluxion, mass wasting, areal erosion, deflation, etc.), if for no other reason, then merely because of the difference in relief energy.

One of the most fundamental features of karsts in the *subarctic tundra region* is that the subsoil is frozen all year round in some instances, and during most of the year in others (more than seven months a year in the karsts of the tjäle zone), and hence any water appearing on the ground surface as a result of a thaw (or more seldom as rain) cannot, over most of the year, seep down into the deeper layers. This water consequently moves about either on the surface, or in the near-surface thawed-out zone, whose depth depends on the amount of heat available for thawing, so that dissolution by this water will largely be confined to the horizontal. In prolonged contact with the atmosphere and the unassuming, but ubiquitous periglacial tundra vegetation, this water acquires a high level of saturation with CO_2; this is also promoted by its low temperature, but it is made possible by the long duration of the contact.

This will, of course, produce hard karst waters. The process of corrosion in this zone, however, is practically irreversible. That is, any calcium carbonate once dissolved will stay in solution practically indefinitely, as the water in this zone is exposed to no influence, either physical (change of temperature, for instance) or chemical, that would cause the precipitation of the calcium carbonate content. In this zone, the drainage factor, incorrectly generalized by Corbel to other climatic zones, does indeed serve as a measure of the rate of dissolution: if this were not the case, the saturation of the solutions would, in the absence of any means of secondary precipitation, forestall any further dissolution.

There is a further factor of precipitation, specific to this zone; it is usually disregarded by workers concerned with the problem, but we have succeeded in proving its reality by experiment. The phenomenon in question is that, if freezing is very slow, the freezing water will expel some of the alkaline-earth carbonates dissolved in it, similarly to the freezing of chlorides out of sea water. Ground ice thus formed is lower in dissolved calcium carbonate than the original water before freezing, and in the pools of water left over in liquid form the concentration automatically rises.

If this process is repeated a sufficient number of times in an area of periodic freeze-and-thaw, ground water of unexpected hardness may result; there is still no precipitation, however, because at the very low solution temperature prevailing (close to 0 °C), ionic diffusion in the solution is so slow that, by the time the release of gas could affect the balance of calcium carbonate precipitation significantly, the highly concentrated residual solution will itself have frozen. (This phenomenon is analogous to the Forelian stratification of sea ice.)

In the periglacial regions, the corrosion mechanism just outlined will entail intense leaching, resulting in the formation of lapies on the ground surface, in the soil and rock zone accessible to freeze-and-thaw. Rock fissures, the initially invisible bedding-plane joints, etc. will be widened and a meagre skeletal karst will develop, in which caverns due to corrosion may come to exist: the waste subsequently washed in may even contribute some erosional sculpture. Over more accidented reliefs, especially at the points weakened by tectonic preformation, a few scattered sinkholes might develop; depending on their function, these may subsequently turn into funnel-shaped doline wells. The conditions for the development of true dolines are usually lacking, however.

In the views of Rohdenburg and Meyer, Schauenberger, Rasmusson, Munck and Tell, this is the genetic process reflected by the limestone caverns in Northern Scandinavia, Greenland and North Alaska. Tell, who made careful studies in the Lumelunda cavern of North Sweden gives more emphasis than most of his colleagues to the role of linear erosion in cavern formation. His views are borne out by the observation that rock debris continually produced by frost comminution on the surface, and even in the near-surface ground and in the lapies clefts, and washed into the caverns by water, turns up in the interior of these caverns mostly in rounded or flattened, worn forms indicative of a fairly long subterranean journey.

A comprehensive illustration of karst features in subpolar hilly regions with permafrost ground is given in *Figure 42*, largely after a block diagram conceived by CORBEL (1952/2, 1954), with some slight, non-essential changes based on the work of RATHJENS (1951, 1954/2) and BAUER (1958).

Karstification in periglacial regions is invariably a fairly low-intensity process. The old, mature, and conspicuous karst forms usual on the karstic surfaces of the temperate zone (large dolines, uvalas, poljes, well-developed lapies) are generally absent. Caves formed purely by dissolution are also usually of negligible size, whereas the genesis of the comparatively large caverns (Lulletjarro, Grönligrotten, Stokkvikgrotten, etc.) bears witness not so much to the advance of karst corrosion as to the less climate-dependent and less time-consuming process of stream-bed sculpture by erosion.

All these incontestable facts are nonetheless insufficient for the clear-cut derivation of the theorem that corrosional karstification in the glacial and periglacial zones is a low-intensity process; one of the highly essential prerequisites of the sculpture of conspicuous relief forms by karstification is absent from the subpolar and mountainous subnival zones: the time factor. As opposed to the majority of temperate, Mediterranean and tropical karsts, these karst reliefs are invariably very young: erosion by inland ice during the glacial periods having annihilated any preglacial relief forms, the beginning of relief evolution by karst processes could only take place

120

after the end of the last phase of Pleistocene glaciation and the final retreat of inland ice.

The workers (e.g. Bauer, Horn and Rathjens) who attribute not more than 8,000—10,000 years to karstification in periglacial situations in the Alps and in Scandinavia are probably right. In contrast, in the temperate karsts of today, which were at worst in a periglacial state throughout the Pleistocene, post-glacial karst evolution is merely the last phase of a much longer evolutionary history in the Tertiary, and in some instances continuous since the Mesozoic.

The phases of peneplanation and the evolution of macro-forms (at least to the point of the preformative lay-out of the present set of karst forms) are evidence of pre-Pleistocene erosion in these regions.

Processes of a wholly different origin have been described by Soviet scientists working in the periglacial tundra and taiga regions of Siberia. In this respect, the publications of SHOSTAKOVICH (1927), GRIGORIEV (1930), BARANOV (1940), KACHURIN (1940), MAKSIMOVICH (1947), GVOZDETSKY (1947, 1950), APRODOV (1948), PARMUZIN (1954), GVOZDETSKY and CHIKISHEV (1966) and especially of BOTS (1957) merit particular attention; the problem has also been touched upon by authors of other nations, such as TROLL (1944/2) and RASMUSSON (1958), these phenomena being known in other parts of the world also, including Iceland, North Sweden and Northern Canada. Irrespective of the nature of the bedrock, the permafrost areas of the tundra and taiga zones are observed to exhibit drainageless oval or circular ground depressions ("kettle holes") reminiscent of typical karst dolines. Some are only a few metres wide, but others exceed 100 m in diameter, a typical range of depths being 1 to 10 m. These depressions, whose morphological features reveal an origin by collapse, are often occupied by lakes, and may pockmark the relief densely enough to call to mind landscapes

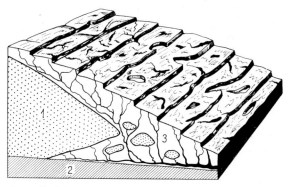

Fig. 42. Diagram of mountain tundras in the tjäle zone (after CORBEL). (The block diagram represents the situation around Tromsö in North Norway or on the Dachstein in Austria.) The permafrost zone becomes the thinner, the deeper the layer thawed out in the summer. Even in the thawed-out zone, however, there remain lenticular bodies of frozen ground. The relief recalls in many respects those developing above permafrost ground, but lapies sculpture on the surface and seepage in the near-surface formations are much more intense; indeed, small swallow-holes and streams disappearing underground are present. Caverns may be formed by corrosion and erosion at the level of horizontal ground-water flow, but there are no deposits of dripstone and calcareous tufa worthy of mention. After the final thawing out of the permafrost ground, dolines may develop on the surface

1 — zone of permafrost ground; 2 — impermeable bedrock; 3 — limestone zone of subdued karstification

Photo 7. Sölle of thermokarst origin near Neubrandenburg in the GDR (photo by the author)

usual on Mediterranean doline-pitted peneplain surfaces (e.g. in Albania).

The negative forms, however, are interspersed with protuberances, mounds ("pingoes") 10 to 200 m in diameter and 1 to 6 m in height. The principal difference from true limestone-karst forms is that these forms may disappear and reappear after a few years, or even annually.

This remarkable and interesting group of phenomena has been termed *frost karst or thermokarst* by the Soviet workers, as it was possible to prove beyond all doubt that they represent phases of the ground's "ice household". In the summer half of the year, when the upper levels of the tundra thaw, the melting of ground ice results in underground cavities whose collapse gives rise to the microrelief just described.

The thermokarst dolines are consequently not products of corrosion, but temporary forms indicative of a special phase of solifluxion, accompanying the partial thawing of permafrost ground in the summer half of the year: as such, they merit classification merely as a pseudo-karst phenomenon.

The positive forms (mounds) of the tundra are also due to ground ice; they are the winter forms corresponding to the preceding summer ones. In ground which contains water in the form of lenticular bodies, which freezes in the cold period will lift up the overlying soil horizons dome-fashion. The flat mounds (pingoes) thus formed have been called "hydrolaccoliths" or "ice laccoliths" by Soviet workers; the terms being expressive of their origin.

122

When a permanent warming of the climate puts an end to permafrost, the kettle holes of the thermokarst may, under favourable conditions, survive for a certain period. The conditions for such conservation exist especially in former alluvial outwash plains *(sandurs)*, where the high-permeability moraine deposits and the lenticular sand bodies of periglacial accumulation provide a soil structure ideally suited for both the evolution of thermokarst forms and their postglacial survival. We attribute the *solls* of the North German and Polish lake districts — at least in part — to thermokarst phenomena, in contrast to the traditional geomorphological view found in the textbooks; we further assume that, by analogy, the thermokarstic sculpture of the relief must have played a part too in the evolution of the Canadian "pitted plains" (see *Photo 7*).

It is worth pointing out that, in the more recent geomorphological literature, there is an increasing number of references casting doubt on the origin of solls (kettle holes) as the pits due to the melting away of huge buried masses of inland ice; this early view is replaced here and there by a hypothesis of origin very similar to ours. One of the pioneers of these ideas was PÉCSI who, in his interpretation of depressions formerly taken as dolines of a loess karst in the region between the Danube and the Tisza, adduced frost action as far back as 1961.

* * *

The periglacial (subnival) karst morphological subregion of the mountains includes those occurrences of karstified rock (primarily limestone) between the snow line and the forest line. Owing to differences in climate resulting from differences in latitude and intracontinental position, these zones occupy a variety of altitudes, but, petrographic conditions being identical, their denudation involves approximately the same phenomena of karstic and non-karstic erosion, producing approximately the same forms anywhere in the world. There are at most differences in dynamism between them, due to different abundances of precipitation, but these are not reflected to any significant extent in the forms sculptured by erosion. The karst phenomena of this subregion were recently studied in some detail by RATHJENS (1951, 1954/2) and two renowned Austrian workers, BAUER (1953, 1959) and TRIMMEL (1957).

Karstification bears the stamp of a meagre soil cover whose gas content is comparatively deficient in CO_2; rock debris comminuted by frost; and the sculpture of lapies by sub-areal corrosion, stronger under the snow than on the bare rock faces. Owing to the steepness of the relief, lapies furrows or channels usually follow the dip of the slope (consequent orientation). Subsequent orientation and microstructural preformation are rather subordinate in orienting lapies, restricted largely to the hilltops and gentler valley flanks; even there they characterize the lapies formed under a scanty soil cover.

The formation of pure lapies, however, is a rarity since the more persistent, more intense processes of wasting, including primarily frost comminution, either repress it completely or impress upon the developing forms the stamp of a polygenetic origin. This is why mountain karsts invariably exhibit fewer classic forms of karst corrosion than could have in fact developed.

The situation is altogether different with underground phenomena, and particularly erosion caverns; the subnival zones of the mountains usually hide many more of these than would be expected merely from the degree of surface karstification. We can cite here the huge limestone mass of the Salzburg Alps in Austria (the Dachstein, the Tennengebirge and the Hagengebirge), whose surfaces bear the signs merely of an embryonic karstification, whereas their interiors contain such vast systems of caverns as the Eisriesenwelt, 42 km long, or the Dachsteinmammuthöhle and the Dachstein-Eisriesenhöhle (both 20 km), the Tantalhöhle (15 km), or the famous Koppenbrüllerhöhle.

This situation is due in part to the reasons expounded above, and in part also to the circumstance that the caverns in the depths of these mountains may be products of pre-Pleistocene karst processes, that is *forms surviving the periods of glaciation.* For instance, as suggested by terrace morphological research in the Salzburg Alps, the Austrian caverns just cited can be linked with late Tertiary valley-bottom levels; as far as evacuation is concerned, they are all inactive today. In contrast, owing to large-scale glacial erosion, the surface karst forms in most mountains may not precede the beginning of the Holocene. That is, the underground phenomena of mountain karsts are as a rule older than the surface phenomena, so that they reflect the karst evolution of earlier periods.

Another noteworthy feature is the scarcity of dripstones in these caverns. Further, accumulations of calcareous tufa in the stream beds are absent or very slight, both underground (tetaratas, tufa weirs) and on the surface (spring limestone). This is partly due to the absence of significant differences in temperature and pCO_2 between the atmospheres surrounding the areas of infiltration into the lithosphere and the points of egress of the water from the fissure network of the rock.

Recent caverns in mountains are mostly vertically oriented. Precipitations and meltwaters can flow rapidly and unhindered off the steep rock slopes on the surface and through the fissure network of the limestone. One of the consequences of this situation for karst genesis is that the seesaw of freeze-and-thaw will not act twice on the same water, and the unimpaired calcium carbonate aggressivity of the water will permit the dissolution of the rock even in the deeper spheres of the joints.

We have already seen in the course of our considerations that the colder the infiltrating water, the more slowly it will attain hydrocarbonate saturation, since the rate of dissolution varies inversely as the temperature. Hence, despite the lower intensity of dissolution, the vertical dimension of a rock body sculptured by corrosion is much greater than in the temperate and especially the tropical karsts. This is why, even under several hundred metres of limestone, the caverns of a mountain karst will exhibit abundant and often quite large-scale underground lapies due to corrosion (*Photo 8*). It also explains why the active period of evolution of shaft caverns *(avens)* in Hungarian hills can be dated as contemporaneous with the Pleistocene glacial periods, at the time when, in keeping with their then

Photo 8. Cavern lapies very typical of the caverns of high-mountain karsts, indicative of local expansions in the vertical reach of recent corrosion in the limestone. Such lapies occasionally form too in caverns under temperate climates, in hilly regions, particularly beneath a comparatively thin cover of limestone rock that is barren on the surface: even there, however, they are too rare to be considered a typical zonal feature (photo by BENICZKÝ)

climatic situation, these peneplains were karstified under the influence of a combination of mountainous (periglacial) factors.

In other words, we may formulate this finding as follows: *the formation of shaft caverns (doline wells),* often of great depth, *is a typical feature of subnival (mountain) karsts* or, almost equivalent as far as the karstifying effect is concerned, of karsts in a hilly or low-mountain region under a periglacial climate. Of course, this does not refer to funnels or dolines formed by the collapse of the roof of a larger cavern underground (Ma-

125

cocha, Skocijan, etc.), but to the majority of shaft caverns (avens), structurally or stratospecifically preformed and excavated by aqueous corrosion, such as include in Hungary the 110 m deep Kiskőhát well, the Almás well (93 m) and the Szeleta well (90 m), and also the deepest known caverns on earth [the Gouffre Berger in France (1122 m), Pierre St. Martin in the Pyrenees (1138 m), Antri di Corchia in Italy (805 m), etc.].

Of course, natural phenomena cannot and should not be handled according to hard and fast genetic schemes and systematic-taxonomic categories, since the differences in lithology, stratigraphy, structure, climatology, biology, environment and anterior evolution history of karsts cover such a wide range, and the resulting set of forms are so diverse and individual, that the exceptions may be said to be the rule. Still, the adopted research *methods of morphometric analysis* permit us to recognize and formulate the most important general trends. It is in this sense that our above findings and *Figure 43* (providing a summary of these) are to be understood, as well as *Figure 44*, reflecting a different method of processing the mass of morphometric data underlying these findings.

Our research results reviewed so far demonstratively prove the profound truth that in climatic karst morphology, distinctive qualitative features are decisively influenced by the intensities of the contributing factors. The climatic conditions which bring about increases and reductions in pCO_2 control the nature of the developing set of forms by influencing the degree of corrosion dynamism. Temperature, which among others affects the rates

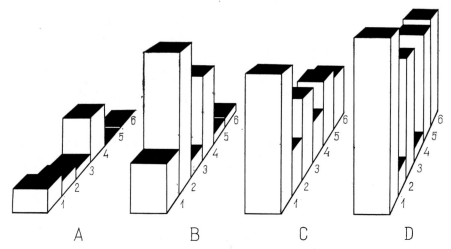

Fig. 43. A comparative statistical presentation of some intensity parameters of karstification in European folded mountains, according to altitude zones

A — mountain surfaces above 3000 m; B — subnival high-mountain barren karsts above 2000 m; C — hill karsts above 1000 m, bearing a plant and soil cover; D — hill karsts between 0 and 1000 m

Meaning of the numbers of columns:

1 — intensity of karstification; 2 — depth of reach of corrosion; 3 — intensity of calcareous tufa deposition and dripstone formation in caverns; 4 — formation of furrow lapies; 5 — formation of root lapies; 6 — intensity of doline formation

126

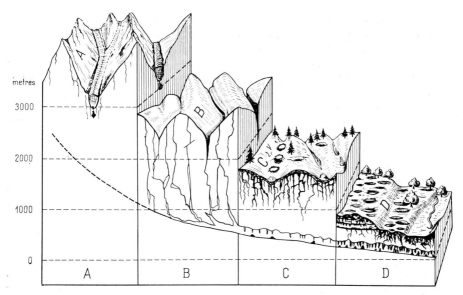

Fig. 44. Diagram of the distribution by vertical zones of the basic formal features of karstification in European folded mountain regions

A — embryonic lapies, possibly the corrosion of shallow caves by water under pressure beneath glaciers; B — low-intensity but deep-reaching karstification by corrosion, usually reflected on the surface by protogenic furrow lapies and young precipitous valley gorges, with the formation of avens in the depth of the karst mass; caverns contain few and ill-developed dripstones; C — medium-intensity and not particularly deep-reaching karstification by corrosion; dolines, inactive valleys evolving aligned dolines along their traces; swallow-holes swallowing surface streams; intense lapies formation, largely including strato- and tecto-orientated furrows on barren surfaces; deposition of calcareous tufa next to karst springs possible; medium-intensity dripstone formation in caverns; D — intense processes of corrosion under soil cover of comparatively small depth, large-scale root-lapies formation; sculpture of dolines, uvalas and possibly of poljes; intense dripstone formation in caverns, copious accumulations of calcareous tufa in valleys

of the absorption and dissolution reactions, influences the vertical depth of the corrosion zone and thereby gives rise to novel features. The period of time involved in the karstification may also become a factor controlling the qualitative aspect of the forms by determining the immediate agencies of denudation.

2. KARST CORROSION IN THE TEMPERATE AND MEDITERRANEAN ZONES

Karstification under temperate and Mediterranean zones occupies a transitional, intermediate position between cold regions and tropical climates, as regards both the intensities of agencies and processes, and their formal consequences. Primarily as a result of the omnipresence and vigour of the plant cover, which also produces a coherent soil cover, the rates of surface and underground denudation are markedly higher as compared with the bare periglacial (or mountainous) limestone areas lacking such soil and plant covers. The mechanisms of corrosion and precipitation typical of karstification in the tropical zone are already present (rhizosphere lapies, large-scale formation of calcareous tufa and dripstones), but the dynamisms of their formation are still seasonal, restricted to the summer half of the year, which in itself results in lowered efficiencies. On the other hand, the seasonal variation of the climatic factors promotes in turn the seasonal rhythm of the karst mechanisms characteristic of periglacial (especially mountainous) types. For instance, especially in the channel and furrow lapies of bare temperate and Mediterranean karst surfaces, we must see the temporary dominance of the cold solutions in the surface sculpture during the winter half of the year.

The annual periodicity, of course, affects most decisively those factors whose intensities depend largely on the atmosphere and the upper soil levels, including primarily the quantity and calcium carbonate aggressivity of the infiltrating water and the rate of reprecipitation (calcareous tufa formation) on the surface, sensitive to ambient temperature. In contrast, the vertical reach of dissolution, and the conditions controlling dripstone formation in caverns, are exposed to no such changes of a similar intensity, as the seasonal fluctuation of temperatures is smoothed out at a comparatively small depth (8 to 25 m); at greater depths, the temperature of the karstic rock mass is usually the annual mean temperature of the region.

This does not mean, of course, that the seasonal meteorological rhythms have no effect at all on either the depth reach of dissolution or the rate of dripstone deposition in the caverns. However, since these rhythms are communicated by essentially one factor only (the chemical composition, the quantity, and to a lesser extent, the temperature of the solution seeping down from above), their significance is less than that of the factors enumerated above. This is corroborated most convincingly in that, whereas the summer and winter carbonic acid saturations acquired by the waters of atmospheric origin in the soil quite regularly differ by a factor of 30 to 50 [our own measurements are in complete agreement with earlier research (FEHÉR 1954)], and summer and winter rates of deposition of calcareous tufa from karst streams cover a similar range (as proved by our measurements at Lillafüred and in the Kecső Valley), the range of seasonal fluctuations in the rate of calcium carbonate deposition from waters dripping off underground stalactites is narrower by at least an order of magnitude (CZÁJLIK and FEJÉRDY 1960, L. MAUCHA 1960/1, L. JAKUCS 1960/2).

Since the corrosional aspect of karst erosion (primarily driven by the biological factors) is very markedly climate-dependent, it is greatly influenced not only by dominant climatic features which, incidentally, also incorporate a statistical background "noise" of a host of minute, concrete local effects, but also in its morphological effect by special topo- and microclimatic conditions. Our own observations suggest that these conditions are sometimes reflected in microform features only, but often also in a lasting manner in the evolution of the relief features of the entire karst region. We have several reasons to assume (this problem will be returned to in analytical detail later) that relief-forming influences especially

128

of microclimatic conditions will assert themselves most in the temperate zone.

In another aspect, certain karst forms causally dependent on the zonal climatic properties of the temperate and Mediterranean zones owe their features predominantly to the climatic extremes characteristic of these. The first such feature that comes to mind is the presence of large erosional karst cavern systems which, although dependent primarily on the lithological conditions of the environment, as will be discussed below, also display the effects of climatic variance. The detritus produced by the freeze-and-thaw of the winter season lending efficiency to linear erosion, and the frequency of strong floods outside the season of vegetation (in the Mediterranean zone), are the fundamental traits of this climatic zone.

It is our intention to give an analytical evaluation of the typical processes of karstification in the temperate and Mediterranean zones and of their formal consequences in a volume to be prepared later, as a sequel to this book, including a detailed description of the forms and their genetic taxonomy.

3. KARST CORROSION IN THE DESERT ZONE

The desert regions are the least endowed of all the climatic zones with facilities for karst corrosion. For such minimal precipitations (less than 10 mm per year, and at times practically none at all), one can hardly speak of dissolution of limestone. Even the annual distribution of this extremely scanty precipitation lacks any uniformity and regularity, so that the conditions for the survival of higher plants and for the evolution of a soil cover are entirely absent. Such precipitation as there is descending in brief but violent rainstorms, part of the rainwater is immediately drained away (areal desert and linear streambed erosion; wadi sculpture) and part of it is avidly absorbed by the ground, where it cannot penetrate to any great depth, as the intense transpiration characteristic of this zone soon results in its total evaporation.

Owing to these conditions, and to the absence of a soil cover that would conserve precipitation for some time at or near the ground surface, contact with the rock of even the small amount of water available is very brief, so that the scarcity of solvent is combined with an insufficient contact time, one of the essential conditions of karst corrosion. If this is viewed in the context of intense comminution by insolation and dynamic relief sculpture by deflation, characteristic of these regions, the conspicuous absence of corrosive limestone forms is quite natural. Accordingly, karsts in true *deserts are typified by the absence of karst phenomena.*

Of course, this does not exclude the occurrence in the desert of certain forms, characteristic as a rule of karst regions, and consequently regarded as karstic in everyday parlance. One encounters for instance caves and grottoes of various sizes (DANES 1916, KOSACK 1952, BULLA 1954/1, H. LEHMANN 1954/1, 1956, BALÁZS 1963/2, MAKSIMOVICH 1964/1), but these occur in any desert rock, not necessarily resulting from a corrosional karst process. Their origin is most often connected with selective wind erosion enhancing lithostructural differences, with linear erosion by rainstorm torrents (especially near the scarps of the stepped tablelands of the deserts, where the relief energy is high), and less often with structural events. The rare caves of corrosional origin, which are nevertheless encountered in certain true deserts, may be attributed to an earlier period, much rainier than the present.

It is worthy of note that the first karst form encountered on progressing from the centre of a true desert towards a marginal region with the climatic features of a semi-desert are caverns indicative of linear erosion. This in itself bears witness to the climatic insensitivity of this evacuating processes, as opposed to the considerable sensitivity of corrosional karst processes in general.

4. TROPICAL KARSTIFICATION

Incontestably, the dynamism of corrosive erosion of limestone reliefs is most intense in the tropical climatic region, where a highly characteristic set of relief forms may be observed. The concept of tropical karstification is usually employed in a very broad sense, however, and is taken, in the zone of torrid climates with two rainy seasons, in the tropical savannah zone with a single rainy season, and in the tropical and subtropical monsoon regions, to include all karst surfaces which exhibit forms of karst erosion different from those of the other climatic zones already described.

Analogous with karst erosion in the other climatic zones, the tropical karst is primarily a landscape of climato-morphologic determinism whose evolution requires certain thresholds of temperature and precipitation. Several authors agree that the thresholds are a mean annual temperature of 17 to 18 °C, and 1000 to 1200 mm of annual rainfall. If either of these two conditions is not met, no tropical karst forms will evolve. That is, an increase in temperature will not in itself counterbalance a deficit in precipitation; nor will an abundant annual rainfall at a low temperature give rise to a tropical karst form.

These climatic minima primarily act through the intermediary of the biosphere, making possible an uninterrupted cycle of vegetation the year round, even in subtropical monsoon regions with deciduous forests. As a result, the edaphon, rich in species represented by large numbers of individuals, ensures very high levels of biogenic CO_2 and organic soil acids all the year round.

These factors, together with the high rates of dissolution by warm rains and ground waters, result in a near-surface calcium carbonate dissolution of striking intensity, because the ground waters, having acquired a substantial aggressivity in the rhizosphere of the tropical aerobic soils with their immensely rich edaphon, start a very intense dissolution as soon as they come into contact with the bedrock, and hence attain saturation within a very short time. In the course of his Cuban studies of 1955, H. LEHMANN showed that water percolating through the roof (only 4 m thick) of the Cueva del Indio cave already contained 150 mg/l of dissolved $CaCO_3$; this must have been the saturation level, since at another point of the cave,

130

where the roof was already 10 m thick, the $CaCO_3$ concentration of the permeating water was 152 mg/l.

The frequent and copious rains of the tropics are well known to effect a strong sheetwash, a sub-areal soil erosion. This is another decisive factor of relief sculpture by tropical karstification, in both the direct and the indirect sense.

The direct relief-forming role of soil erosion is well known and clarified in many respects in the geomorphological literature, but the indirect effects of the process are seldom referred to. We must consequently examine this problem in somewhat more detail.

By the indirect karst-relief sculpture of soil erosion we mean that process which results from the washing together and accumulation of soil particles, resulting in a substantial thickening of the soil cover in places, and the chemical consequences of such thickening. In our interpretation of this phenomenon, we start from the consideration that, even in the early stages of karst erosion, when karst forms are not yet present even embryonically, the peneplain surface is divided into parts where the soil is thinned by rains and others where the washed-off soil accumulates. This effect holds especially for the horizon of mobile organic debris and loose humus. The process entails an areal selectivity in the dynamism of karst corrosion, since under the locally thickened humus cover corrosion is substantially stronger than in the bare spots where the soil has been removed altogether or thinned and its top level removed, and this level plays the most important role in activating calcium carbonate aggressivity.

On the surfaces better exposed to sheetwash the karst may even be laid bare, although under tropical conditions complete soil removal is unusual; tenacious roots of plants, forming an interlocking tangle on the rock surface, usually forestall total ablation; but even minor differences may be extremely significant as concerns the influence on the rate of dissolution. It is necessary in this context to emphasize the following three factors affecting corrosion intensity:

1. In soils with a thick humus, the mere fact that the biologically productive horizon is thicker, results in the production and accumulation of more biogenic CO_2, and in a more prolonged contact of the ground water with the soil atmosphere.

2. A thicker soil has a greater water-storage capacity, and absorbs more rain in a downpour than a thin carpet of soil. Hence, the amount of water acting upon a limestone surface covered by a thick soil will be greater, and the discharge of water from the soil towards the rock surface will be more drawn-out and uniform.

3. In periods of intense evaporation, a thinner soil will dry out sooner, and hence more often. In consequence, its phytedaphon in particular will be much impoverished and restricted to the eurythermic species capable of withstanding a broad range of changes in humidity and hence also in temperature. It should be added that a dry soil is better aerated and thus less suited for the accumulation of CO_2.

Of course, as karstification proceeds and the dolines grow deeper, such differences in corrosion intensity, minute to start with, are enhanced more and more, until the karst plateau is divided up into peak and summit

Photo 9. Cone karst region sculptured by tropical karst corrosion and lateral streambed erosion in Cuba, Pinar del Rio (photo by the author)

regions, bare of soil or almost so, with low-intensity corrosion, and into intermontane depressions, deepened with increasing speed, where a thick dynamic soil layer ensures a considerable intensity of corrosion. These depressions may in time develop into intermontane basins.

In the initial stage of karst erosion, intermontane depressions are analogous in both form and content to the dolines of the temperate zones. Intensive deepening at subsequent stages, however, may give rise to forms qualitatively different from dolines. The new quality of form becomes conspicuous especially if intermontane corrosion wears the limestone down to the local baselevel of erosion, and the further sculpture of forms is combined with the lateral erosion of above-surface streams. A karst region reflecting this compound origin due to both tropical karst corrosion and lateral streambed erosion is shown in *Photo 9,* a view of the Pinar del Rio region of Cuba.

The succession of processes due to selective erosion by karst corrosion and the morphogenetic outlines of the reliefs thus sculptured are presented in *Figure 45.*

Even in the caption to Figure 45 we were obliged to use terminology referring to the most typical tropical karst forms (karst cone, karst tower; inselbergs; intermontane basins, etc.). Clearly, the distinctive features of these forms become more or less self-explanatory once the fundamental agencies contributing to the genetic process are known. In the following, we shall review all the important and typical sets of forms of this high-efficiency type of corrosion.

132

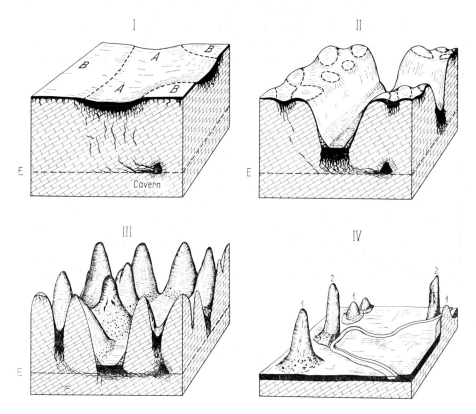

Fig. 45. Four-phase genetic pattern of the erosion of karst surfaces in the tropics

Phase I: Soil and related waste is removed from the hummocks and deposited in the depressions of a pre-karst surface, resulting in more intense karstification in the areas marked A as compared to the areas marked B (E represents the baselevel of erosion)

Phase II: Intense karst corrosion under the soil cover in the A-areas causes the karst surface to be lowered increasingly faster than under the B-areas: the B-areas become progressively dissimilar to the A-areas too, owing to cumulative effects (e.g. to sub-areal erosion, the focal point of our considerations)

Phase III: Phase of evolution of the tropical cone karst. The B-areas themselves are so reduced in size that they are divided into peaks and ridges where the rate of vertical erosion is low, as any soil formed is soon swept off the steep hillsides. The karst cone thus evolves as a permanent form of the tropical karst, whose base, placed where soil may accumulate, can erode ten times faster than at its summit

Phase IV: Lateral erosion and corrosion of the rivers forming in the A-areas at the baselevel of erosion develop the karst cones into karst towers by undercutting. In the process, the formerly underground streams develop surface beds in the A-areas and these latter are widened into intermontane plains, while the ground plans of the karst inselbergs left over from the former B-areas are gradually reduced (1 — cone karst; 2 — tower karst)

The most detailed picture of the contribution of karst forms to relief sculpture in the international karst morphological literature is found in the works of H. Lehmann. Since my own observations concerning this climatic region, restricted to Cuban karsts, are very far from complete, I shall rely heavily on the literature for a presentation of the full range of relief forms.

a) Rain-forest karst

The dynamism of karst erosion is most intense in those regions of the earth where the temperatures are very high all year round (above 25 °C) and the rains very abundant (possibly several thousand millimetres). Regions exposed to such conditions are characterized by a wild labyrinth of fantastically shaped, irregular rock towers, jagged ridges and hogbacks, caverns and canyons, sinkholes and doline wells, the whole covered by an impassable tangle of rank tropical vegetation: the resulting landscape is called a rain-forest karst. Such karsts are known to occur in South Vietnam, Laos, on the Malay Peninsula, in New Guinea, in the Congo, etc. They are practically impenetrable owing to the strikingly accidented relief, the dense growth of vegetation, and the unhealthy oppressive humidity of the near-ground atmosphere. This is why rain-forest karsts are among the least-known regions of the earth; and this is why the study of their forms and of the intensities of the forces forming them will be among the more arduous tasks of the future.

b) Inselberg karst

We have already seen in our interpretation of Figure 45 that erosion by corrosion will result in the sculpture of an inselberg karst, especially in the tropical savannah zone and in regions of subtropical—tropical monsoon climates (mean annual temperature 18 to 27 °C; mean annual rainfall 1000 to 2000 mm). In such a region, the karst plateau undergoing erosion is divided into isolated conical or tower-shaped inselbergs, sometimes separated by broad, flat-bottomed valley plains, known as intermontane karst plains. The summit level of the inselbergs is an approximate indication of the top level of the former connected karst plateau, whereas the valley-floor level usually indicates the local baselevel of erosion.

The "rock-pyramids", of sugarloaf, tent, or tower shape, may be 50 to 300 m tall; they may stand alone or in rows. Many of them are riddled with horizontal cave passages, most of which are inactive, however.

The inselberg karst is called "Kegelkarst" or "Turmkarst" in German, "cockpit karst" or "tower karst" in English, and "mogotes" in Cuban Spanish. The French literature calls them "karst à pitons" or "karst en

134

écumoire", or sometimes also "karst à tourelles". In our opinion it is most correct to use the comprehensive term inselberg karst. It should be borne in mind, however, that within any inselberg-karst region, it is sometimes reasonable to distinguish, as two successive stages of erosion, a *younger cone-karst phase and a subsequent tower-karst state*, the latter being indicative of a more advanced erosion and of the interaction of several agencies of erosion.

The classic, best known areas of inselberg karsts include South China (Kweichow, Kwangsi), North Vietnam, Cuba, Puerto Rico, Jamaica, etc.

c) Karst cone and karst tower

The two most typical positive forms of the inselberg karst are cones and towers. Some inselberg karsts are dominated by cones, whereas in others cones and towers occur together. On the other hand, it is unusual for towers without cones to occupy any sizeable area.

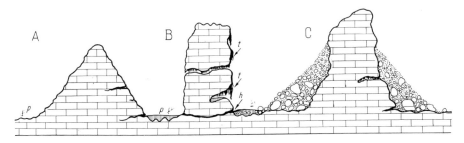

Fig. 46. Fundamental types of karst cones and towers (after BALÁZS)
A — primary karst cone sculptured by corrosion; B — karst tower; C — karst cone covered in its own alluvia; *t* — tufa curtain; *h* — hillfoot cavern; *p* — intermontane plain

Cones may be primary cones of corrosion (A in *Fig. 46*), or secondary cones with an apron of rubble (C). The apron itself may be either primary (a pediment resulting from the erosion of the karst cone), or secondary (accompanying the senile stage of decay of a karst tower).

Karst towers (B in Fig. 46) originate from karst cones in that stage of erosion when the denudation of the intermontane plain has advanced to the local baselevel of erosion, and a surface network of drainage starts to develop on it. A karst tower is thus a form bearing witness to the lateral undercutting erosion and corrosion by streams, although its vertical walls are sometimes due to the collapse of caverns, to structural planes, bedding-plane separation, etc.

Photo 10. Karst marginal plain in tropical karst in Cuba (photo by the author)

d) Intermontane karst plains

Lowlands 50 to several thousand metres wide, of irregular outline, and surrounding karst inselbergs are called intermontane karst plains or karst marginal plains. They usually represent accumulations of alluvia rich in calcium carbonate, occasionally calcareous tufa, or terra rossa (possibly laterite), or mixtures of these in various proportions. At best a few tens of metres thick, this soil cover is invariably underlain by the same massive rock as forms the inselbergs towering above the plains.

The intermontane karst plain may be fully closed, polje-like, or open on one or more sides. In the last case it is usually called a karst marginal plain ("Karstrandebene" in German) (*Photo 10*).

Most of the rain falling upon the plain and its inselbergs during the year evaporates. This is due to a considerable extent to the dense plant cover. Drainage is effected by the rivers of the intermontane plains, which carry away appreciably softened water; the plains closed on all sides, but sometimes also the open ones, are drained through hillfoot caverns.

The evolution of a karst plain agrees in every respect with that of an erosional polje in the temperate region, the difference lying merely in the intensity of erosion. We feel that the differences between a polje and an intermontane karst plain emphasized by H. Lehmann are neither essential nor genetic, but merely a matter of degree. This is why we agree basically with the proposal of BALÁZS (1959/2, 1968) to consider this state of erosion a *tropical polje*.

If an intermontane karst plain or a karst marginal plain is invaded by the sea (e.g. in part of the Gulf of Tonkin), we are confronted with a *karst archipelago or karst island sea*. Karst cones and towers jutting out of the sea are usually made even steeper by wave abrasion.

e) Other characteristic tropical karst forms

The agency decisive in the modelling of the microforms in the bedrock is the enormously vital plant cover of tropical karsts. The roots of these arboraceous and other plants etch tortuous single and branching channels in the hard rock. Most of these channels are of circular section; they occasionally reach down 25 m into the rock; they may locally criss-cross the limestone so densely as to turn it into something of a large-scale skeletal cavernous sponge. The present author has observed at several points around Santiago de Cuba limestone blocks of Miocene age, in which root channels have removed up to 75 per cent of the original rock volume (*Photo 11*).

Under tropical conditions, the evolution of this "root-zone lapies" is an extremely fast process. Four to ten years suffice for the corrosive action

Photo 11. Typical root lapies in a tropical limestone (Cuba, Oriente). High-intensity biochemical corrosion has eaten away more than 75 per cent of the original rock volume (photo by the author)

Photo 12. A characteristic example of the dynamics of biogenic karst corrosion is the trees in Oriente (Cuba), which have grown through 4—5 m long rock channels hollowed out by their root acid and the crowns of which are on the surface, with the trunk resting on the soil of the cavern (photo by the author)

of a penetrating root to turn a primary hairline crack in the rock into a rock channel of arm or thigh thickness. In other words, these spectacular biogenic karst forms may develop even within a single vegetal cycle (*Photo 12*).

In contrast, karst surfaces with a meagre soil and sparse plant cover receiving large quantities of rain may exhibit large-scale furrow and rill karsts. These are, in both formal and genetic respects, entirely analogous to the lapies of the temperate zone. The difference is only one of size, but it may be quite substantial. According to the literature, the lapies in the Yunnan region of South China are 20 to 30 m wide. The rock labyrinths of the canyons between the jagged ridges are well-nigh impenetrable. Utilizing the local Chinese term (shiling — rock forest), we shall call the lapies forms of this size *tropical rock forests* (*Fig. 47*).

Rivers in an intermontane plain often disappear in a swallow cave at the foot of a cone or tower and reappear on its other side. These holes are usually called *hillfoot caves* (the "Fusshöhlen" of H. Lehmann). Genetically, they correspond to the polje-rim swallow cave of the Dinaric region, or to the katavothra.

Cone and tower hills also abound in caves at higher than hillfoot level. They exhibit traces of a former intense dripstone formation, which has entirely filled up some of them. A circumstance worthy of special note, however, is that dripstone formation in the caverns of the inselbergs has generally ceased by now, and the caverns are usually dry. This is connected with the fact that fissures, bedding-plane gaps and other cavities suitable for the conduction of water in the early stages of karst corrosion have been filled up with precipitates in the meantime by the highly saturated calcium carbonate solutions seeping down from the surface, and thus the advance of karstification has itself become the factor defeating any further evolution of the three-dimensional karst. Another incontestable factor is that the cone summits cannot possibly carry soil cover thick enough to store sufficient rain and pass it on at a constant rate to the underlying bedrock after having imparted to it a high degree of aggressivity (*Photo 13*).

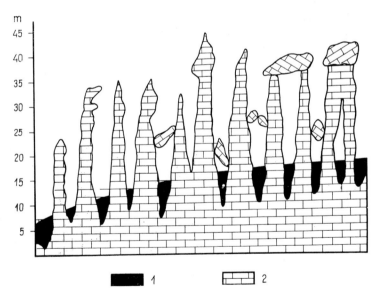

Fig. 47. Profile of part of the "rock forest" in Yunnan (after BALÁZS)

1 — clay; 2 — limestone (lapies ridges)

139

Photo 13. As the entrance to this Cuban cavern demonstrates, the dripstone formation, characteristic of tropical caverns, is discernible at the cavern opening (photo by the author)

On the other hand, owing to the blocking of the fissure grid in the limestone by dripstones and other forms of precipitated calcium carbonate, most of the unevaporated rain will drain off the tropical karst cones in the form of sheetwash. Water trickling down exposed roots and lianas under usually thin soil, or occasionally on the bare rock slopes, precipitates out its dissolved calcium carbonate content on the surface. This process results in another highly typical accumulation of tropical karsts, the *tropical tufa curtain* that, on overhanging slopes in particular, forms widespread huge, stalactite-like tufa bowers, or "petrified waterfalls".

Of course, tropical karsts also exhibit all the forms usual in the well-known classic karsts of the temperate zone (swallow holes, dolines, calcareous tufa mounds, etc.).

5. KARST MORPHOLOGICAL CONSEQUENCES OF SOIL MICROCLIMATES

In the previous sections we discussed the decisive importance of the climate in controlling the intensity of the karst process. Our investigation has disclosed a wide range of arguments for attributing a central position in morphogenetic analysis to the climatic variance of karstification.

On the other hand, we also arrived at the formulation of one of our most fundamental theorems, notably that the karst corrosion of limestone rocks is essentially the formal imprint in the soluble bedrock of the biological and chemical phenomena of evolution of the pedosphere, the soil covering the rock. It was further established that these biological and chemical phenomena are themselves under climatic control.

The karst erosion of limestone regions identical in lithologic, structural and orographic conditions, but different as to climatic conditions, exhibit differences in quality and also in quantity, amounting to several orders of magnitude, for the sole reason that the temperatures and precipitations of these regions are different; as a result, their surfaces bear specific types of plant cover giving rise to diverse soil-biological (and hence chemical) processes.

Research in the last few years has convincingly documented the above assertion. It is thus time to make a further step forward: if the comparison of geographically separate areas confirms the assumption that differences in precipitation volumes and heat quantities induce differences in karst dynamism (largely by the intermediary of biochemical processes), then this same assumption must also hold in the comparison of regions different as regards climatic conditions, even if these are geographical neighbours. That is, distance should play no role at all in determining these relationships.

In other words, within a given microregion the karst process is invariably determined by the microclimatic parameters of the site in question, which are in turn not determined only by the macroclimate of the region.

The global zonality of the macroclimate influences the karst process inasmuch as it determines the features, distribution and proportions of individual microclimatic areas within a climatic region. However, if local conditions of orography, exposure, protection from the wind, etc. modify the climate giving rise to small differences in microclimatic areas, then the local intensities of the karst processes in these small areas, will also differ essentially from the overall karst process typical of the macrospace (region). The intrazonal appearance of most extrazonal features in karst morphology is due to this. Hence, in a given region, the quality of the surface erosion may be interpreted as a statistical average of the observed erosional events in a number of not necessarily similar microspaces.

Our primary task is to determine the smallest physico-geographic landscape unit which may still reflect in its forms the microclimatic divergences giving rise to differences in degree in the general karstification process.

This set of problems has not so far been tackled by geomorphologists. However, in addition to our own investigations, we rely on the results of certain pioneering colleagues mainly in the fields of climatology, pedology and biology. We first turn to the studies of Wagner, which provide

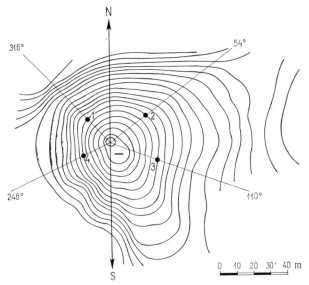

Fig. 48. Relief map with one-metre contours of a doline on the Középbérc (Bükk Hills) microclimatically surveyed by WAGNER (1956). The figures 1 to 4 mark the sites and azimuths against the doline centre of the four recordings of soil temperatures in Figs 49 and 51

a mass of data covering long periods of time, for the assessment of possible morphogenetic connexions (WAGNER 1954, 1955/1—2, 1956, 1960, 1964, FUTÓ 1962, BÁRÁNY 1967, etc.). Other significant research includes investigations into soil respiration by soil scientists [among which the work of FEHÉR (1954) is the most relevant to our subject], as well as the studies aimed at a microclimatic interpretation of plant associations in karst regions of homogeneous lithology (BACSÓ and ZÓLYOMI 1934, P. JAKUCS 1954, 1956, 1961/2, 1962).

Largely as a result of the above authors, it is known that, for instance on the karst surfaces of the Hungarian hills, there are significant differences in soil intensity due to microclimatic causes; these differences arise not merely in connexion with the rhizospheric processes of this or that plant association, forest type, shrub wood or steppe, as a consequence of the northerly or southerly exposure (that is, different even within a single doline), but on an even smaller scale (e.g. in the root spheres of two plant species directly adjacent to one another). This is especially true of the interplay of soil respiration and of carbon dioxide production in the soil, which is very sensitive to the activity of soil microorganisms. It is these factors which are most significant in determining aggressivity as regards the karstification potential of water seeping from the soil into the karst.

Consequently, if it can be proved that significant differences in heat availability, their warming and cooling graphs, the soil moisture, etc. exist such as on the slopes of northerly and southerly, and of easterly and westerly exposures, this entails further differences in the natural plant cover, the related bacterial flora of the pedosphere, the soil respiration, etc., which in turn result in a partial dynamic differentiation of the karst process within the doline. That is to say, karst erosion will be different on slopes of different exposures within any given doline. It follows that the form of a karst doline results from the distribution of the corresponding micro-climatic zones.

Let us next examine some of the premises to the above-stated theorem as a working hypothesis.

WAGNER (*Fig. 48*) has given detailed recordings of microclimatic param-eters from a doline on Középbérc Hill on the Bükk Plateau, Hungary; these permit an accurate, quantitative assessment of the characteristic temperature differences within dolines and the trends of these differences (WAGNER 1960, 1963, 1964, AMBRUS 1965, GÖMÖRI 1967). It is found that warming is as a rule strongest and most prolonged on the south-easterly and southerly facing slopes of dolines, whereas the north-easterly and northerly slopes remain coolest. A comparison of easterly and westerly slopes in a doline invariably reveals the easterly facing slopes to be warmer.

Temperature differences between opposite slopes are most pronounced in the morning, when the near-ground air layers above the easterly and south-easterly facing slopes may exhibit gradients of as much as 10 °C or higher in the summer. In the afternoon, on the other hand, when the westerly facing slopes are exposed to direct solar radiation, the heating effect is not so marked.

The differences in daily warming and insolation between southerly and northerly, and also easterly and westerly facing slopes are strikingly dem-onstrated by a comparison of ground temperatures. *Figure 49* presents

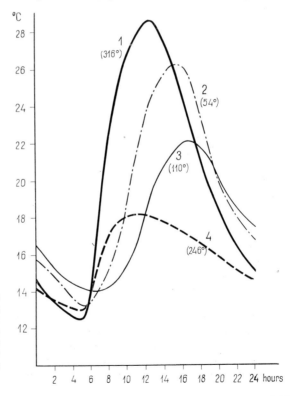

Fig. 49. Soil temperatures at 2-cm depths recorded in a doline on Középbérc (cf. Fig. 48). The 24-hour diagrams represent averages of the recordings by WAGNER on four consecutive cloudless days (6—9 August, 1965)

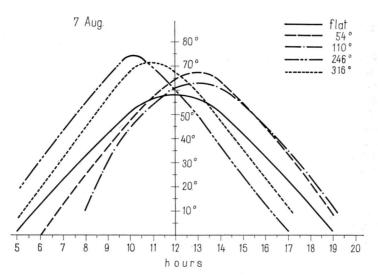

flat
———   54°
—·—   110°
—··— 246°
········ 316°

Fig. 50. Angles of incidence of solar rays at the four recording sites in the Középbérc doline of Fig. 48. The insolation curves were calculated by GÖMÖRI (1967) from the following parameters:

Station	Azimuth of site as observed from doline centre, degrees	Exposure of site by compass point	Slope at site, degrees
1	316	SE	17
2	54	SW	12
3	110	WNW	13
4	246	ENE	24

the recordings of four ground temperature stations implanted at 2 cm depths on different exposures.

The amplitudes, as expected, primarily reflect the differences in slope angles (*Fig. 50*), but the peculiar trends of the temperature curves for the various exposures, the displacements of the maxima, and the rate of change of the upward branches of the diagrams all reflect a more marked continentality in the easterly facing exposures.

These phenomena are due to the complex interaction of several factors.

1. In the summer, the mornings and forenoons are usually less cloudy than the afternoons.

2. Eastern facing slopes receive the heat of direct irradiation responsible for the warming of the ground early in the day, while the western slope, warmed only by air convection (of low specific heat) warms up very slowly. In the afternoon, on the other hand, when the western slopes receive direct sunshine, the cooling of the eastern facing slopes by radiation is retarded by the air which, having been warmed up considerably during the day by contact with the ground, is now at its warmest. Hence, the eastern facing slopes are warm throughout the entire duration of sunshine, whereas the western facing slopes are warm in the afternoon only.

3. Summer rainstorms are more frequent in the afternoon than in the morning. Hence, direct solar heat is more often used to evaporate precipitation from the western facing slopes (that tend to be warmer when the rain falls) than from slopes of easterly exposure.

4. As the dominant rain-bringing wind in Hungary is westerly or north-westerly, the western facing slopes receive more rain than the eastern slopes. This factor is particularly significant in the summer when the strong winds accompanying rainstorms cause raindrop trajectories to include acute angles with the horizontal.

The peculiar daily trends of the soil temperatures in the various exposures do not, of course, affect the soil merely to a depth of 2 cm; on the contrary, they determine the heat balance of practically the entire soil profile. Hence, the pedological processes of the eastern and southern doline flanks are invariably more extreme than those of the western and northern flanks. This is especially obvious in the daily temperature graphs for a depth of 30 cm (*Fig. 51*); the fluctuation is almost nil in the westerly exposure.

These significant differences of heat transfer and ground temperature within a given doline have a complex effect on the CO_2 production in the soil cover of the doline, as well as the intensity of soil respiration, the soil moisture, the qualitative and quantitative compositions of the plant cover and of the soil microflora, etc.; all this will affect the karst process itself and impart to it local differences in dynamism.

The close relation of soil moisture to the degree of warming on doline flanks of various exposures can be exemplified by a detailed survey of a doline on the North Borsod Karst (Northeast Hungary); at the time of the survey (May 1962), the doline had been ploughed and hence was practically vegetationless. Curves of identical moisture content, established by drying soil samples taken from a depth of 10 cm, are shown in *Figure 52*.

We have shown above that, even within a single doline, the differences in ground temperature and soil moisture may be quite marked, and that the distribution of these factors is linked with the various conditions of exposure. The extension of this line of thought towards completing the proof of the micro-climatic control of differences in karst dynamism is quite straightforward.

One of the fundamental textbook-level theorems of biology is that life functions of the microorganisms living in the soil are sensitively dependent upon ground temperature changes.

W. H. RUSSELL's diagram, published in 1926, is a clear illustration of the daily fluctuation of bacterial abundance in the soil, obviously closely related to the daily temperature fluctuations (*Fig. 53*).

After a series of tests and recordings, FEHÉR (1954) pointed out that an optimum temperature is in itself insufficient for the stimulation of the microbial population in a soil; what is required is the simultaneous availability of optimum temperature and optimum soil moisture. Fehér's findings, more recently corroborated by BECK (1968), show that optimum conditions for the virulence and multiplication of the soil bacterial flora include a temperature of 25 °C, and a soil moisture of about 25 weight per cent, provided the soil is sufficiently aerated. An increase or decrease in either of these factors entails an immediate, sharp decrease in bacterial abundance. The nature of the relationship can be assessed by inspecting *Figure 54*.

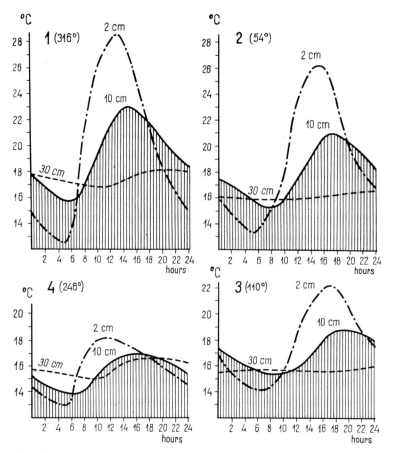

Fig. 51. Daily temperature fluctuations at various depths in the soil at the recording sites in the Középbérc doline. Extremes typical of slopes with an easterly component (1 and 4) are conspicuous even at 30-cm depth. The graphs represent averages of recordings by R. WAGNER on four consecutive cloudless days (6—9 August, 1965)

Under Central European climatic conditions, the ground temperature and soil moisture tend to vary in opposite senses. In the summer, when temperatures attain a maximum, the soil moisture content is usually low. If, on the other hand, the moisture content is temporarily boosted by heavy rain, the subsequent cool weather and/or evaporation again inhibit the optimum development of bioactivity.

This antagonism between the two factors is enhanced by the substantial differences of exposure of the doline flanks. The fast-warming south and east facing slopes experience brief periods with the temperature and moisture conditions of bioactivity nearly optimum at almost the same time (strong sunshine, after a summer rain at night or in the morning). In such cases, the bacterial abundance and the resulting increase of CO_2 production in

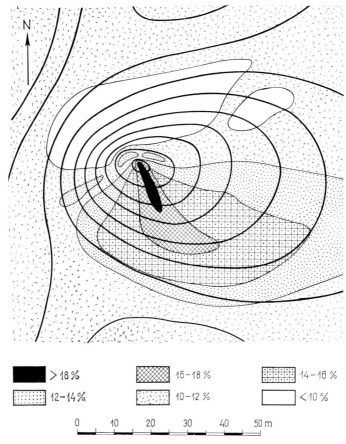

Fig. 52. Example of soil-moisture distribution at 10-cm depth in a vegetationless (ploughed-up) doline with a uniform soil cover. Soil moistures expressed as weight per cent. The isolines are one-metre relief contours. The map is based on 81 observations made on a 10-by-10 m grid pattern

the soil attain abrupt peaks. Usually, however, as far as the life conditions of the microorganisms are concerned, the strong and often protracted summer drought in the soil is unfavourably combined with higher temperatures, and hence, on slopes characterized by such extremes of ground temperature and drought, the large fluctuations of bioactivity give rise to equally appreciable fluctuations in karst-corrosion intensities.

In contrast, it has been seen that the soils on the north and west facing slopes of the dolines do not exhibit such extremes either in temperature or in moisture content. The lower, but more uniform temperatures and the higher soil-moisture content determine a different, but more uniform abundance of microorganisms in the soil. Implicitly, therefore, we have already arrived at the most decisive cause of the less intense fluctuation,

10*

147

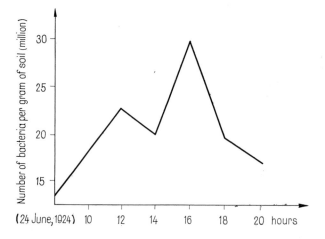

Fig. 53. Twelve-hour fluctuation of the number of soil bacteria as a function of the temperature in the soil layer examined (RUSSELL 1926)

but also of the reduced corrosivity of the ground waters on slopes of such exposures.

It should be pointed out in this context that Wagner, in his assessment of the morphogenetic effect of the differences in exposure of doline

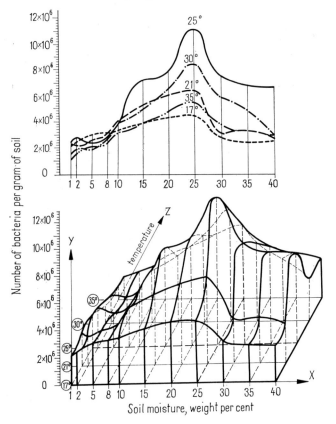

Fig. 54. Block diagram representing the biological activity of soil in terms of bacterial abundance as functions of temperature and soil humidity. The top part of the figure is a projection of the block diagram onto the XY plane (after FEHÉR 1954)

148

flanks, also emphasized the more intense comminution due to the stronger insolation on the more rapidly warmed, rocky eastern facing slopes, as well as the influence upon physical weathering of the stronger jointing resulting from thermal expansion. Research to verify this very plausible assumption has not yet been made, so that Wagner's views as to the intensity of the morphological influence of this factor must for the time being be regarded as a working hypothesis only.

Of course, the microclimatic exposure parameters just discussed determine not only the quality and quantity of the phytoedaphon in a doline, but also the structure of the macroflora as well. In the Bükk Hill of Hungary, for instance (Hosszúbérci-rét, Kismező, Nagymező, etc.), or on the North Borsod Karst (Verőtető, etc.), the usually rocky south slopes of unwooded dolines grow steppe-grass associations rich in species of the wooded steppe (*Festucetum sulcatae* = association of *Festuca sulcata*), whereas the eastern and western facing slopes and the rims with a thin soil cover carry mesophile hill lawns (association of *Festuca ovina*). The north slopes exhibit either the above, or a hazel association (association of *Corylus avellana*) where the soil is stonier; on the gently sloping northern shoulders, and on the flatter doline floors, where the soil is deep, there are matgrass lawns (association of *Nardus stricta*). If the doline bottom is steep and funnel-shaped, then it usually develops an association of tall weeds (with species of *Aconitum, Gladiolus*, etc.; P. JAKUCS 1961/1—2, 1962). These plant associations exhibit an inverse zonality in the dolines.

Such inversions incidentally, were also recorded by GEIGER (1961) from the Gstettneralm doline of Lower Austria, and by HORVAT (1953) from the dolines of the Yugoslavian Karst.

Clearly, other zones of vegetation (zones of altitude) will exhibit different plant associations: the mere fact that a doline is under forest cover drastically changes the situation. Nevertheless, differentiation according to exposure will prevail there, too. By the intermediary of the pedosphere, therefore, all this significantly affects karstification under a soil cover; the various plant species differ in their demands on the soil, and also in their influence upon the evolution, chemistry, microbial abundance, moisture, aeration, etc. of the soil.

For understandable reasons, these relationships have not so far been investigated on the natural plant covers of karst regions, but concrete and relevant recordings have long been available concerning certain cultivated plants and some others, especially certain types of trees. *Table 15* (after STOKLASA and DOERELL 1926) presents the soil CO_2 productions of six cultivated plants,

Table 15

Specific soil CO_2 production of various agricultural crops and soil bacteria (after STOKLASA and DOERELL 1926)

Plant or bacterium	24-hour CO_2 production in milligrams
Sugar beet	0·3 — 5·4
Barley	63·2 — 76·4
Wheat	87·6 — 94·8
Rye	100·7 — 131·0
Oat	111·5 — 135·4
Buckwheat	212·5 — 274·0
Clostridium gelatinosum	480
Bact. hartlebi	600
Azotobacter chroococcum	1 270
Bacillus mesentericus	13 000

149

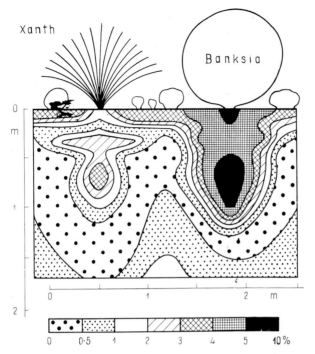

Fig. 55. An example of how the rhizospheres of various plant species concentrate and preserve soil moisture. Distribution of soil moisture below an Australian grassland after rain (after SPECHT 1958)

and of four species of soil bacteria. The data refer to 1 g of dry matter of roots or bacteria.

This table clearly shows that, as regards the edaphic production of carbon dioxide, the importance of bacteria (but also of microorganisms in general) is much greater than that of plant roots. There is nevertheless an undeniable connection between the formation of root-lapies channels and certain plants of the karst association (e.g. *Nardus stricta*: cf. P. JAKUCS 1956); this may result from the root zones of different plants harboring bacterial populations different in composition and abundance; moreover, in a sympathetic relationship with this, the local soil humidity in the rhizosphere also depends (especially at times of drought) on the plant species growing above (*Fig. 55*).

THOM and HUMFELD (1932) gave a quantitative evaluation of the connection between plant roots and the abundance of bacteria in the soil (*Table 16*).

Table 16

Abundance of soil microorganisms in various types of soil (after THOM and HUMFELD 1932)

Type of soil	Number of bacteria per gram of soil	Number of fungi per gram of soil
Soil without roots	5,500,000	100,000
Rhizosphere in general	26,000,000	800,000
Direct vicinity of capillary roots	136,000,000	7,000,000

150

Since the production of CO_2 in the soil is greatly dependent on edaphic abundance (Fehér 1954, Geiger 1961, Fekete 1952, 1958, Stefanovits 1963, Fekete, Hargitai and Zsoldos 1964, Beck 1968), it follows almost automatically from the above considerations that soils differing in plant cover (and hence also in humus concentration and in plant associations) will exhibit significant differences in carbon dioxide production too. That this is indeed the case is proved by the now classic observations of Stoklasa and Ernest (1922). Some of their findings are given in *Table 17*. Even though these observations do not refer to karst regions, similar tendencies prevail there.

Table 17

Calcium dioxide production in various types of soil
(after Stoklasa and Ernest 1922)

Type of soil	Depth	CO_2 production in mg/kg of soil at 20 °C over 24 hrs
Loam	top-soil	49·7
Loam	deeper layer	7·6
Limy soil	top-soil	18·5
Limy soil	deeper layer	9·8
Swamp soil	top-soil	41·2
Forest soil	top-soil	36·4
Forest soil low in humus	25 cm	9 − 12
Forest soil high in humus	25 cm	20 − 26
Meadow	25 cm	10 − 16
Infertile soil low in humus	25 cm	8 − 14
Soil good for rye and wheat	25 cm	30 − 48
Soil good for clover	25 cm	53 − 60

A comparison of Tables 15 and 16 immediately reveals that the limestone corrosivities of the roots of certain plants (together with the related phytoedaphon) are much greater than those of the other plants living in the same relief form (e.g. the same doline), but whose rhizospheres demand a bacterial symbiosis different in both quality and quantity. Hence, to the question raised at the beginning of this section, as to what is the smallest relief unit of physical geography in which microclimatic differences controlling the intensity of karstification may be reflected in formal features, the only possible answer is that there is no such minimum size.

This is so because in under-the-soil karstification, where the usual superficial, areal processes of planation (erosion by wind, water, etc.) play no role, even the smallest detail of the relief is composed of innumerable minute, juxtaposed patches with different weathering dynamisms; these patches may range in size from the square metre to the square millimetre. Each of these microspaces, even if of practically infinitesimal dimensions, has its specific degree of corrosion, and develops its peculiar microforms of dissolution; collectively, these constitute the form types of traditional karst morphology, such as the lapies field, the doline, etc.

It would be entirely wrong, of course, to conclude from all this that the evolution, nature and distribution of macroforms in a karst are due exclusively to a statistical superposition of processes controlled by the micro-facies: in reality, there is a reversible causality that also acts in the opposite sense: the variances in the zonal macroclimate of the region, its lithology, relief, structure, hydrography, etc., determine the features, proportions and distribution of areal types of microclimates and association groups. That is, the processes of erosion themselves act in a mosaic of microspaces, but the pieces of the mosaic constitute one or several larger-scale patterns, whose fundamental traits are not controlled by the mathematical sum of the partial processes of the individual mosaic elements.

a) Methods of testing soil gas for carbon dioxide content

The investigations most relevant to our problem have been seen to come not from the field of research of geomorphology, let alone from karst morphology; on the contrary, they originate primarily from agricultural science, pedology and biology. It is thus natural that the data provided by these investigations do not refer to the processes of karsts with undisturbed soil and plant covers, or to their circumstances of CO_2 production, but primarily to concrete cultivated plants. The few relevant references in the literature of karst genesis (TROMBE 1951/2, 1952, SMYK and DRYZAL 1964, etc.) are either conclusions based on small numbers of measurements, or generalizations of observations concerning different pedofacies found in the pedological literature. Although this reliance on analogies (quite natural as long as there are no particular series of measurements in karst regions to rely on) may give fairly good approximations , it has nevertheless become necessary to approach the problem via more direct research.

This is not a simple task, however, and our investigations into this set of problems is far from complete. One of the outstanding difficulties initially was that it was necessary to develop a suitable research methodology, as the current methods of recording soil respiration and analysing soil atmospheres were not applicable in our case.

The CO_2 fraction of the soil atmosphere is usually determined in an undisturbed soil sample taken by some suitable means (usually in a one-litre metal cylinder with a sharpened rim). The hermetically sealed sample is transported to the laboratory where its gas content is expelled with water or with a 10 per cent NaCl solution, and collected in a funnel. The soil gas thus obtained is fed to an Orsat stack-gas analyser, where its CO_2 content is determined by absorption in a potassium hydroxide solution, or assayed by the Gorbunov barium hydroxide (hydrochloric acid titration) method (BOROVYEV, YEGOROV and KISELYEV 1951, DI GLÉRIA, KLIMES, SZMIK and DVORACSEK 1957, BALLENEGGER and DI GLÉRIA 1962).

If the purpose of the test is to determine the CO_2 production in the soil per unit of time, the procedure is modified inasmuch as a slow current of air is sucked through the soil sample in the laboratory; its CO_2 content is determined both before and after its passage through the sample (by absorption, volumetry, gravimetry or titration). The difference is related to the duration of the test and to the amount of soil used.

In another procedure, a metal bell open at the bottom, tailor-made for the purpose, is pressed into the soil to a certain depth; the bell serves to capture the gas released by the soil under natural conditions. The bell is connected to a suitable apparatus (e.g. a Lundegardh device), and the quantity of CO_2 absorbed in $Ba(OH)_2$ is determined by titration with hydrochloric acid, as mentioned above (BALLENEGGER 1953, FEHÉR 1954).

In our early investigations into the CO_2 content of the soil cover of karst we employed these same methods, but as our experience grew we were prompted, primarily by the time and laboratory-space requirements of these methods, to develop faster, on-site test methods. This was also justified on several other grounds. It was observed that, as far as the CO_2 content of the soil is concerned, the time between the taking of the soil sample and its processing in the laboratory is by no means irrelevant. When two soil samples were taken side by side from the same depth and from under the same plant cover, the one processed later invariably releases more CO_2 on the displacement of its soil gas content. This is quite understandable, since there is no reason at all for the processes of biovegetation and other processes of oxidation to cease in the hermetically closed soil sample as long as the oxygen content of the soil atmosphere lasts. In serial test runs, where the comparability of the results is vital, this means that the method is useless.

When an attempt was made to record soil respiration, the problems became even more serious. Each test is so time-consuming (the recording of a single datum requires 5 to 10 hours either in the laboratory or in the field) that this in itself precludes the collection of statistically meaningful series of data.

Since it was required to perform simultaneous recordings of the CO_2 contents at various adjacent sites with different soil covers and microclimates in a given karst area, the development of a rapid on-site testing method was imperative. Our efforts to this end led to two methods, detailed below.

Method I. Soil gas is extracted by means of a slim copper probe about 5 mm in external diameter, whose wall has been perforated close to its bottom end. The probe can simply be pressed into the soil to the desired depth. It is about 40 cm in length, with a conical bottom end. A steel rod fitting snugly into the copper tube is inserted in the tube prior to impression. This serves to lend mechanical strength to the thin-walled copper tube, and also to prevent the clogging of the perforations by soil particles, but its principal purpose is to prevent the premature escape of soil gas and its mixing with above-ground air.

After the insertion of the probe, the ground surface is rendered impermeable within a radius of some tens of centimetres, for instance by the spreading of a film of viscous oil. (If the soil is highly porous, or granular, it may be better to use molten paraffin or stearin.) The soil gas is sucked up by a small turbo pump driven by a spring, or a low-voltage electric motor fed by torch batteries, designed for the purpose and fitted to the top end of the probe. The pump output is collected in an empty rubber balloon (the bladder of a football, for instance; *Fig. 56*).

After the extraction of about 0·15 litre of soil gas (which, depending on the air permeability of the soil, takes about 10 to 150 sec to collect), the rubber balloon is shut off by means of a clip and then connected to an

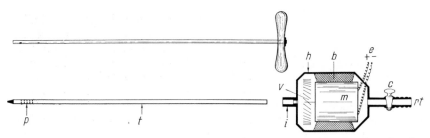

Fig. 56. Principle of the soil probe used for soil gas recovery (devised by the author)

t — thin-walled probe tube; *p* — perforations in the probe wall; *i* — airtight inlet coupling of pump housing; *v* — 16-blade fan-type impeller; *m* — low-voltage (12 V) electric motor; *b* — baffles fixing the motor; *e* — power leads with airtight inlets; *h* — housing of the pump-case; *c* — aircock; *rt* — corrugated pipe for connexion to a rubber tube; *r* — rod to be placed into the probe during insertion into the soil

Orsat gas analyser. The first sample is used to flush the analyser, while the second sample is titrated for CO_2, using a potassium hydroxide solution as an absorbent (*Photo 14*).

This method, first used in 1965, permits one person to carry out 4 or 5 on-site tests per hour. If the tests are to be repeated at a later date (e.g. next day), it is reasonable to use several probes and to leave these inserted in the ground between tests.

In 1965 and 1966 we used this method in series of analyses in almost all karst regions of Hungary (the North Borsod Karst, Bükk, Pilis, Gerecse, Bakony and Mecsek Hills, and also in the Sopron Basin at Fertőrákos). After about 300 runs, however, we were forced to recognize that, although these tests had demonstrated significant differences (up to several per cent) in the CO_2 contents of the pore gases of various soils and soil horizons, even between points of observation very close together, and had often revealed quite abrupt and substantial changes in concentration (depending on the time of day and other factors) in the soil gas at a given point of observation, the data thus collected were still insufficient to permit the unravelling of the basic relationships.

As regards the cause of the unsatisfactory results, it was first thought that the admixture of extraneous air trapped in the pump housing could lower the accuracy of the measurements. Although this factor incontestably affected the results, the air added to each sample was a constant quantity (about 30 ml), which modified the absolute values but not the relative concentrations.

Improvement of the accuracy of the method was necessary for other reasons, too. The minimum amount of about 150 ml of soil gas required for the test was extracted from a depression sphere of unknown size in the soil, surrounding the perforated end of the probe. The size and shape of this sphere depended on a number of unknown quantities, such as the permeability of the soil, its moisture content, etc. In particular, the specific CO_2 productions of the rhizospheres of different plant species growing close together could not be investigated adequately by the method as it was.

154

Photo 14. Soil gas extraction by Method 1 (devised by the author) on the Bükk Plateau. On the right-hand side the Orsat-type gas analyser is visible. On the left the probe inserted in the ground is seen, together with the attached suction unit and rubber bladder

155

In order to overcome these problems a microanalytical method was required permitting the high-accuracy analysis of a much smaller quantity of gas, because the extraction of such a gas quantity from a well-defined point of the soil space is much simpler to ensure. The solution, in the form of Method II below, was found in 1967.

Method II. The amount of soil gas required for analysis by the second method is not more than about 5 ml. This quantity of gas is drawn from the chosen point of the soil by means of a medical syringe. (The plunger should be smeared with paraffin oil to ensure a perfect seal in the syringe.) After the insertion of the needle, whose length is chosen in keeping with the depth of soil to be reached, it is advisable to leakproof the ground surface within a radius of some 20 cm in this case, too. A further point to be noted is that during the insertion of the needle it is necessary to leave the mandrel in place, and to remove it only just before the application of the syringe.

In our experience the extraction of 5 ml of soil gas does not present any particular difficulty except if the soil is either a clay totally impermeable to air, or soaked with water; nor does the diameter of the depression sphere exceed a few centimetres. The gas can thus be drawn from a well-defined, selected, soil sphere (e.g. the root zone of a single tuft of grass).

Analysis of the extracted gas sample is performed by means of the device shown in *Figure 57*.

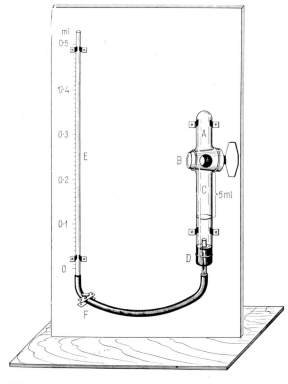

Fig. 57. Principle of gas microanalyser using a calibrated capillary (devised by the author)

A — potassium hydroxide solution container; B — wide-aperture ground-glass stopcock; C — reaction chamber consisting of a 5-ml calibrated upper section and an uncalibrated lower section for the insertion of a rubber stopper; D — a single-bore rubber stopper with a short length of glass pipe, connected to a rubber hose; E — spring-loaded clamp; F — calibrated capillary open at top, for reading off the result

The test tube is divided into two parts (A and C) by a wide-aperture, polished glass stopcock (B). With the tube inverted and the valve open, potassium hydroxide solution is added to fill part A and the valve aperture entirely and without bubbles. The solution is composed of one part KOH and two parts H_2O. After closure of the valve, any solution remaining in part C is poured out, and all traces of potassium hydroxide are removed by careful repeated flushing with water. Part C is then filled with a 10 per cent NaCl solution, which is useful to dye either red or a dark blue. The tube is then inverted and stood, mouth downwards, in a flat glass basin filled with an identical NaCl solution. Sufficient gas is bubbled from the syringe into the test tube to displace the liquid in part C to the 5 ml mark. The tube — with its mouth still immersed in the liquid in the basin — is next stoppered with the rubber stopper D.

The glass and rubber tubes providing the connexion with the calibrated capillary E are also filled with the same dyed NaCl solution as above.

After connexion, the two parts of the apparatus are wiped dry and fixed onto a suitable stand in the position shown in Figure 57. The clamp F is opened, and the rubber stopper D pushed in slightly; the slight excess pressure in the space C raises a liquid capillary column in the tube E. Any overspill at the end of E is carefully taken up with a shred of blotting paper. After the capillary column has become stabilized in the tube (which may take up to two minutes owing to the required equalization of temperatures), the position of the meniscus is recorded. Cock B is now turned to establish communication between parts A and C. The KOH solution flows into C, and some of the gas replaces it in A. In the process, the CO_2 content of the gas mixture is absorbed by the KOH solution. Hence, the total volume of the liquid and gas phases in A and C prior to the opening of the cock is reduced by the volume of the CO_2 in the gas mixture. The elimination of the partial pressure of CO_2 therefore reduces the height of the liquid column in the capillary.

With a capillary in which 0·5 ml of liquid forms a column 50 cm high, each per cent CO_2 content lowers the liquid level by 5 cm. In this case, assuming that levels 0·5 mm apart can be distinguished, the apparatus permits measurement of CO_2 contents up to 10 per cent with an accuracy of 0·01 per cent. Capillaries of different length and internal diameter can be used to give an apparatus with higher or lower sensitivity.

The only factor requiring careful attention is the extreme sensitivity of the device to temperature changes. It is therefore necessary to operate it in the shade. The test tube containing the reagents should be handled exclusively with wooden forceps; warming by the hand or by the breath of the observer should be avoided.

After the operator has acquired sufficient practice, the method gives accurate and very rapid results. We used it in 1967 and 1968 to perform some 940 measurements, some of them in Hungary, but most in Yugoslavian karst regions. A brief account of the results and of the typical findings most worthy of generalization are given below, as these measurements have given irrefutable proof of quantitative differences in karst corrosion intensity between adjacent microspaces.

b) Examples of typical carbon dioxide contents in soil atmospheres of karst microspaces differing in biological and climatic features

Our first investigations of soil atmospheres convinced us that CO_2 concentrations in the soil gas differ by several orders of magnitude, not only as regards observations made simultaneously at different points, but also when observations were made at the same point at different instants of time. The fluctuations in question are not restricted to the long-range seasonal waves of CO_2 abundance discussed in the pedological literature,

157

but also include marked changes of gas composition over much shorter periods. In the majority of cases it is impossible to obtain identical results even in two consecutive measurements at a given point of observation.*

All this induced us not to be contented with numerous but sporadic data, but to compare simultaneous series of measurements, possibly covering the entire area of a certain karst form (e.g. a doline), and also to collect background information against which the trends of short-range events in test runs at selected observation points could be evaluated. Accordingly, in 1968 we made runs of experiments lasting one day or several days on end, with measurements at intervals of two hours, or if necessary, even of one hour.

These studies produced some highly informative findings touching upon the core of the matter; one of the most interesting was a test run in a doline on a low terra rossa-covered limestone plateau to the south of the town of Karlovac in Croatia (Yugoslavia). We installed pairs of needle probes on both the south and north facing flanks of the doline, with one probe inserted to a depth of 5 cm and the other to 20 cm. It should be added that the entire doline was covered fairly uniformly by eagle fern (*Pteridium aquilinium*). On both flanks stations were sited at points of roughly equal slope angles (ca. 20°) and each needle probe was inserted directly beneath the stem of a *Pteridium*. Observed with the naked eye, the soil showed no significant differences in constitution between the two sites, except that on the north slope it was much wetter even at a depth of 5 cm. (Lacking the means of making quantitative determinations, we were reduced to estimation in this latter respect.)

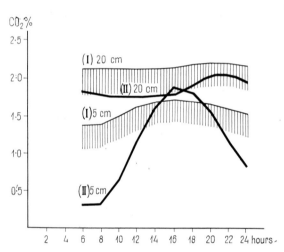

Fig. 58. Eighteen-hour fluctuation of CO_2 content in soil gas extracted from the root zone (5 and 20 cm depths) of well-developed specimens of eagle fern *(Pteridium aquilinum)* on a cloudless calm summer day (14 July 1968). Recording in northerly (I) and southerly (II) exposures in a Croatian doline (some 12 km south of Karlovac, beside the highway towards Plitvice). Slope angles about 20°. Recordings at 2-hour intervals. Soil profile: at 20 cm, largely rendzina with red clay, at 5 cm a mull-type crumbly humus-rich topsoil

The first test day (14 July 1968) was warm, calm and cloudless throughout. The observed CO_2 contents of the soil gas are plotted in *Figure 58*.

The daily concentration trends evident in the figure give rise to a number of

* Our experience with the 5 ml microanalytical method indicates that it is necessary to allow for a period of at least one hour for gas regeneration between measurements.

158

conclusions. Since no contradictory findings have so far been obtained anywhere else, these may possibly even now be formulated with a substantial claim towards general validity:

1. On karst surface under a plant cover, the CO_2 content of the soil gas over the entire depth range of 20 cm covered by our tests exhibits a pronounced daily fluctuation, sensitive to and approximately covariant with the temperature fluctuation of the soil.

2. Gas-concentration fluctuations are more extreme at both 5 and 20 cm depths in southerly exposures than in northerly ones.

3. On a daily average, the CO_2 content of the soil gas in

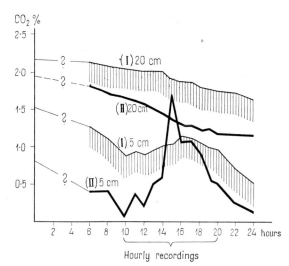

Hourly recordings

Fig. 59. Fluctuations of the CO_2 content of the soil gas of the sites specified in *Fig. 58*, on a summer day with a cloud cover of about 40 per cent, moderately windy from the late morning on 15 July 1968

the southerly exposure remains below that of the northerly exposure at both sampling depths. (We shall see later that this relationship holds only when the soil is drier on the south than on the north facing slope.)

4. CO_2 concentration is usually higher at 20 cm than at 5 cm depth. (It will be seen later that this relationship too is valid only if the topsoil is much drier than the deeper soil layers.)

Comparison of point 1 with points 3 and 4 reveals a certain antagonism between the assertions formulated above. If the CO_2 content of the soil gas indeed varies as the soil temperature, one would expect higher concentrations of CO_2 on the south facing slopes, where stronger sunshine gives rise to higher temperatures, and the same should also hold for the warmer topsoil layer of 5 cm depth. In the case in hand, however, there are two circumstances to be kept in mind; both will annul the biostimulating effect of the higher temperature, or at least impede its realistic manifestation in the CO_2 concentration. These are the marked aridity of the soil on the southern slopes, and the enhanced aeration of this soil, due among others to the aridity.

The fact that the effect of soil moisture upon the biological activity of the edaphon (and hence upon its CO_2 production) is by no means negligible, was evident from our discussion of Figure 54. Nevertheless, the enormous importance of the state of aeration of the soil's pore space was disclosed only by the following day's recordings in the Croatian doline. On that day, the calm of the previous day was replaced by moderate squalls, that were reflected in a most remarkable manner by the recordings (cf. *Fig. 59*). The essential features of this influence may be summarized as follows.

1. Even a gentle breeze markedly lowers the CO_2 content of the soil atmosphere.

159

2. This decrease in concentration is not due to the lessening of CO_2 production in the ground, but to an enhanced aeration of the pore space. This is implied, for example, by the abrupt peak at 3 p.m. in graph (II) 5, associated with a short period of calm: the explanation of its sudden appearance requires the assumption that the biological activity of the edaphon had already intensified during the preceding hours characterized by low values, whereas the conditions for the gaseous products of metabolism to remain *in loco nascendi* became satisfied only during the calm. What is more, we must assume that flushing due to the wind stimulates the aerobic processes in the soil, and that consequently squalls in fact impair only the conditions of gas accumulation.

3. The more moist the soil, the slower and less efficient the gas exchange wrought by the wind. This is revealed especially by a comparison of graphs (II) 5 and (I) 5. These differences, however, imply once more that at both depths investigated, the average concentrations of CO_2 in the soil gas remain higher in the northerly than in the southerly exposures.

4. The relatively significant but brief surges in CO_2 concentration in the topsoil have practically no effect on the slowly falling tendency of the gas concentration of the deeper soil levels in windy weather.

Continuation of our Croatian measurements into the third day was justified by a fairly abundant rainfall in the night of 15–16 July. During the rain and afterwards, the soil CO_2 graphs showed remarkable trends at both 5 and 20 cm depths. The recordings plotted in *Figure 60* admit of the following straightforward interpretation:

1. In the topsoil, wetted directly by the rain (in the case in hand to 5 cm depth in both exposures), the infiltrating water absorbs almost the entire CO_2 reserve of the soil atmosphere in the process of infiltration

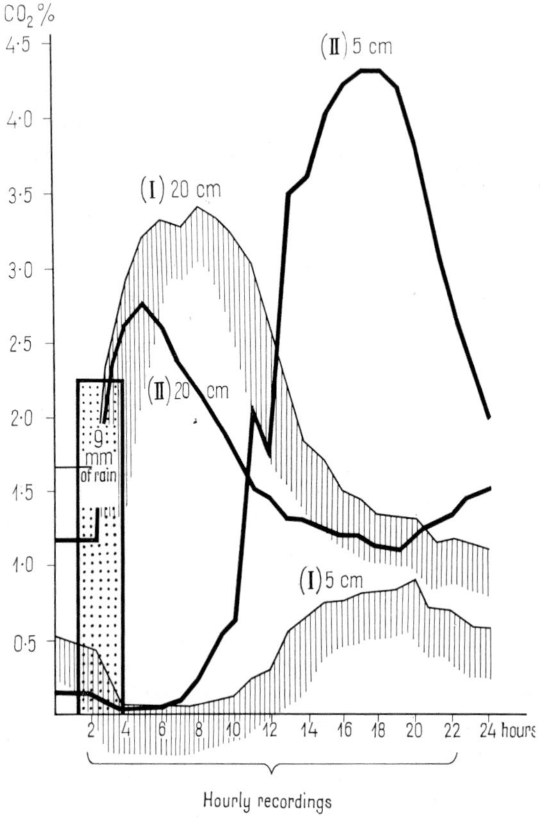

Fig. 60. Fluctuations of the CO_2 content of the soil gas of the sites specified in Fig. 58, on a clear calm day following a night rainstorm delivering about 9 mm of rain. The rain which fell between 1·10 hrs and 3·35 hrs of the night was initially heavy, followed by repeated periods of gentler rain

2. In the deeper soil horizons, not affected directly by the rain, the CO_2 content of the pore gas undergoes a sudden surge; the developing concentrations are unexpectedly high as compared with the previous values. This entails a striking inversion of the CO_2 contents between the 5 and 20 cm soil horizons, which is essentially maintained throughout the next day (provided sunshine in the daytime results in a marked warming).

As for the cause of this remarkable night time event, we can only assume it to be due to a strong swelling under the rain of the wetted topsoil, sealing off the deeper soil-gas spaces, preventing their separation, and promoting the accumulation of the gaseous products of decay and other processes of oxidative metabolism.

That this may indeed be the main cause of the effect described is confirmed by a comparison of the 20-cm-depth graphs of the southerly and northerly exposures. In the southerly exposure, where the soil had been drier before the rain (graph II, 20), the seal provided by the wetting was destroyed sooner (before 5 a.m.) than in the northerly exposure where the soil had been more moist to start with, and (graph I, 20) the same amount of rain could result in a more prolonged effect. Here, the decrease in gas concentration did not begin before 8 a.m.

3. Next day's warming due to sunshine and atmospheric convection made the production of CO_2 at 5 cm depth in the southerly exposure (graph II, 5) surpass all the values previously recorded in the area, by a coincidence of optimum temperature with optimum humidity on this particular day. It is noteworthy, however, that the peak was retarded by several hours against the peaks of (II) 5 on the previous days, presumably owing to the heat loss resulting from the stronger evaporation in the forenoon.

We have no explanation for the switchback in the graph between 10 and 11 a.m., but it might be due to a gentle breeze that we failed to observe.

4. The daytime drop in CO_2 concentration at 20 cm depth is hard to explain, especially where it coincides with a simultaneous increase in the CO_2 concentration of the topsoil. However, one cannot exclude the possibility of this being due to absorption by the soil moisture which has by this time attained the deeper level.

5. The rising trend in graph (II) 20 after 7 p.m. presumably reflects the diffusion of some of the abundant gas in the topsoil.

6. The highly significant difference between the afternoon rises in graphs (II) 5 and (I) 5 proves that, given identically favourable soil humidities, the production of CO_2 in the more strongly warmed soils of the southern slopes can exceed by several times the production on the slopes with northerly exposure (cf. point 3 in the interpretation of Fig. 58).

7. Under favourable conditions of soil moisture, especially in southerly exposures, CO_2 may be more abundant in the topsoil than deeper down in the soil at the same station (cf. point 4 of the evaluation of Fig. 58).

From our several-day test runs in Hungarian karst regions, let us pick out for discussion our recordings on 17 and 18 August 1968 in an unwooded doline of Létrástető in the Bükk Hills. In addition to north and south stations, we recorded characteristics of soil CO_2 in easterly and westerly

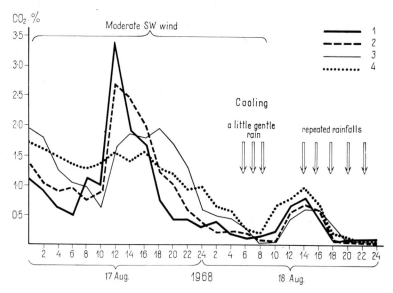

Fig. 61. An example of the influence of slope exposure upon the intensity of karstification. Fluctuation of the CO_2 content of the soil gas collected from the rhizospheres of *Festuca* specimens growing on slopes of approximately identical angles but different exposures in an unwooded doline at Létrástető in the Bükk Hills, on a warm sunny day, and on the next rainy cooler day. Gas samples were extracted from the root zone at 2-hourly intervals on 17 and 18 August, 1968

1 — *Festuca sulcata*, easterly exposure; 2 — idem, southerly exposure; 3 — idem, westerly exposure; 4 — *Festuca ovina*, northerly exposure

exposures, too, on a moderately windy and sunny day followed by a rainy, cooler one (*Fig. 61*).

In order to eliminate all possible fortuitous factors from the recordings of soil-gas concentration trends as a function of exposure, all stations were installed on slopes of identical angles, in the root spheres of steppe-grass tufts of identical species (*Festuca sulcata*) at the same stage of development. On the north facing slope no well-developed *Festuca sulcata* was found: accordingly, a tuft of *Festuca ovina* was chosen, the roots of which are somewhat less dense. All soil gas samples were collected from the 5 cm level. In choosing the doline we took care to have a soil cover of approximately identical thickness and constitution in each exposure.

The two-day measurement run led to the following conclusions.

1. On 17 August, a southwesterly wind of 4 deg. Beaufort disturbed the daily course of the CO_2 content; its influence was least marked in the easterly exposure, which was essentially the lee slope. At noon, a daily peak content of 3·35 per cent CO_2 was recorded there, a very high value for a windy day; it was probably due to optimum sunshine in the forenoon, combined with favourable soil humidity. On the southern facing slope, and even more in the westerly exposure, the daily peak CO_2 concentrations were lower,

despite a favourable insolation all day long. The flattening of the daily peak by dynamic soil aeration is most conspicuous on the western slope.

2. The peaks of the westerly and easterly exposures were about 6 hours apart on the first day of the run. Such a displacement can only be due to warming by direct sunshine. (On the next day, overcast all day, the peaks of the various exposures almost coincided.)

3. On the north slope, where the stimulation of CO_2 production, due to the daily warming by air convection, was practically totally nullified by the wind, the graph's almost uniform falling tendency reflects the decrease in gas concentration characteristic of a windy day.

(The fact that comparatively high CO_2 concentrations were recorded in all exposures during the night of 16–17 August is probably due to a favourable combination of sunshine, soil moisture and calm on the 16th, which had probably resulted in extremely high daytime peaks in each exposure. Unfortunately, in the absence of appropriate measurements this hypothesis cannot be verified.)

4. Although the results thus far do not permit disentanglement of the influences of all the possible contributing factors, it can be stated with confidence that the fluctuations of CO_2 content in the soil gas, a function of an exceedingly large number of effects, is in the main exposure-controlled. The differences in gas concentration and rates of daily production revealed by our measurements between the eastern and western facing slopes of dolines are quite often of the same extent as the corresponding differences between southerly and northerly exposures.

Since the production and overall concentration of CO_2 in the soil is the decisive factor in the aggressivity of the waters seeping through the soil, and hence also the main factor controlling the local intensity of karstification, it may be stated that the lack of circular symmetry of dolines is almost certainly due primarily to the microclimatic factors just discussed rather than to the lithologic and structural causes (dip and strike orientation) suspected by earlier authors. This is the only plausible way to explain the fact that the axes of symmetry of dolines formed in limestone strata of various dips and strikes are parallel all over a given group of hills, as shown by our relevant measurements in the Bükk Hills, in the North Borsod Karst, and in several Croatian karst planinas (in this context cf. Fig. 88).

Incidentally, the various plant specimens and types of associations doubtless play specific roles in determining CO_2 production in the soil as well as in controlling soil aeration; and this must also be valid for the plant associations of the karsts. This is illustrated rather strikingly by a comparison of soil gases from under a forest and a steppe lawn with no arborescent plants, the former being almost invariably higher in CO_2 than the latter. This difference is due to a number of causes. We presume the following to be the most important.

1. The humidity of a forest soil is more favourable and less subject to fluctuations then that of a steppe soil.

2. The forest soil is protected from the wind by the foliage.

3. The forest soil is most often covered by a horizontally stratified, uninterrupted layer of fallen leaves, which may contribute greatly to the prevention of evaporation.

4. The broad and deep rhizospheres of arborescent plants give rise to a much deeper bioactive soil zone, significant for the subcutaneous production of CO_2, and to an increased abundance of edaphon per unit of ground surface area.

Figure 62 presents some of our typical recorded data, on which the above statements are based. It seems that the soil gas conditions most favourable for a karst process in Hungary are encountered under stands of oak and beech with the corresponding plant associations; the gas production even of a karst shrub wood is more meagre, and that of a grassland even poorer. Even under a pine forest, the CO_2 content of the soil is higher than under a grass association!

With regard to the rhizospheres of grass species, we were somewhat astonished to find the highest CO_2 concentrations under hydrophilic and thermophobic *Nardus stricta*; this is presumably a specific property of this kind of grass, as soil moisture conditions during our experiments were also optimum at the root levels of the *Festuca* and *Carex* species examined in sites where soil temperatures were much closer to the optimum.

The valuable findings of BALÁZS (1964) concerning the consistent relationship between the composition of karst-spring waters in the temperate zone and the plant covers of the karstic drainage areas belonging to them have likewise confirmed higher CO_2 concentrations in forest soils, thereby emphasizing the significant influence of the plant cover upon the dynamism of karstification (*Fig. 63*).

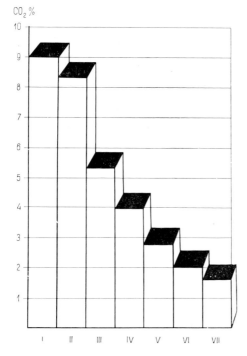

Fig. 62. Comparative diagram of spring CO_2 contents in soil gases extracted from the rhizospheres of various karst-lawn associations and from 5 to 10 cm depths in various forest soils. Recordings on calm clear days in April and May (1967, 1968) in the Bükk Hills and on the North Borsod Karst

Origin of soil gas samples:

I — oak forest, from under several centimetres of two-year-old, wet, compact vegetal compost; II — beech forest, idem; III — pine forest, from under a carpet of decaying needles, from a depth of about 8 cm; IV — from the root zone of a *Nardus stricta* lawn thriving in a thick acid soil at the bottom of a doline on the Bükk Plateau; V — from the root zone of a *Festuca sulcata* lawn from a doline south-easterly facing flank with outcrops of rock; VI — from the root zone of a *Festuca ovina* lawn from a doline northerly facing flank with outcrops of rock; VII — from under a specimen of *Carex humilis* from 5 cm depth from the south-easterly flank of a doline at Aggtelek

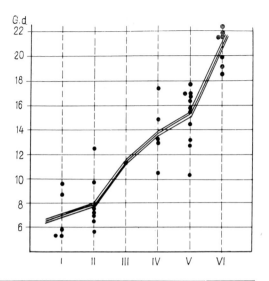

Fig. 63. Hardness of waters of karst springs in the temperate zone plotted against the plant cover types and relative coverage in the karstic drainage area supplying the springs. The numbers refer to the groups characterized below (BALÁZS' data)

Group	Distribution of plant cover types in the drainage area, per cent			Mean hardness of water samples tested, G.d.
	forest	lawn, meadow, shrub wood	rocky, barren	
I	—	0 — 10	80 — 100	7·0
II	—	30 — 60	40 — 70	7·8
III	max. 10	60 — 90	10 — 40	11·2
IV	0 — 25	75 — 100	max. 10	13·7
V	25 — 75	25 — 75	max. 10	15·0
VI	75 — 100	0 — 25	max. 10	20·7

In an assessment of these problems, of course, the animal life in the soil must not be forgotten, since the metabolism of the zoo-edaphon incontestably contributes to the composition of the soil gases. However, research into the contribution of this factor to the general effect and into its influence upon karst corrosion has not yet been carried out.

AUTHIGENIC AND ALLOGENIC KARST EVOLUTION (THE ROLE OF EROSIONAL VARIANCE IN KARST EROSION)

As emphasized earlier (L. JAKUCS 1952/1, 1956/1—2, 1960/1—2, 1968/1), in addition to the factors of petrovariance, epeirovariance and climatic variance discussed in the foregoing chapters, the quantitative and qualitative control of the dynamism of karst erosion also depends on *the orographic relationship of the karstic rock to its non-karstic environment*; this relationship exerts a multifarious influence upon the proportion of the various factors of erosion active in any given karst region. In this respect, one of the most important problems is whether linear, downward streambed erosion may play a part in the sculpture of a limestone relief, or whether erosion takes place without this factor, primarily by the subareal and spatial corrosion of the limestone.

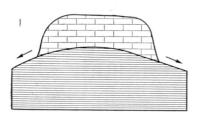

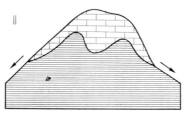

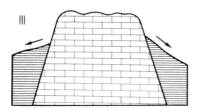

Fig. 64. Schematic diagrams of the possible variants of A-type (authigenic) karsts

The various possibilities, which we shall collectively term the erosional variance of karstification, are of considerable symptomatic significance: we must accordingly analyse them in some detail below.

The geological and structural setting of the limestone region and its orographic relation to its non-karstic surroundings permit first of all two clearly distinguished fundamental types: *A-type (authigenic) and B-type (allogenic) karsts.*

By an *authigenic (A-type) karst* we mean a limestone mass in an elevated orographic position, dominating its non-karstic surroundings. This prevents any surface water in the non-karstic surroundings from flowing towards or into the karst mass. In an authigenic karst, water invariably flows off (or out of) the karst and towards the lower-lying non-karstic surface. Hence, only waters infiltrated into the karst mass proper can influence the genetic factors of the hydrography of that karst.

The group of authigenic karsts includes the majority of inselberg karsts and most mountain karsts. (Schemes of the various types of authigenic karst are shown in

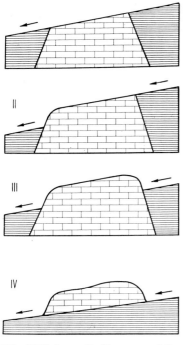

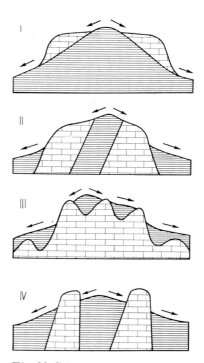

Fig. 65. Schematic diagrams of the possible variants of B-type (allogenic) karsts

Fig. 66. Schematic diagrams of the possible variants of B-type (allogenic) karsts

Figure 64. These drawings may be construed as profiles through the authigenic karst mass in any arbitrary direction.)

An *allogenic (B-type) karst*, on the other hand, means that karsted limestone is so situated that linear water-courses draining from non-karstic surfaces may reach the limestone region. The criterion of allogeny in a karst, then, is that its hydrography should involve contributions from waters arriving from alien (non-karstic) surfaces. (Schemes of allogenic karsts are shown in *Figure 65.*)

A karst mass may often seem A-type overall, but be B-type in its details. This is the case when the rock of an extensive karst plateau — satisfying the criteria of authigeny overall — includes syngenetic intercalations or postgenetic (structurally determined) pinched-in outcrops of alien, impermeable rock. The Great Plateau of the Bükk Hills in Hungary is a case in point (*Fig. 66*).

Another frequent occurrence is that an orographically pure authigenic karst plateau gradually evolves in the advanced stages of its erosion towards the B-type, owing purely to accumulations of dissolution residues, terra rossa, or to

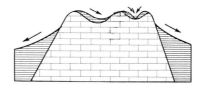

Fig. 67. Profile through a B-type karst, developed from an A-type one by surface pedogenesis and eluvial weathering resulting in terra rossa deposits

167

a humus-rich soil cover, rendering the plateau surface impermeable (*Fig. 67*).

In general the only pure type in nature is the authigenic karst, whereas in the allogenic karst the formal features of the B-type are invariably combined with A-type hydrological and formal features.

1. FEATURES OF AUTHIGENIC KARST EROSION IN THE PRESENCE OF AN UNCHANGING LOCAL BASELEVEL OF EROSION

The initial stage of authigenic (A-type) karst erosion can be studied in limestone masses rising above the local baselevel of erosion. The fundamental lithologic condition for the process to start at all is a primary fissure and joint system in the rock. This condition is diagenetically ensured in most limestones occurring in nature.

Most Tertiary and older limestones bear the traces of postgenetic, geomechanical effects (SCHMIDT 1954, 1957) that can in some instances even be correlated with phases of orogeny. The fissure permeability of the rock is thus to be regarded as a universally satisfied primary condition of karst erosion.

Even at the outset of the period of erosion, precipitation falling onto the limestone mass rising above the local baselevel of erosion may seep into the fissure network, where it exerts hydrocarbonate dissolution in three dimensions. The depth of the karst zone where such corrosion actually takes place seldom exceeds 15 to 20 m in the Central and Eastern European low-hill karsts, or in their Mediterranean counterparts which we have also investigated, that is, depending on their carbonic acid saturation, the infiltrating waters corrode only to a limited depth. According to the analyses of VENKOVITS (1949/1—2, TROMBE (1952, 1956), LEHMANN, KRÖMMELBEIN and LÖTSCHET (1956), BÖGLI (1960) and L. JAKUCS (1960/2, 1966), in a majority of cases the fissure water seeping down by gravity into the deeper levels of the karst has attained calcium carbonate—carbonic acid equilibrium; in view of the reaction time required for hydrocarbonate-type dissolution (discussed in the relevant chapters of this book), the area of the limestone surface exposed to unit mass of water, and the extreme slowness of downward seepage by gravity (KESSLER 1956), this becomes a necessary consequence of the chemical and physical parameters of the water.

The lower limit of downward seepage of karst waters descending under gravity is the level of karst water saturation (i.e. the karst water table), the altitude of which is a function of the local baselevel of erosion; only where the karst rock does not reach so far down is the karst water table kept suspended by an impermeable underlying formation. The motion of water particles below the karst water table is no longer directly controlled by gravity, but by the laws of hydrodynamics governing the motion of water in a spatial network of fissures, according to the principles of communicating vessels (HORUSITZKY 1942, LOUIS 1956/1, NÉMETH 1959, LEBEDEV 1963). However, as long as the water particles and the gas spaces trapped by them do not reach the karst water table, they are exposed to no hydrostatic pressure that could upset the calcium carbonate—carbonic acid equilibrium attained in the top 15 to 20 m of the karst. Consequently, the karst includes a depth interval where the primary fissure network of the rock is not widened by dissolution by the waters, which merely use it as a passage in their downward journey under the joint influence of gravity and adhesion. This neutral zone, inactive as far as the karst process is concerned, is the more extensive vertically, the higher the karst surface above the karst water table, or above the local baselevel of erosion determining its altitude.

It is known that in the interior of the karst mass the karst water table is higher than at the points of outflow (springs), assuming an inverted meniscus shape (GRUND 1912/1) rising from the vicinity of the local baselevel of erosion towards the interior of the karst mass. This phenomenon is the more conspicuous, the younger the karst, that is, the less the capacity of its primary fissure network as related to the water throughput to be drained per unit time. Still, even a rock with a well-developed fissure system will not be able to handle the water seeping down the three-dimensional fissure network and drain it towards the points of outflow without a certain pressure head represented by a swelling of the water table.

The less developed the communicating fissure network in the rock, and hence the more swollen (convex) the karst water table, the deeper the zone within the karst mass in which the flow of water is controlled by the position of the points of outflow and the depression caused by them. Hence, the flow of karst water towards the springs is three-dimensional rather than areal. A vertical profile of the zone where the water particles are in a motion that is horizontal overall shows it to be lenticular in section, provided the karst mass reaches down below the level of springs (*Fig. 68*).

In those authigenic karsts, on the other hand, where the geometry and position of this karst water lens are not determined by the local baselevel of karst erosion, but by the impermeable formations underlying the limestone (suspended karst aquifer), the lens is convex above only, while its bottom surface follows the surface of the impermeable bedrock (*Fig. 69*).

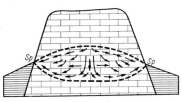

Fig. 68. Lenticular zone in an authigenic karst where the limestone body extends below the baselevel of karst erosion

Sp — springs. Arrows indicate the flow pattern of the karst water

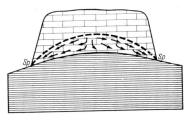

Fig. 69. Lenticular zone in an authigenic karst of the suspended type

Sp — springs. Arrows indicate the flow pattern of the karst water

In the karst water lens, all the communicating fissures and clefts are filled with water, and hence the water particles and gas bubbles joining it become exposed after a while to some hydrostatic pressure. The karst water in the lens thus again becomes capable of dissolution, and depending on the pressure increase acting upon it, and also on the absorption and the activating effect of the carbon dioxide contained in the gas bubbles, it indeed dissolves some of the rock (L. JAKUCS 1960/2, 1966). Pressure increase plays the most important role along the bottom boundary of the lens; it is there that secondary dissolution is most effective. Together with this effect, there is a secondary activation of the dissolution potential by mixing corrosion, since it is essentially the lenticular zone that brings together and mixes the karst waters of different hardnesses, seeping down in comparative isolation in the various vertical fissure systems.

Secondary corrosion does not only widen the horizontal joints of the rock, however, but by reducing their resistance to flow also affects the shape of the lens, flattening its upper boundary and thereby decreasing the hydrostatic pressure differential. This is why, even in the early stages of karst evolution, the upper boundary of the lens attains an equilibrium position which (apart from short-range displacements of the karst water table following precipitation on the karst surface) undergoes no essential changes in the later stages of karst erosion.

Figure 70 shows the zones of typical authigenic karst erosion in a hilly region of the temperate zone, in the first stage of karst evolution.

The volume of karstic rock lying beneath the lenticular zone plays no role in karst erosion. Even though the water in the fissures of the rock is under hydrostatic pressure, this water is removed from the karst water hydrographic cycle; it therefore attains equilibrium with its surroundings and effects no further dissolution. With this feature in mind, it is justified to call this zone the inactive deep karst.

It follows from our above considerations concerning the lenticular zone of the karst mass that the tendency towards limestone dissolution is most intense close to the bottom boundary of the lens. Accordingly, the principal layer of flow in the lenticular zone also develops close to the bottom boundary; it is there that water-bearing fissures are most pronouncedly widened by corrosion. In any karst mass including an inactive

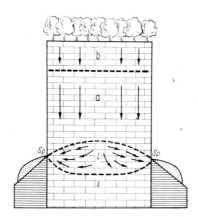

Fig. 70. Zones of karst erosion in an authigenic karst body showing the early effects of karstification in the low-mountain facies of the temperate zone

b — zone of infiltration, with significant primary dissolution of calcium carbonate; a — zone of downward filtration without calcium carbonate dissolution; l — lenticular zone with calcium carbonate dissolution by pressure and mixing corrosion; Sp — spring zone with deposition of calcareous tufa in spots; i — zone of the inactive deep karst

deep karst zone, this level of karst cavern, cavity and water-passage sculpture lies somewhat deeper than the karst-spring level.

In the course of advancing karst erosion, the process just outlined may result in the evolution of corrosion caverns under the karst water table. The karst water passages, which may possibly evolve into caverns, thus lie more or less horizontally near the base of the lens, and exhibit abrupt upgrades next to the spring (*Vaucluse*-type spring channel).

The further stages of karst erosion are expressed by advancing doline development on the surface. This process, however, is restricted to the top

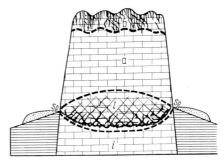

Fig. 71. Second stage in the erosion of an authigenic karst. Doline evolution in the b-zone, reduction of thickness in the a-zone, and evolution of corrosional cavities in the lenticular zone are the characteristic features of this stage. For an evaluation cf. also Fig. 70

15 to 20 m of the karst rock, its *zone of infiltration (b-zone)*; it involves the formation of depressions on the surface, the considerable widening of fissure systems by corrosion, and occasionally the coalescing of cavities and the collapse of the ground surface. The lowering of the surface owing to doline evolution, on the other hand, gradually lowers the bottom boundary of the b-zone, too (*Fig. 71*).

The second stage of erosion of an authigenic karst is the *period* when the *zone of infiltration by gravity (a-zone)* is gradually eaten away by the slow descent of the b-zone, which in the end comes into direct contact with the lenticular zone. The karst enters its third and last stage of erosion when this happens.

The first and second stages of evolution were characterized by the widening of cavities by corrosion in the lenticular zone. In the third stage, this process is arrested and even reversed, owing to the disappearance of the a-zone which formerly acted as a filter to the dissolution residues and solid mineralic weathering products swept in from the surface: in the third stage, direct contact between the wider passages and channels in the b-zone and in the lenticular zone, where it silts up some of the passages. Thus, whereas the second stage was dominated by the gradual clogging of vertical passages in the b-zone (the evolution of "geological organ pipes"), in the third stage the site of this process advances into the horizontal passages of the lenticular zone.

In the second stage of erosion it is precisely this clayey, terra rossa-like sediment, trapped by and locally accumulating in the fissures of the b-zone, that plays a decisive role in smoothing out the effects of karst erosion in that zone and confining them to a horizontal band. The evolution of an impermeable layer of this terra rossa at the bottom of already developed dolines, isolates these places (initially more accessible to karst erosion) from sub-areal sheetwash and dynamic soil corrosion, the attack of these agencies being shifted to the rises among dolines formerly more or less spared. (Classic examples of temporarily clogged dolines are those of the

171

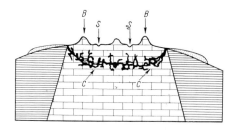

Fig. 72. Third stage in the erosion of an authigenic karst: the nearly-flat karst (limestone peneplain) *S* — surface streams; *B* — buttes of limestone; *C* — silted-up, inactive cavities in the former lenticular zone

Karlovac karst plain in Yugoslavia, and of the Vöröstó uvala near Jósvafő in Hungary.)

It may be mentioned in passing that in tropical karstification this mechanism of action is impossible, since the soils washed into the depressions of the limestone surface are very rich in calcium carbonate due to intense ground-surface corrosion and ground-surface precipitation of calcium carbonate. They are consequently more porous and permeable than the decalcified clayey terra rossa of the temperate zone.

As a statistical result of the above temperate-zone process, the lowering process, the lowering of the karst plateau by erosion proceeds more or less uniformly, resulting in the preservation of the plateau feature, even though the smaller spatial and temporal units making up the mosaic of the plateau may exhibit marked differences of dynamism. In the end, while the b-zone and the lenticular zone gradually coalesce, the planation of the karst, or its erosion down to the impermeable bedrock, is completed (*Fig. 72*).

Thus, only the thickness of the a-zone affects karst erosion processes by influencing its duration. The thicker the a-zone at the outset of karst erosion, the longer its complete erosion will take. In other words, the higher a limestone mass rises above the local baselevel of erosion, the longer is the time available for corrosive karst erosion to sculpture superficial karst forms usually on an ever larger and larger scale.

2. EROSION OF AUTHIGENIC KARST WHEN ACCOMPANIED BY DISPLACEMENTS OF THE LOCAL BASELEVEL OF KARST EROSION

We have so far studied the evolution of A-type karst in the hypothetical, ideal, fundamental case that the local baselevel of erosion relevant to karst evolution (the level of karst springs) is not displaced during karstification. In nature, however, authigenic karsts do not have such a steadfast baselevel of erosion except when the spring level and hence the position of the lenticular zone too are fixed by an impermeable bedrock, and consequently the entire thickness of the limestone mass participates in karst evolution.

On the other hand, in karst masses including inactive deep karst zones, the local baselevels of erosion relevant to karst evolution tend to be displaced fairly substantially in the course of karstification. This circumstance is invariably reflected in peculiar features among the products of erosion.

An elevation of the local baselevel of erosion might be due to orogenic or epeirogenic movements, or to a relative elevation of the surfaces surrounding the karst as a result of intense deposition (cases I and II in *Fig. 73*). Most often, however, the erosional baselevel is displaced downwards in the course of time. Such a process can be inferred from a structural uplifting of the karst mass and/or from the retreating incision of the valleys draining the karst (cases I and II in *Fig. 74*).

Any displacement of the baselevel of karst erosion may thus be due to a wide range of causes, but in the final analysis there are only two possible results, the relative rise or the relative subsidence of the karst mass. The changes in the features of karst erosion as a result of these changes in relative baselevel are discussed below.

A relative rise of the baselevel of erosion, or an equivalent subsidence of the mountain mass, essentially entails a shortening of the duration of karst erosion, due to the raising of the level of corrosion of the lenticular zone to a higher secondary level.

The former lenticular zone is thereby displaced into the inactive deep karst zone corresponding to the new situation and is accordingly inactivated. The cavities of the former lenticular zone continue full of karst water. This water is under hydrostatic pressure, but its circulation (flow) has either ceased or been reduced to such an extent as to preclude any further widening of corrosion cavities. The lack of flow prevents any clayey sediment from reaching and silting up these cavities. At a depth of a hundred or even several hundred metres below the new baselevel of karst erosion, therefore, the corrosive cavities of a fossil lenticular zone may be conserved over periods significant even on a geohistorical time scale, as a system of cavities contributing to the karst-water storage capacity of the deep karst.

Since the passages of such zones have been developed by the lateral motion of water in a former lenticular zone, they will be characterized in

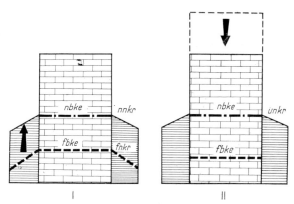

Fig. 73. Displacement of the baselevel of karst erosion if the non-karstic surroundings of the karst mass are uplifted (I), or the karst mass itself is lowered (II) *nbke* — new baselevel of karst erosion; *fbke* — former baselevel of karst erosion; *nnkr* — new non-karstic relief; *fnkr* — former non-karstic relief; *unkr* — unchanged non-karstic relief. The arrows indicate the displacement of the relief

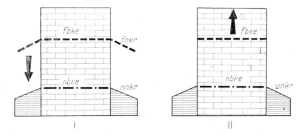

Fig. 74. Displacement of the baselevel of karst erosion if the non-karstic surroundings of the karst mass are lowered by erosion or tectonic movement (I), or the karst mass is comparatively uplifted (II)

The arrows indicate the displacement of the relief. For symbols see Fig. 73

the new situation too by wide-ranging lateral interconnection. In mining operations under the karst water table, inrushes of karst water out of cavities of such lowered fossil lenticular zones may be catastrophic.

Clearly, the likelihood of karst-water inrushes in a mining area is also influenced significantly by a number of other factors, such as the density of fault planes, their position, their gaping or closed nature, etc., and this permits the pinpointing of the zones of gravest jeopardy (KASSAI 1948, ALBEL 1950, SCHMIDT 1953). Nevertheless, the above insight may perhaps bring us closer to an interpretation of unexpected inrushes that do not take place along fault planes and yet may flood an entire mine with karst water fast enough to frustrate any preventive measures. Unfortunately, in the present stage of our knowledge, it is impossible to give even a probable estimate as to where such inrushes are to be expected. In contrast, it is possible to give an approximate indication of the most menaced horizons, by a karst morphogenic analysis of the mine region, including the identification of blocks with lenticular zones that have been downfaulted or otherwise lowered.

The relative lowering of the baselevel of erosion during karstification, or the equivalent relative rise of the karst mass, results in a downward displacement of the lenticular zone, and in a consequent thickening of the karst's a-zone: the result is the lengthening of the duration of karst erosion. In such karsts, then, doline formation is intensified precisely because of this prolonged duration compared with the neighbouring, unaffected karst surfaces.

In an authigenic karst, relatively uplifted in the course of karst erosion, the former lenticular zone is displaced into the a-zone and a new lenticular zone starts to develop at the level determined by the baselevel of erosion. The cavities of the uplifted lenticular zone are thus left high and dry, and the erosion cavities, formerly full of karst water under pressure, are now filled with air.

If the evolution of the former lenticular zone was sufficiently long prior to its uplifting, its actual position is marked by a number of now inactive spring caves due to corrosion. On the other hand, if the preceding evolution was shorter or possibly contemporaneous with glacial phases of the Pleistocene, unfavourable to the dynamism of karst corrosion, then the place of the former lenticular zone is indicated only by a level with somewhat widened clefts and fissures with corroded walls within the karst mass.

The mixing and pressure corrosion caverns evolved in the lenticular zone invariably exhibit features clearly revealing their origin whose nature may be inferred from the following considerations:

1. The entry of the cave (the former spring outlet) lies higher than the rest of the cave, so that any more or less horizontal passages are accessible only through the former spring funnel. Two of a number of Hungarian examples are the István Cave at Lillafüred in the Bükk Hills and the Legény Cave in the Pilis Hills.

2. These caves are never through-caverns: their only aperture open to the surface is the one that has served as the spring outlet. (Second outlets, if any, may possibly be due to fortuitous influences alien to the karst genetic process, such as structural events, a cave-roof collapse, etc.)

174

3. The cave has no well-defined bottom- or roof-level plane. Narrower passages and channels due to corrosion connect more spacious halls, likewise due to corrosion. There are numerous corrosion-sculptured funnels, and the floors of the cavities are situated at a variety of levels.

4. The caves exhibit no streambeds or rock terraces due to linear erosion.

5. In the ground plan, the caves are capriciously labyrinthine; they nowhere exhibit the tree pattern of a surface drainage network, involving a main branch and tributaries.

6. The trends of structural preformation are conspicuous in the determining of the caves' ground plans.

These caves dissolved by karst water under pressure in the lenticular zone resemble in many respects, in forms as well as in origin, the caves dissolved by thermal waters. In Hungary, this type includes for instance the István Cave of Lillafüred (Bükk Hills), and the Legény and Leány Caves (Pilis Hills); it is open to discussion whether the sculpture of the Solymár, Mátyás Hill, Pál Valley, and Ferenc Hill caves, and of the Devil's Hole on Szoplak Hill, etc. is due predominantly to thermal waters or to the cold karst waters of the lenticular zone.

In the gravity-controlled zone (a-zone) of the karst the cavities and fissures of uplifted and thus inactivated ancient lenticular zones receive the descending karst water, that can be considered a saturated calcium carbonate solution. In the cavities with free water table offering a chance of gas exchange, this water can now lose some of its CO_2 and so form dripstones by precipitation. The process of dripstone deposition may result after some time in the filling-up of the cavities, and in the elimination of any evacuation space.

In the aerated cavities of the authigenic karst, then, the condition of CO_2 loss required for the formation of dripstones is satisfied. However, since the zone under consideration is the a-zone of the karst, where the water seeping down into any cavity has not yet been exposed to any significant hydrostatic pressure, the difference between the pCO_2 of the atmosphere of the cavity and the tension of the dissolved carbonic acid in equilibrium with the actual calcium carbonate content of the water is not so great as in the caverns of an allogenic karst (to be discussed later), where the calcium carbonate concentration of the water is further boosted by the hydrostatic pressure distribution in the active lenticular zone. Hence, dripstone formation in the cavities of the authigenic (A-type) karsts is invariably less intense than in the cavern tunnels sculptured by linear erosion in the active lenticular zones of allogenic (B-type) karsts. (Our own comparative studies in the A-type (authigenic) Legény Cave of the Pilis Hills and in the B-type (allogenic) Béke Cavern at Aggtelek, for instance, have revealed a dripstone coverage of not more than 10 to 15 per cent on the roof surfaces of the former, as compared with 100 per cent in the latter).

To summarize our most important findings concerning authigenic karst erosion:

1. In the b-zone (the top 15 to 20 m) of an authigenic karst mass in the temperate climatic zone, limestone dissolution of fluctuating intensity effects the sculpture of dolines and lapies, a process that — if sufficient time is available for erosion — will develop a typical karst plateau relief.

(As we have seen earlier, lapies and doline formation is a process of corrosion controlled primarily by the plant cover and by the humus-rich soil cover connected with it.)

2. In the second horizon (a-zone) of the karst, no dissolution of calcium carbonate takes place; the precipitation of calcium carbonate is restricted to the case that the a-zone includes aerated cavities or fissures with a free water table.

3. Accessible empty cavities in an a-zone will occur only if the karstified mountain mass has, in the course of its karstification, been uplifted with respect to its non-karstic surroundings.

4. These caves are not large as a rule; they have labyrinthine ground plans; their spatial extent is not purely horizontal but, especially in the vicinity of former spring outlets, has an appreciable vertical component, too. The general morphology recalls the features of hydrothermal caverns.

5. The duration of the individual, successive, qualitatively different stages of the process of karstification and karst erosion are relative and non-objective, and even within a region of given lithology, climate, etc. depend on the thickness of the rock's a-zone. Under the influence of certain structural or non-karstic processes of erosion and deposition, the rates of karst erosion of even a single given karst mass may be accelerated or retarded.

6. The lenticular zone of the karst is characterized by the cavity-forming activity of the mixing corrosion, as well as of the secondary pressure corrosion of a water flow confined within a given system of horizontal ducts. The top boundary of the lenticular zone, the karst water table, is convex upwards, with its top level above the spring level of the karst, whereas its bottom boundary (if not limited by an impermeable bedrock) is convex downwards, with its bottom level below the local baselevel of erosion.

7. The zone of the inactive deep karst plays no role whatever in controlling the nature of karst erosion.

8. Dripstone formation in the caves of an authigenic karst is less intense than in the erosional caverns of an allogenic karst of identical age.

3. ALLOGENIC (B-TYPE) KARST EROSION

Most karsts occurring in nature are allogenic; that is, the molding of the hydrography and even of the morphology of the karst receives contributions from alien streams flowing in from non-karstic surfaces. These contributions play a dominant role in controlling the qualitative character of the karst process, so much so that karst erosion may in such cases take a course entirely different as to both dynamism and geomorphological products from the karst erosion of an authigenic karst.

Earlier geomorphologists failed either to recognize or to assign appropriate importance to the fundamental differences between authigenic and allogenic karsts, and indeed, to the often opposed trends of karst relief sculpture under the influence of opposed agencies: they were consequently unable to interpret a number of phenomena correctly. The uncertainties that characterize the standpoints of various authors, e.g. in respect of

176

karst-valley genesis, can almost always be traced to this
failure. For a full interpretation
of karstification, and of the
morphological aspect of the
karst and its origin, the study
of the differences and interactions between authigenic and
allogenic agencies of denudation is indispensable.

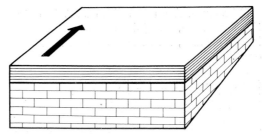

Fig. 75. A limestone mass covered with an
impermeable formation as the fundamental
type of the confined B-type karst. The arrow
indicates the slope of the ground surface

The analysis of allogenic
karst denudation must be com-
menced with the case where
authigenic karstification is al-
most totally excluded from the process, that is, where the features of
B-type karst erosion are recognizable as (almost) pure types. This is realized in those karst regions covered with a more or less thick impermeable
non-karstic formation (*Fig. 75*).

In a limestone mass covered by impermeable deposits, there is no possibility of A-type karstification. Hence, when a valley formed by linear
erosion, and incised into the non-karstic cover formation, cuts its way
through to the karstic bedrock, the underdeveloped system of joints in the
limestone is unable to swallow the waters of the stream, especially as the
contact between the two is confined to the linear. Hence, valley sculpture
by linear erosion is epigenetically impressed from the non-karstic higher
surface upon the limestone zone (*Fig. 76*).

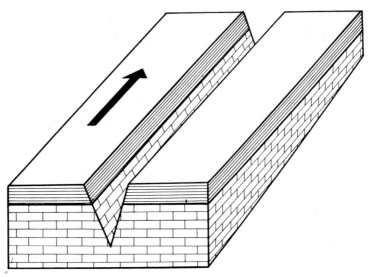

Fig. 76. A stream valley sculpture by linear erosion is epigenetically
impressed upon the limestone mass

Of course, from the time that the streambed starts to incise itself into the limestone, the joints of the limestone start to drain part of the water in the stream, and the uncovered karst immediately embarks upon A-type erosion.

Since the contact between water and limestone is only linear, however, the amount of water infiltrating into the karst mass (early in the process in particular) is much less than in an authigenic karst of open surface, where karstification is areal rather than linear. Hence, the widening of the passages in the limestone by corrosion is very slow in the b-zone as well as in the lenticular zone.

Incision by superficial linear erosion remains the dominant process of valley sculpture in the limestone until the linearly confined attack of A-type karstification manages to expand the primary fissure system of the rock sufficiently to permit the water passages thus sculptured by corrosion to tap, or indeed fully to drain the water in the stream somewhere along the streambed trace.

If the non-karstic cover formation of the karst was initially absolutely impermeable, totally preventing the infiltration of any waters into the karst, then the widening of the deeper passages in the limestone by corrosion will be so slow that, by the time the karst develops a network of clefts and fissures of sufficient capacity to tap the river, the continuing linear erosion and the resulting incision of the valley may advance down to the bottom of the karst, to the karst water table. In our opinion, the deep gorge-like valleys in karst regions (Békás Cap, Torda Defile, Sajó Gorge, Szádelő Gorge, Stracena Gorge, the gorge at Máriaremete near Budapest, Cuha Gorge, etc.) are all due to this process rather than to the collapse of cavern roofs. This would uphold the views of LÁNG (1937) and other geomorphologists contesting the theory of valley formation by collapse.

If some or all of the impermeable cover is eroded off the karstic surfaces during the incision into the inherited erosional valley pattern of the karst,

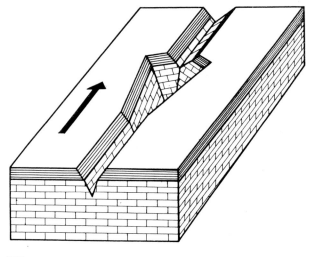

Fig. 77. Principle of swallow-hole formation and bathycapture (stream piracy by an underground streambed) in an epigenetically formed limestone valley

178

then a more intense authigenic karstification of the limestone may start, and the passages in the lenticular zone become sufficiently developed to drain the water out of the river from below. We have called this phenomenon *underground river piracy* or bathycapture (L. JAKUCS 1956/1, 1957/2) and consider it to be a regular process widespread over all the karst regions of the earth (*Fig. 77*).

A watercourse deflected underground by bathycapture will of course retain all the erosion potential of the surface stream, since the nature and lithology of its drainage area, and the composition of the stream's load, are not changed by the act of piracy. Indeed, the inevitable increase in the slope angle of the streambed results in an intensified scour. Hence, the process of valley sculpture by linear erosion displaces its theatre of underground operations.

The scouring efficiency is particularly high in the swallow hole connecting the two erosion levels, since it is here that the angle of descent of the water is steepest. This results in such an energetic and dynamic process of reaming compared with the slow widening of the passages in an authigenic karst by corrosion, that a qualitative change amounting to a variable revolution in the mechanism of action sets in, and scour by the streamload takes over almost entirely — the role of further sculpturing of the karst water may play at best a very subordinate role in widening the karst passages.

The vertical passages, suddenly and intensely widened after piracy, conduct stream water and its heterogeneous granular content into the depth of the karst, and discharge them into the cavities sculptured by A-type corrosion in the lenticular zone. As we have seen, these passages, excavated by mixing corrosion and pressure dissolution in the lenticular zone, occur largely in the bottom regions of the karst-water lens, below the level of the karst springs. Accordingly, allogenic water inundating the cavities of the lenticular zone is unable to remove all the waste washed in through the spring openings, and hence this waste, especially the bottom load, accumulates in the passages. This entails the narrowing of the passages and an acceleration of the flow in them.

In the passages depressed below the spring level of the lenticular zone, the fast-flowing scouring water understandably sculptures the near-roof portions and the roofs proper of the passages with its suspended load, until the roof-level of the cave gradually rises everywhere above the spring level; this puts an end to the syphon effect obliging the B-type water to flow very fast. Allogenic water thus effects an enlargement of passages by upward scour in the lenticular zone of the karst (*Fig. 78*).

Roof scour in a passage converted to B-type will of course proceed only until the profile of the passage is reamed all along its length so as to surpass a certain baselevel of erosion, determined by the altitude of the spring level and by the rate of discharge of water to be handled by the passage. This level does not coincide with the top boundary surface of the lenticular zone of the former authigenic karst; it is a much less convex flatter surface, that rises just a few metres above the spring level even deep in the mountain. One of the reasons why it would be impossible for the underground stream to scour its way up to the top surface of the former karst water

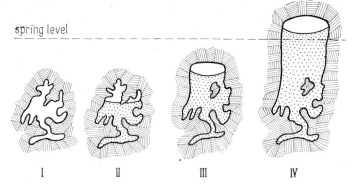

I   II   III   IV

Fig. 78. Upward enlargement by scour of cavern passages in a
B-type lenticular zone

I — cross-section of a passage sculptured by corrosion in an
A-type lenticular zone; II — deposition of sediment by the B-
type stream at the bottom of the cavern; III — upward enlargement of the cavern profile by scour towards the spring
level as the sediment is deposited; IV — a state of equilibrium
sets in as determined by the stream gradient and the position
of the spring level

lens is that in that case the slope of the streambed would become so steep
as to entail the incision of the stream into its own sediment. A state of roof-
level equilibrium develops in B-type caverns, therefore, reflecting the
dynamic flow equilibrium of the B-type karst water table in the karst.

In all allogenic karsts there are consequently two karst water tables. The
A-type table coincides with the top boundary of the authigenic lenticular
zone, whereas the scoured-out channel of the B-type table is situated farther

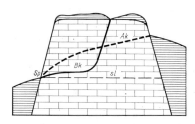

Fig. 79. Interpretation of the
double karst water table of B-type
karsts

Ak — A-type karst water table,
i.e. the top boundary of the A-
type lenticular zone; *Bk* — B-
type karst water table, i.e. the
level of evolution of the cavern
passage sculptured by scour; *sl* —
theoretical spring level; *Sp* —
spring

below, and rises only slightly above the
spring level (*Fig. 79*).

It would seem logical to assume that
a wide allogenic channel scoured right
through the lenticular a-zone would de-
flate the pronounced convexity of the
A-type karst water table. In reality this
does not happen because for a considerable time the channels scoured upward
into the lenticular zone do not yet represent an axis of depression for the
higher-lying mass of karst water in the
A-type lenticular zone, as the vertical
water passages, widened by corrosion in
the lenticular zone, are connected with the
horizontal passages in the bottom region
of the lenticular zone. Their drainage thus
continues to be ensured by the syngenetic
horizontal passages, rather than by the

180

postgenetic, allogenic scour channel, whose genesis is essentially alien to the karst process. In contrast, our observations have obliged us to admit that, simultaneously with the evolution of a B-type channel at spring-level height, the convexity of the A-type karst water table increases rather than decreases.

The reason for this phenomenon is that the sediment deposited in the karst region lying beneath the newly-formed allogenic scour channel blocks all passages formerly ensuring the drainage of A-type water, and thereby chokes the former internal drainage network sculptured by corrosion within the karst mass.

To summarize, the evolution of a scour cavern in the lenticular zone will make the A-type karstification regress to a more rudimentary state, necessitating the evolution of a new lenticular zone of more pronounced convexity. We have termed the new lenticular zone, whose axis of depression is the allogenic cavern channel, a B-type lenticular zone.

The B-type lenticular zone differs from the A-type one in two fundamental characteristics.

1. Even in a limestone mass including an inactive deep-karst zone, the B-type lenticular zone has only one convex boundary, the top one, whose expansion below the level of the scour channel is prevented by the obstruction of all the previously existing passages farther below.

2. The strong initial convexity of the B-type karst water table, gradually deflating during the advance of karst denudation, eventually fits the B-type karst water table: as a consequence, the B-type lenticular zone gradually dies off, as opposed to the A-type lenticular zone of the authigenic karst, which persists up to the end of the process of karst evolution. The deflation and eventual dying-off of the B-type lenticular zone proceeds in step with a reorientation of the earlier corrosion passages, and the establishment of new drainage connexions, which have adapted to the new axis of depression and internal baselevel of erosion represented by the scour cavern.

The above considerations shed light on the intriguing problem of why the rate of dripstone formation is fastest in the early stages of cavern evolution, and why the mass of dripstone formed per unit time is less in the senile stage. (It may be recalled (L. JAKUCS 1960/2, 1966) that the recent dynamism of dripstone evolution is more intense in the more juvenile Béke and Imre Vass caverns than in the senile Baradla (Hungary). It has also been seen, however, that in the Baradla the present-day rate of dripstone formation is much lower than it was in the youth of the cavern, and that the problem of the now inactive decaying giant dripstones of the cavern system can only partly be attributed to soil erosion and the consequent laying bare of the limestone as a result of deforestation.)

One of the fundamental reasons for this phenomenon is incontestably the fact that accessory dissolution of calcium carbonate, induced by the increase in hydrostatic pressure, remains intense in the B-type lenticular zone, whose convexity is considerable in the early stages of evolution of the scour cavern; this situation results in an intense dripstone formation in the air space of the scour cavern, where pressures become equalized. This pressure-dependent process of calcium carbonate dissolution loses intensity in the later stages of scour, however, when the lens is deflated, and gradually ceases to act as one of the factors of dripstone formation.

We have seen that allogenic water pouring into the karst will sculpture its own passage by upward scour, up to the static level of the B-type karst water table. However, gradual erosion in the adjacent non-karstic formations that determine the position of the baselevel of erosion in the karst, also gradually lower the karst-spring level. Further contingencies of the scour channel are also influenced by the incision of the above-ground valley downstream from the karst spring: retreating streambed erosion starting outside the cavern increases the slope of the underground streambed, results in the incision of the underground stream into its own non-karstic deposits, and thereby increases the clearance between the cavern roof and the water in the stream. Even at the beginning, an air gap opens between the water in the stream and the cavern roof, and occasional syphons also open up one by one. Thus, a through-cavern with a stream gradually forms, characterized by increasing height and an increasingly voluminous air space.

This process is no longer a widening of passages by a karst process, however, since the underground stream incises itself in its own earlier-accumulated non-karstic deposits, rather than into the limestone bedrock underlying these. During the secondary deepening of the passage, allogenic water contacts the limestone only along the side walls. Laterar scour and hydraulic erosion by the stream may locally cut into, or form terraces in these latter.

The underground stream, incising itself into its own deposits, does not of course remove these deposits from the entire pre-depositional cavern system of the limestone mass. Hence, gravel terraces and sand banks are left behind here and there, as witnesses to a previous stage of cavern evolution in which the entire cavity was filled with sediment.

Another obvious conclusion is that not all the gravel terraces in caverns sculptured by stream-scour are due to this type of process. In certain types of allogenic karst (see below) the streambed in the scour tunnel incises itself into the limestone. These caverns likewise exhibit gravel and sand terraces, but with the difference that these latter are contemporaneous with the process of incision, and with the deepening of the cavern profile, whereas the gravels forming the terraces in the allogenic covered karsts discussed so far are not contemporaneous with the deepening of the cavern, but relics of the period of upward scour.

To summarize, the typical features of scour caverns of the covered-karst type include the following:

1. The limestone floor of the cavern passage is buried under a deep accumulation of non-karstic waste.

2. The now inactive passages not used by the underground stream are filled up to their roofs with erosional waste brought in from the non-karstic drainage area (sand, gravel, silt, etc.), and even in the profiles of the active passages there are uncountable lateral conglomerate terraces.

3. The roof of the cavern passage is a broad flat horizontal surface, rather than a pointed arch.

4. The bottom profile of the cavern, hidden under the thick layer of sediment, is not a smooth flat surface like the roof, but a relief of irregular

depressions, ridges, wells and labyrinths, all filled with sediments and continuing downwards into the cavities of the former A-type lenticular zone.

The above features are comprehensively illustrated in *Figure 80.*

The Sloup cavern system of the Moravian karst or the Castellani Cavern in Apulia lend themselves best for a study of this genetic type.

Let us now direct our attention to the surface relief sculpture in an allogenic karst region.

The beheaded and dewatered valley section cut down to the limestone cannot be sculptured any further by streambed erosion; this is replaced by the sub-areal corrosion characteristics of authigenic karsts. The inactivated above-karst stream valley develops into a *string of dolines.* As these dolines now constitute the deepest-lying parts of the relief, they collect all the waste washed off the neighbouring areas where the karst is still covered. Many of the dolines making up the string may be clogged, depending on the permeability features of the waste deposited in them, but some of them may reopen at a later stage. The doline hollows, however, invariably contain huge masses of terra rossa and other, largely non-karstic waste.

In dolines formed on the more remote, higher limestone surfaces of the karst laid bare by the erosion of the cover formation, this accumulation of foreign waste, so typical of the aligned doline, is almost totally absent. Accordingly, karstification under the soil cover is less intense and the dolines are smaller.

An instructive example for the above assertion is the comparison of the profiles of accumulated deposits within lone dolines and string dolines of one and the same karst mass. For example the aligned dolines along the highway linking Aggtelek to Jósvafő in Hungary are filled with thick sequences of redeposited terra rossa-type clay, and so obstructed that one of them even contains a small lake (the Vöröstó). In contrast, the non-aligned dolines of Somostető near Jósvafő are lined with only a thin layer of rendzina soil that hardly covers the limestone; further, these dolines are much smaller than those that are aligned.

We may now formulate those implications of *aligned-doline formation* highlighted by our investigations into allogenic karst evolution:

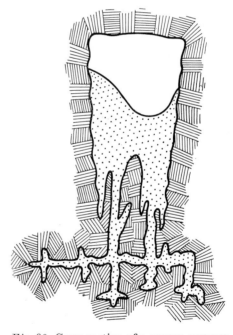

Fig. 80. Cross-section of a cavern passage originally of the A-type, sculptured by B-type processes. The section of the profile due to corrosion is totally silted up by sediment, but that due to scour is partly visible

183

Photo 15. Terrace grooves due to streambed scour on a rock in the doline of the Vörösto near Jósvafő

1. The layout of aligned dolines is determined by the former streambed axes epigenetically impressed from the covered karst into the limestone. This layout is determined by structural preformation in so far as the lines attracting surface streambeds in the formation originally overlying the karst mass are usually structure-controlled.

2. The aligned dolines are invariably older and deeper-lying than the lone dolines.

3. The aligned dolines are more developed and larger than the lone dolines.

4. The conspicuous presence of a doline series on a karst surface may indicate that the area was more or less covered at the outset of erosion.

5. If the aligned dolines contain a more substantial filling of non-karstic waste than the lone dolines, this invariably makes it a certainty that the karst was at least partially covered at the outset of erosion.

6. At the bottom of the aligned dolines, beneath the secondary deposits of waste, any uncovered limestone rock often exhibits traces of scour by a former surface stream (terraces, etc.; cf., for example, the terrace grooves of the Bear Rocks near the Vörösto of Jósvafő, in *Photo 15*).

In the still active sections of epigenetic valleys incised into a limestone body, the bathycapture phenomenon may be repeated several times in

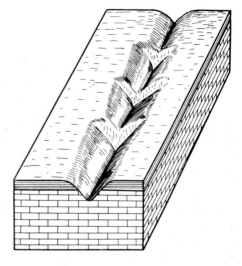

Fig. 81. Evolution of a multi-stage chain of swallow-holes in an epigenetically formed limestone valley

a retreating, upstream direction (the direction of the area of drainage). As a result, a stepped string of swallow-holes may develop on the surface (*Fig. 81*), and the scour cavern is prolonged each time by a new upstream section (*Fig. 82*).

If in the course of this process the karstic mountain mass is also uplifted, or the baselevel of erosion is lowered so much that the underground streambed cannot adjust to it rapidly enough by incision, then a deeper, second cavern level (a lower cavern) develops, and any further bathycapture naturally drains the waters of the river into this lower, active cavern level. This results in the interesting phenomenon of the older swallow-holes still discharging into the upper cavern while the more recent ones are already in hydrological communication with the lower one. Examples of this state are known among others from the Aggtelek Karst in Hungary, where a young swallow-hole, the Bábalyuk, having beheaded by bathycapture the feed valley of the Acheron swallow hole discharging into the upper level of the Baradla system, today discharges the waters deflected from the Acheron directly into the Lower Cavern (*Fig. 83*).

* * *

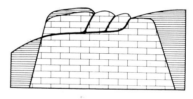

Fig. 82. Schematic profile of multistage bathycapture by retreating erosion in an epigenetically formed limestone valley

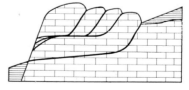

Fig. 83. Interpretation of a two-stage B-type karst water table by multistage bathycapture where there has been a substantial lowering of the baselevel by karst erosion

185

Let us continue our study of allogenic karst denudation with an analysis of diagrams I and II in Figure 65. In these examples, the non-karstic, impermeable formations contiguous with the karstic rock mass are higher on one side, and on that side the non-karstic surface slopes towards the karstic mass. Hence, its streambeds due to linear erosion discharge onto the limestone surface: even at the outset of the period of karst erosion, valley sculpture in the non-karstic region transgresses upon the limestone zone.

In the case studied, however, the incision of valleys into the limestone by linear erosion must be long-lived, for, as the karst in question is an open one, authigenic karstification is active right from the start of the erosion process. Hence, a system of passages sculptured by corrosion, much better-developed than in the case of a covered karst, is available early in the course of valley sculpture for draining the allogenic waters of the surface karst valleys into the depths of the karst mass.

Hence, in allogenic karsts not covered by an impermeable formation, the first stage of erosion combines subareal doline formation with valley sculpture by linear erosion. This holds everywhere except in those B-type karst regions where the limestone mass is higher to start with than all the adjacent non-karstic formations surrounding it (cf. diagram III in Fig. 65).

Under the conditions reflected by diagrams I and II of Figure 65, allogenic water is denied any role in surface sculpture by the time the second stage of erosion sets in. Hence, relief sculpture proceeds in accordance with the laws of authigenic karstification, for as soon as the stepwise retreating bathycaptures in the limestone valley attain the border of the limestone mass (and it is from this point in time that the second stage of erosion begins), the non-karstic surface undergoes intense degradation in the zone of contact with the karstic mass, as a result of retrogressive erosion reaching up from the cavern to the surface through the marginal sinkholes. The process eventually results in a dominant central position of the limestone mass, in the state shown in diagram III in Figure 65. It is thus essentially the B-type denudation proper that has made the karst more accessible to A-type relief sculpture.

In nature, however, it frequently happens that the situation shown in diagrams III and IV of Figure 65 is due not to the working of a preceding phase of erosion, but to various structural factors operative before the actual phase of erosion. In this case, karstification starts at once with the sculpture of allogenic scour channels, and consequently the A-waters of more subdued dynamism are unable to form an A-type lenticular zone prior to this event. The lenticular zone is therefore directly developed as a B-type one, and the surface of the limestone plateau exhibits no linear streams and streambeds, and no land forms due to linear erosion, not even in the embryonic stage of erosion.

In such a karst then, the allogenic channel adjusts to the sinking local baselevel of erosion by gradual incision into its own streambed, and consequently has a smooth limestone bottom. At the same time, the cavern, whose width varies as the size of the non-karstic drainage area (L. JAKUCS 1956/1), exhibits a triangular rather than a trapezoidal cross-section; in this case the scour channel evolves syngenetically and simultaneously with the drainage network of the non-karstic drainage area, so that the various

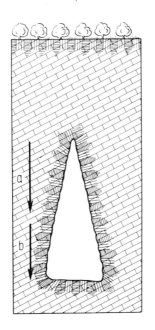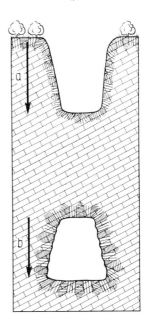

Fig. 84. Schematic profile of a complete (I) and truncated (II) period of cavern sculpture by scour. In diagram II that portion of the streambed due to scour represented by the arrow marked "a" is developed as a surface stream

sectional widths at various heights in the passage reflect the evolution of discharge during the full history of evolution of the non-karstic valley sculpture. Triangular cross-sections of passages are therefore indicative of a complete cycle of cavern formation, whereas the truncated, trapezoidal ones of certain caverns indicate that the first stage of valley sculpture did not take place in the cavern but in the now inactive stream valleys or doline strings on the karst surface (*Fig. 84*).

It is obvious at this stage of our considerations that karst surfaces over-lying caverns, indicating a complete cycle of erosion, will lack aligned dolines (e.g. in the vicinity of the Skocijanske Jama in Slovenia), whereas caverns with truncated passage sections (Bükk Hills, Aggtelek Hills, Mecsek Hills) are invariably accompanied by aligned dolines on the surface.

* * *

This chapter has so far been limited to a review of the characteristic types of allogenic karst denudation: we have seen how the various fundamental

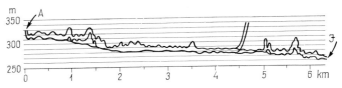

Fig. 85. Longitudinal section of the Main Branch of the Baradla Cavern between Aggtelek (A) and Jósvafő (J)

187

Photo 16. A view of the Domica Cavern (the Slovak section of the Aggtelek Cavern) (after BENICZKÝ). The fossil streambed is clearly visible even though the passage is inactive at present

morphological forms of scour-type karst caverns may be attributed to thi or that stage of evolution under different conditions of surface structur and relief. We have also seen how, depending on the various initial condi tions, the variants of B-type karstification in their turn influence surface modelling and also the evolution of the karst hydrography. So far, we have looked for the individual, the particular within the general; let us now attempt the inverse approach by looking for general traits in the particular cases. Let us therefore review the features common to every B-type cavern and, at the same time, absent from every A-type cavern.

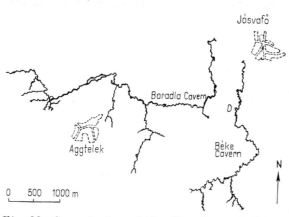

Fig. 86. Ground plan of the Baradla and Peace Caverns of Aggtelek, Hungary, reminiscent of a surface drainage pattern

Photo 17. Typically occurring profile uniform in height and width (Domica Cavern) (after BENICZKÝ)

1. In allogenic caverns, a given generation of passages is confined to a given subhorizontal plane, or almost so. All passages slope from the swallow-hole towards the spring. There are no adverse gradients (*Fig. 85*).

2. The ground plans recall the pattern of tributaries of a surface river: there is a capacious main trunk with narrower tributary passages opening into it (*Fig. 86*).

3. There are readily recognizable streambeds in every passage; these may either carry water or be inactive (*Photo 16*).

4. Disregarding secondary distortions due to roof collapses and differences in lithology, the width and height of the passage cross-section do not deviate sharply from a typical average in the middle course of any cavern branch (*Photo 17*).

189

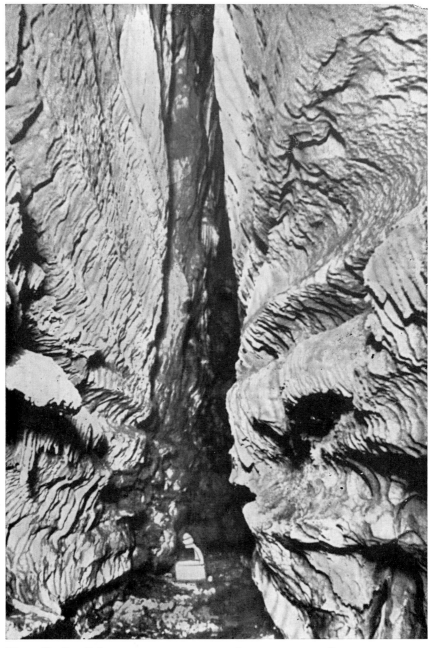

Photo 18. Parallel scour grooves on the side-walls of the "Radish Branch", Baradla Cavern, Aggtelek

190

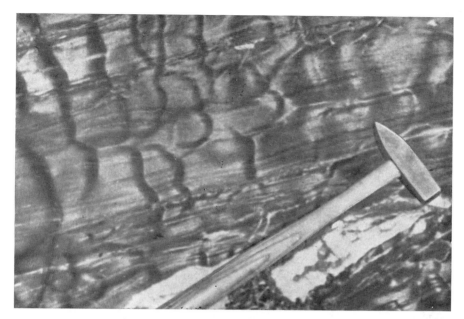

Photo 19. Conchoidal depressions on the wall of a cavern

5. The widest and tallest passages occur in the swallow-hole zone or in its vicinity, since the sudden change in gradient and the steep slope make scour strongest precisely in these parts (the baselevel of erosion within the karst usually being much deeper than the bottom level of the valley section upstream from the swallow-hole), and also because the swallow-hole branches of various ages and levels within the karst have a tendency to coalesce there (cf. the X-zone in *Fig. 87*).

6. If the baselevel of erosion (the spring level) was sinking in the course of cavern evolution, the passage exhibits a vertical digitation next to the spring outlet. In such cases, cavities of extreme size come to exist in the zone of digitation, e.g. the "Halls of Giants" of the Baradla, of the Béke Cavern and of the Freedom Cavern at Égerszög, or the "Hall of Cyclops" in the Imre Vass Cavern, to cite only Hungarian examples (cf. the Y-zone in Fig. 87).

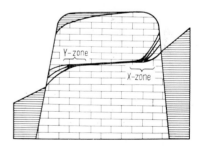

7. The side walls exhibit horizontal, parallel rock-terrace grooves (*Photo 18*).

8. The rocky walls of the passages, and the rocky islets in the streambed exhibit characteristic conchoidal depressions due to cavitation (*Photo 19*). Whirlpool holes

Fig. 87. Zones of divergence (Y-zone) and convergence (X-zone) in a B-type system of caverns, with extraordinary scouring in both zones, either resulting from the relative uplifting of the limestone block or of the relative lowering of the surroundings by differential erosion

191

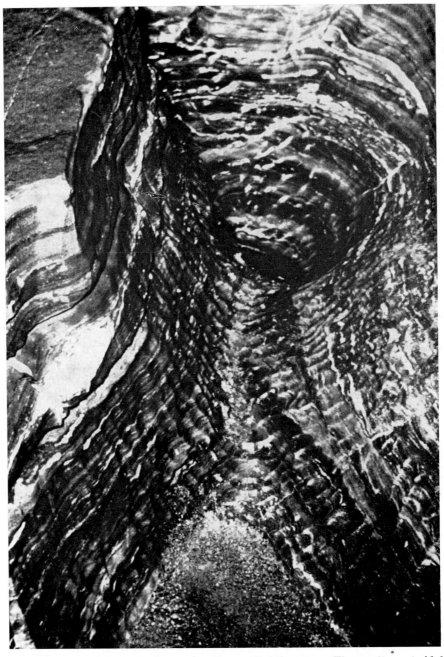

Photo 20. Pits due to evorsion in a well-stratified limestone. The small conchoidal depressions are also visible (Lulletjaro Cavern, Sweden)

Photo 21. Typical forms of corrosion (scour) by suspended material in the stream in the Javoricko Cavern (Moravian Karst)

scoured out by vortex action (*Photo 20*) are also frequent. Wall surfaces sculptured by corrosion, although not excluded, are subordinate and highly localized in any scour cavern under a temperate climate, but the typically corrosional, parallel rock grooves permit one to distinguish them with ease from the forms due to scour, the latter exhibiting capricious microforms unselectively overriding bedding planes, veins in the rock and any other changes in lithology (*Photo 21*).

9. The rate of dripstone formation is much more intense in these caverns, especially in their youth, than in cavities sculptured by corrosion in an authigenic karst.

10. The streambed sediment of passages in allogenic caverns invariably includes stream-laid waste differing in lithology from the rock mass in which the cavern is sculptured, and often even of a non-karstic nature. In large caverns, these accumulations include gravels of quartz or other substances more resistant to wear than limestone, as well as sand, silt and rock debris.

As the upshot of our considerations concerning A- and B-type karsts, we may now formulate one of our most important conclusions:

B-type karst erosion is essentially none other than a peculiar facies (confined to the depths of a karstic rock mass) of a non-karstic process of relief sculpture, notably of valley sculpture by linear streambed erosion. Its occurrence in a karst mass is purely accidental, a function of extraneous circumstances, and not an inevitable stage in the process of evolution of each and every karst mass. The classic interpretations of karstification as the corrosion of limestone failed to account for the presence of this extraneous effect, or for the morphogenetic consequences of its presence for that matter, limiting themselves as they did to the contemplation of authigenic karstification only. This is one of the reasons why the classical concept of karstification must be regarded as an overstrict definition reflecting only part of reality. If we were to equate karstification with corrosion, we would be obliged to exclude from the karst concept (in the genetic sense) all of the largest and most magnificent cavern formations in the depths of limestone masses all over the world.

INFLUENCE OF RELIEF CONFIGURATION UPON THE KARST PROCESS (THE GEOMORPHOLOGICAL VARIANCE OF KARSTIFICATION)

Our observations have completely convinced us that the geographical distributions of the components of karst erosion include certain features that are unexplained either by differences in lithology, by concrete differences in climatic factors representing the situation of the karst region in a climatic zone, by structural pre- or postformation, or by the relationship of the karst to its non-karstic surroundings.

When it is recalled, for instance, that most dolines on a karst surface have a ground plan that is not circular but elongated in some direction, such that one of the doline flanks is almost invariably much steeper than the others, we are already in possession of a relationship with a bearing on the causal relations of this problem. Mapping of the asymmetries of a variety of dolines revealed that the factors determining the ground plan of the doline in the course of its evolution are other than the relationships studied and published by early authors (Cvijić, Grund, Cholnoky, etc.), such as the dip of the strata and the lines of structurally preferred orientation; these other factors overcome the preferred orientation due to the dip and strike of the strata, and impress upon these forms an orientation depending on the points of the compass. In other words, independent of whether the strata dip north, south, east or west, the doline flanks with by far the highest relief energy in the Bükk Hills and on the North Borsod Karst are invariably the easterly or north-easterly facing flanks (*Fig. 88*).

However, although we have recognized this phenomenon we cannot jump to general conclusions without analysing a number of further examples.

It is known that the karsts of our planet are in various stages of erosion, and of geographic relief evolution. The present-day aspect of the landscape provides us with the resultant of all the forms from previous episodes of relief evolution. The actual (temporal) cross-section of the succession of events, reflected in the set of relief forms, is not merely the complex upshot of all the preceding episodes of relief evolution, but is itself a dynamism-controlling factor affecting relief formation in the present and in the future through its qualitative and quantitative driving factors.

This rather general statement, intentionally formulated rather broadly, expresses an important feature of the evolution of any relief, and not just of karsts; however, in adducing proof for it we shall remain within the confines of karst science.

Given a leaching solution of fixed quantity, temperature and chemical composition, surface karst corrosion is more efficient, the more extensive the rock surface in contact with unit volume of the solution during unit time. The extent of the surface is relative, however, and a function of

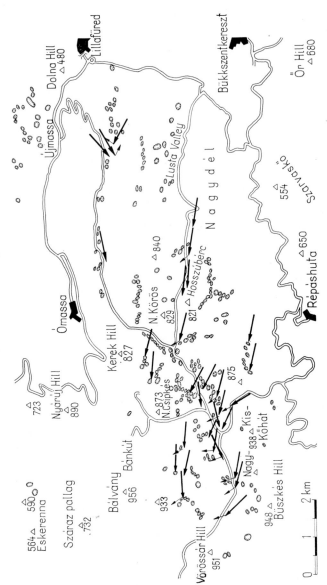

Fig. 88. Orientation of asymmetric dolines on the Bükk Plateau and its relationship to the sculpturing of the bedding about the dolines. The bold-line arrows point from the gentlest toward the steepest slope of the dolines. The small arrows represent the dip of the bedding

paleogeographic events. At the beginning of the process of erosion, a limestone plateau not yet provided with a karst relief offers to erosion one square kilometre of surface per square kilometre of map area (disregarding, of course, the internal fissures and joints). However, owing to the intense dissection of the relief by advanced doline sculpture on a limestone plateau of advanced karstification, one square kilometre of map area may actually correspond to 1·5 sq. km or more of actual rock surface. The rates of erosion of a young and an old karst relief differ purely for this reason, if for no other.

There are other reasons too, however. Karstification widens part of the fissure grid draining surface waters into the rock mass. The widened fissures with their reduced wall drag attract a substantial proportion of the water pulled downward by gravity. Hence, early in the process of karst evolution when all the fissures were still narrow and the three-dimensional karstification of the young karst mass was still homogeneous, even the narrowest fissures could contribute to the drainage of the descending waters; the advancing maturity of karst evolution gradually resulted in a linearization of vertical drainage, thereby reducing the total surface area in contact with the leaching solution in the interior of the karst mass.

As a consequence of all these factors, as erosion advances the efficiency of surface corrosion increases, while the efficiency of corrosion within the karst mass gradually wanes.

This set of examples may be followed still further. The partial increase in slope angles resulting from the formation of dolines promotes not only a faster surface run-off of precipitation, but also soil erosion and hence the natural exposure of the karst rock. This process may reduce the efficiency of karst corrosion in the areas of steep doline and valley flanks, whereas it may be enhanced on the doline and valley floors characterized by the confluence of waters and the deposition of sediments; in contrast, beyond a given limit (that of the critical impermeability of the deposits), it may inhibit the process altogether.

In order to present a wider proof of our postulate, some other retarding effects should be pointed out.

In numerous karst regions, including Yugoslavia, Italy, Austria, Cuba, South China, etc., it is obvious that the size of the karst mass itself may result in qualitative differences in karst erosion. For instance, in the authigenic karst mountains of Slovenia, Croatia, Albania, etc., several hundred sq. km in extent, even the A-type lenticular zones exhibit a B-type motivation, purely because of the volumes of water involved in their sculpture.

To consider another example of a different nature, snow accumulated in the hollows of well-developed deep dolines on karst plateaux, fallen in the winter and swept together by the wind, may persist well beyond the general snow-melting characteristic of the region as a whole. Masses of snow in striking contrast to the blossoming countryside can be encountered quite frequently in May and June in the peculiar microclimatic spaces of temperate-zone dolines (*Photo 22*). Beneath these snow-covered spots the karst process is, so to speak, put in a deep freeze; that is, it will be many times less efficient than in the snow-free surroundings: even though the gradual melting of this long-lived snow ensures a continuous supply of infiltrating

Photo 22. Patches of snow retention in late May in a doline of the middle karst plateau (1100 to 1200 m altitude) of Chatyr-Dagh Mountain (1525 m) on the Crimean Peninsula

cold water, this cannot vie with the high corrosive potential of the soil solutions, due to the vegetative production of CO_2 in the rhizospheres of the verdant surfaces close by (*Fig. 89*).

Similar examples could be enumerated, as the retarding effects of karstification, once developed, may and do effect the complex mix of morphogenetic processes controlling the further course of evolution. We have included all these retarding effects under the heading of *geomorphological variance in karstification,* as they express the many diverse and significant influences on the geomorphological features of the present-day landscape, developed during the prior evolution history of the karst. In a concise formulation, probably unusual on a first hearing, but certainly expressing the essence of the matter, we might say that geomorphological variance in karstification means the influence of the karst topography upon karstification.

Karst forms and, of course, the relief forms typical of any other types of landscape as well, are not in this sense mere passive products of erosion, etc., but undeniably active, indirectly relief-forming, and process-controlling factors.

We maintain that a systematic analytical study of the above effects, and of a number of other effects not touched upon here, may be one of the primary tasks of karst morphogenetics in the future, since a full and realistic genetic understanding of a landscape on today's exacting level of sophistication renders an analysis of the diverse interactions initiated by earlier erosion

198

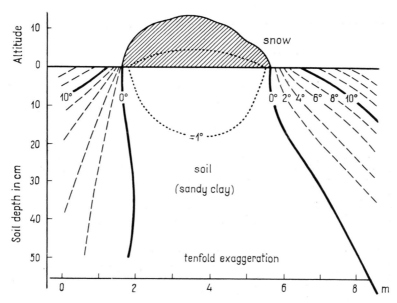

Fig. 89. Influence of a late-melting snowpatch upon the ground isotherms (after Köhn 1948)

in the qualitative and quantitative parameters of subsequent erosion
indispensable.

We are convinced that a profound understanding of cause-to-effect relationships in morphogenetics will be impossible without studies of the sort
outlined above.

THE ANTHROPOVARIANCE OF KARSTIFICATION

Indisputably any natural landscape and the human society living on it will interact on many levels. We must investigate which agencies are enhanced and where at any given instant in the interaction of region and society, and in what measure these enhanced agencies affect the tendencies of continuing evolution of the human community and of the landscape itself.

The influence upon the evolution of society of the orographic, hydrographic, climatologic, petrographic, etc. features of a geographic environment has been studied in the last few decades with a great deal of care and widely discussed by modern geographical science. As a result, it has been possible to reject most of the one-sided distorted approaches: geographic determinism as one extreme, and the total negation of the importance of all these effects at the other, or the exaggeration of the role of society to the point of a geographic biologism.

Present-day geographical science attributes to these problems an importance in keeping with their real weight, and devotes much painstaking effort to the study of the effective relationships; by learning the laws of their spontaneous manifestation, it is hoped to find reasonably practicable ways of applying these laws to a positive control of nature, most appropriate to the requirements of society. The final aim and the raison d'être of the scientific research is brought together in these studies.

Human communities living in and off a karst region interact with their environment perhaps even more strongly than in regions of a different nature. The almost total lack of available water on extensive karst plateaux, most often coupled with a practically complete absence of agricultural land, is highly unfavourable to the settling and evolution of cultures, where even the minimum human requirements are barely supplied. This is the main reason why, in the largely karstic state of Črna Gora (Montenegro) in Yugoslavia, the population density is only 33 per sq. km, whereas in the adjacent state of Serbia it is 86 per sq. km, with corresponding significant differences in the ways of life, the living standards and the cultural demands of the two peoples.

In keeping with the morphogenetic aims of the present book, however, we do not intend to highlight this aspect of karst regions and the social communities supported on them, but rather the types of anthropogenic effects in the qualitative and quantitative evolution of karstification.

These anthropogenic effects usually influence the karst process very intensely, even though their reflection in land forms may as yet be unmeasurable, the duration of their action having been too short on a geological time scale. They may fundamentally and recognizably alter the

200

tendencies of surface evolution, however, by initiating a completely new "cultural denudation", giving rise to a landscape altogether different from a landscape solely subject to its own laws of spontaneous evolution.

We shall now illustrate all this by presenting certain important anthropogenic modifiers of erosion.

1. MODIFICATIONS IN EROSION DUE TO CHANGES IN THE NATURAL PLANT COVER OF A KARST REGION

It is common knowledge that the huge demands for industrial timber required for the building of Venice, and for the construction of the Adriatic fishing fleets, the men-of-war and trading vessels of more recent times were tantamount to a death sentence for the forests in near-shore areas of the Croatian and Dalmatian karst. Complete deforestation was naturally followed by large-scale soil erosion, and the karst-type denudation of the steep hillsides soon resulted in the total and irreversible denudation of the region.

In Albania and especially in Greece it was the tremendous multiplication of goats some centuries ago that was responsible for deforestation and denudation; feeding on buds and young shoots, and thereby killing off replacement growths, goats caused the aging, senility and decay of woods and forests, thus opening up the way for the total areal erosion of the soil deprived of its reinforcing network of roots.

Soil erosion was also promoted and accelerated by the mechanical effect of trampling by the herds. In a short while, the multiplication of stray goats and its undesirable consequences reached such a degree that the animals could not find sufficient food, while the limited agricultural land that did remain could not provide even the minimum sustenance to a population living on a meagre agricultural produce even at the best of times. Thoughtless interference with nature therefore resulted not only in the upsetting of the biological equilibrium, but also in a profound change in the character of the land, in a reduction of its agricultural productivity and naturally also in qualitatively new features of erosion.

Based on the comparative analysis of wide-ranging phytogeographical data, P. JAKUCS (1956) first demonstrated consistent connexions between the form types of limestone lapies and the plant associations thriving in the karst regions. One consequence of these connexions is that, whereas the primary lapies reliefs (*Photo 23*) of karst areas bearing a sufficient soil and plant cover are places of intense subcutaneous lapies formation, resulting as a rule in rounded microforms and root holes of irregular pattern, these forms have been altered by subsequent denudation and exposure on the surface, giving rise to the typical furrow and rain-rill set of karst forms typical of high mountains, as a result of these secondary processes (*Photo 24*).

This effective "metamorphism" of lapies forms is so regular, even quantitywise, that, for instance in the various areas of the Dalmatian Karst, the state of advancement of this reshaping permits (via comparative morphoanalysis) a good approximate estimate of the time elapsed since the denudation of the rock in any particular locality. *Photos 25* and *26* illustrate this.

201

Photo 23. Rounded limestone lapies with root holes, the typical result of evolution under a soil cover, on a flank of Baradla-tető at Aggtelek (photo by HOLLENZER)

The removal of the plant and soil cover also has other consequences, of course, resulting in a distortion of the karstifying process.

Prior to degradation, karst soils covered with forest, and even those supporting only a lawn association, supply an evened-out flow of ground water to the underlying limestone. This is a consequence of the natural water storage capacity of the soil, which enables it occasionally to take in and transitorily store quite substantial amounts of precipitation. In the process, a large proportion of the pores between the soil particles become filled with water; some soils swell considerably as a result.

On the other hand, rain immediately runs off denuded karst surfaces, being partly absorbed into the fissure system of the karst rock, and so even a few hours after a summer shower the limestone surface is again completely dry. This is why drippings of comparatively uniform discharge, active the year round, invariably occur in any dripstone caverns beneath wooded karst surfaces, whereas stalactites with markedly variable dripping rates occur almost without exception in cavern sections underlying barren karst surfaces. The water discharge of some of these latter dripstones may cease altogether at intervals.

This is borne out convincingly by our recordings of the water discharge rates of some stalactites in the Baradla and Béke caverns at Aggtelek (*Fig. 90*).

Photo 24. Secondary dissection of barren lapies of the Dalmatian Karst by parallel runoff furrows: the lack of a preferred orientation among the blocks of rock clearly indicates the subcutaneous sculpture of the basic forms

Our Slovenian observations in the nineteen-sixties convinced us that there are also other sensitive relationships between the plant-cover pattern of the ground surface and the resulting state of the soil, and also the nature of the karst process. First and foremost, there are considerable differences in the dynamics of dripstone formation in cavern sections lying beneath covered and barren karst surfaces. Forest-covered reliefs show greater dripstone formation rates than degraded planinas by several orders of magnitude. Especially in short-range comparisons, rates can differ by a factor of 10^3. This is understandable since some drippings of water occasionally entirely dry up under barren karsts.

A significant decrease in the original water-storage capacity of the soil and thus in the non-uniform water infiltration from the surface cover in eroded karsts will cause the volume of water emitted from karst springs to vary with time. The advance of surface degradation results in increasing extremes in the spring water yield and even in the water composition of the springs. Whereas prior to general soil degradation the peak discharge may exceed the minimum by a factor of ten at most, after degradation the peak discharge may exceed the minimum water discharge by as much as a factor of one hundred (KESSLER 1954, 1956). This also has a deleterious influence on the purity, the natural filtration, the possible bacterial contamination, etc. of the water, even in the case of A-type springs.

203

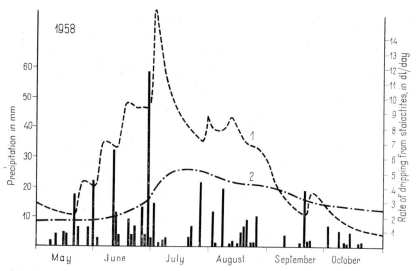

Fig. 90. Typical differences in water runoff from stalactites underlying a completely barren karst (graph 1) and a karst covered with a thickish humus-rich soil under a forest (graph 2). The histogram shows the rainfall in the region under study during six months of 1958

1 — stalactite 3 in the Hall of Columns of the Baradla; 2 — stalactite 4 in the Béke Cavern

Photo 25. A lapies field laid bare by total soil erosion subsequent to deforestation, near Hercegnovi, Yugoslavia. The lapies still reflect the influence of the subterranean processes; the evolution of runoff furrows is embryonic. Deforestation took place about 80 to 100 years ago (cf. also Photo 26)

Photo 26. A lapies field laid bare by total soil erosion subsequent to deforestation, near Hercegnovi (about 2 km from the site shown in Photo 25). The lapies show hardly any remains of the initial subterranean process; the well-developed runoff furrows are indicative of an advanced stage of barren-karst corrosion. The time elapsed since deforestation is at least 400 to 600 years

It seems that although the degradation of the karstic drainage area increases the total waterspring yields of that area on a year-round average, by increasing the proportion of infiltrated water, at the same time the extreme fluctuations of volume discharge and the deterioration of the water quality are very unfavourable for supplying human settlements for example. Consequently, the afforestation of karst surfaces within the drainage areas of one or several karst springs ensuring the water supply of a town is a high-priority task for the society. Neglecting to do so, or even allowing the processes of degradation to continue, will inevitably result in the deterioration of the reliability and quality parameters of the spring.

Almost invariably anthropogenic influences affect the evolution of the natural plant cover over a karst region by degrading that cover; there are also some other sensitive intensity indicators of the connected karst processes, however. One of these is the changing colour of dripstones in caverns, perhaps the most sensitive record of rates of degradation in the past as well as in the present.

Reference can be made in this context to our examinations concerning the colour, structure, chemical and mineralogical composition, locality of occurrence and abundance of dripstones in the caverns of the North Borsod

Karst in Hungary (L. JAKUCS 1960/3, 1962), which clearly led to the following inferences:

1. The abundance of non-carbonate contaminations is least in the dripstones of those cavern sections under a relief with an uninterrupted forest cover and a natural soil profile.

2. The dripstones under barren karsts are often inactive, dull of surface, and usually yellow, brown, ochre or a clayey-grey in colour.

3. Where the plant cover has died off recently, the surfaces of stalactites and stalagmites show a marked change in colour, usually towards a red tint. Subareal erosion on the surface and the increased infiltration into the karst of the eroded clays and iron compounds results in a lower calcium carbonate content in recent dripstone formations; such layers tend to be friable and rich in non-carbonate contaminating substances.

4. If the forest on the karst is renewed after a brief period of barrenness, the dripstones grow lighter once more, and the most recent layers are then clear again. In this way it is possible to infer the phases of surface degradation from the cross-sections of heterogeneous dripstones in caverns; such phases may reflect either an anthropogenic influence, or a natural destruction of the forest, e.g. by fire. Not only do the interiors of such dripstones exhibit concentric shells of dripstone differing in colour and composition, but some of the calcium carbonate layers even wear a coating of clay. The calcium carbonate content of this intrastalactic clay may be as low as one per cent. The clay coating is in turn surrounded by a calcium carbonate shell, this pattern possibly being repeated 5 or 6 times. This may occasionally reach such a degree that a broken-off stalactite can be drawn out telescope-fashion by deforming the plastic layers of clay contained in it (*Fig. 91*).

In caverns underlying limestone planinas, where the terra rossa-type soil is rich in ferric oxide, the degradation of the soil and of the plant cover is clearly indicated by the redness of large masses of wall linings and dripstones, since in karst areas where the forest cover was destroyed, the upsetting of the long-standing equilibrium of the soil cover permitted the waters to wash the degraded soil through the fissures of the limestone in the caverns. Comparison of cavern and surface maps reveals (L. JAKUCS 1960/2, 1962) that in the vicinity of the "Red Hall" or of the "Stone Toadstool Gate" in the Béke cavern of Aggtelek, for instance, where the red lining on the cavern formations is especially con-

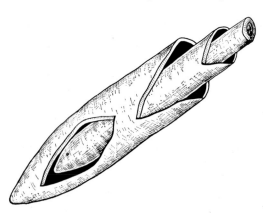

Fig. 91. Structure of a telescoping stalactite indicative of ancient forest fires or other episodes of surface denudation. The soft clay sand wiched between the calcite shells, deposited during periods of denudation, can be washed out subsequently, in which case the broken-off stalactite readily slides apart

spicuous and ubiquitous, a denudation caused by total deforestation has taken place over the last hundred years or so.

The washing of clay into the barren karst may occur locally at so high a rate that even over a few centuries it may result in a significant, and locally even complete silting-up of inactive cavern sections. Sedimentological and pollen-analytical methods applied to the muddy fillings in the "Fairytale Land" and "Golden Street" of the Aggtelek cavern and in the upper passage of the "Radish branch" (L. Jakucs 1957/2), as well as in numerous upper-level syphon bypasses in the Béke Cavern, etc. have demonstrated that silting-up over the last few centuries (during a period of general surface denudation in the neighbourhood) has deposited a bed of clay thicker than the aggregate deposits of the previous three or four millennia.

Such a rapid process of silting-up and clogging of underground cavities justifies the statement that any anthropogenic interference with the natural plant cover of a karst region will initiate a period of intensive changes and decay in earlier-formed karst features both on the surface and underground.

Of course, the above considerations do not imply that it is unfeasible to displace the process in the opposite sense, that is, to halt degradation already under way, and even to reverse the trend. There are many examples to show how successful a timely and well-chosen method of reafforestation may be. According to P. Jakucs (1954, 1955, 1956), however, the task is far from simple. "Reafforestation must always start from the already shrub-covered areas remaining from the former forest; the tree genera of the prior natural plant cover that may be found still thriving on similar slopes of adjacent hillsides must be employed. Reafforestation must proceed gradually, with due regard to the natural succession of plant associations. (For instance, a lawn-covered area should first be planted with shrubs, and only after these have gained a foothold may one think of planting trees (in Hungary primarily hairy oak, *Quercus pubescens*)."

Any change in the natural plant and soil cover of a limestone planina will, as a matter of course, affect the intensity of every karst process connected with corrosion, including for example doline sculpture, or calcareous tufa deposition next to a spring. We have nevertheless picked out above only the formation of lapies and the phenomena of hydrology and sedimentation in caverns; the slowing of doline formation accompanying the advance of degradation, as well as the reduction or cessation of calcareous tufa deposition from a karst spring whose waters are gradually softening, are processes whose morphological consequences are not conspicuous in the short term, or not recordable at all by the tools available today, and this makes their discussion very largely theoretical.

2. MODIFICATIONS IN EROSIONAL PROCESSES ACCOMPANYING ANTHROPO-GENIC INTERFERENCE WITH THE NATURAL HYDROLOGY OF A KARST

Over and above the effects already outlined, man can influence the natural hydrological state of a karst region most effectively in the following ways, which in turn also affect the further course of erosion to various extents:

1. By interfering with the intake capacity of swallow-holes at the downstream end of the surface valley section of a B-type linear streambed.

2. By interfering with the discharge capacity of a spring at the down-stream end of the underground (cavern) section of the stream.

3. By river conservancy works on karst streams, both surface and underground.

4. By artificially damming up streams.

Since any one of the above classes of interference may have unexpected consequences involving not only the features of erosion in the region, but also the human communities inhabiting it, we outline the results of our relevant studies in more detail below.

a) Problems connected with human interference with the intake capacity of swallow-holes

Our earlier analysis of the problem has revealed that in a B-type karst a swallow-hole may conveniently be regarded as a flux gate, through which a linear stream, flowing up to that point in a surface bed, enters an underground section. Downstream from the swallow-hole, the water continues to flow in a bed, with the single difference that this bed is enclosed in a rocky archway, a cavern tunnel.

Disregarding caverns in an embryonic stage of development, the discharge capacities of the surface and underground streambed sections of the stream are as a rule equal, both sections having been sculptured by the incisive, valley-forming energy of one and the same body of water. It is thus quite natural, and indeed a necessary consequence of this situation, that the genetic discharge capacity of the swallow-hole section is in no way subordinate to the other sections, connecting as it does the two typical streambed sections of the stream, the open surface and the covered underground one.

Despite this, one often finds that the swallow-capacity of the hole is less (possibly many times so) than the discharge capacities of the adjoining streambed sections. This occurs time and time again in inundations by dammed-up floods in the swallow-hole. The prolonged, ominous inundation of Yugoslavian poljes are usually due to such situations, but even in Hungarian karst regions many instances of temporary flooding in swallow-hole areas can readily be cited (L. JAKUCS 1956/2).

The cause of such an event is invariably a secondary obstruction or post-genetic narrowing of the swallow-hole passage. The explanation for such a set of circumstances is as follows.

The bottom level of the streambed section on the surface is determined basically by the altitude of the non-karstic environment. That of the underground passage, on the other hand, has been seen to be determined by the B-type lenticular zone matched to the spring (outflow) level. Thus, in the majority of cases the open streambed upstream of the swallow-hole is, so to speak, in a suspended position above the underground streambed section, this latter being matched to the local baselevel of erosion (*Fig. 92*).

For the reasons given above, within the swallow-hole the water drops as in a waterfall before reaching the cavern. At the static level of the B-type karst water table, on the other hand, the waterflow is regular so that

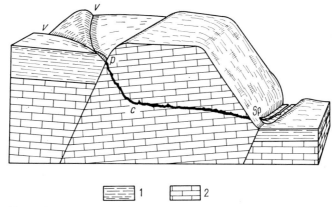

Fig. 92. Interpretation of the inherent tendency to clogging in the swallow-hole section. The "suspended" surface valley between V and P, usually of gentle slope, is succeeded first by a very steep section between P and C, and then by another section of gentle slope between C and Sp. Both sections $V-P$ and $C-Sp$ are characterized by lateral streambed erosion accompanying downward incision, whereas in the section $P-C$ the only agency at work is strong linear streambed erosion. As a result, the passages in the swallow-hole section are tall but narrow, easily obstructed by driftwood, timber, etc. swept in from the surface. No such obstruction occurs in the wide passages between C and Sp

1 — impermeable beds; 2 — limestone

the bed is sculptured evenly by lateral erosion. Hence, the passages of narrowest section in the entire underground system occur in the swallow-hole, where any large-sized chunk of driftwood may become caught and form an obstruction (*Fig. 93*).

Obstructions in swallow-holes most often form in the vicinity of the hole's inlet, where the hydrostatic pressure acting on the total obstruction is least, and the obstruction is able to resist it better than farther below where higher hydrostatic pressures develop. An obstruction resisting the flood close to the swallow-hole inlet might well be broken down at greater depth, since the hydrostatic pressure increases by one atmosphere per ten metres of depth: for instance, a stoppage formed at a swallow-hole depth of 20 m must support 20 tons per sq. m pressure, provided the channel above it is filled with water.

Swallow-hole obstructions are practically unknown in those caverns where the streambed section upstream of the swallow-hole does not lie significantly higher than the underground section, as this eliminates the above-discussed hydraulic break in the swallow-hole section. In such systems, the inlet of the swallow-hole tends to be as wide as any other cross-section of the underground passage, as the water acts there by lateral erosion just as in any other streambed section at maturity stage.

This formulation was made possible by a study of the swallow-hole regions of the great swallow-hole caverns of the Slovenian karsts (Škocijanska-jama, Rakek-Škocjan, Postojanska-Jama, etc.).

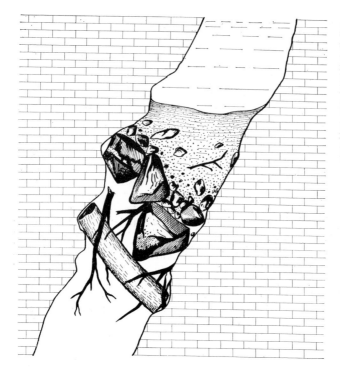

Fig. 93. Temporary obstruction in a steep swallow-hole. A length of timber or a block of rock swept into the swallow funnel will at first hold up tree branches and boulders of stone, but later on will trap the finer sediment and finally even silt up, thus completely obstructing the passage

An accurate knowledge of the cause-and-effect relationships concerning these phenomena may incidentally also turn out to be highly fruitful in an economic context, as it provides a key to efficient flood prevention in karst regions. It is known, for instance, that many of the Yugoslavian poljes are inundated over longish periods each year, and the bodies of water flooding them are drained rather sluggishly (*Photo 27*). The particular importance of the problem is due to the fact that in the karsts of the Dinaric region almost all of the arable and agriculturally workable land is concentrated on the extensive flat bottoms of the intercolline basins in the poljes.

At times of snowmelt and copious summer rains, the poljes are flooded by waters discharged by the underground drainage network of the karst, and they are likewise drained through cavern passages. If the cavern passages discharging into the polje have a higher capacity than the passages draining it, then the polje bottom will become flooded periodically.

Often, however, the polje bottom lies lower than the top flood-level of the karst water table whose altitude varies as a function of the abundance of precipitation. The openings at the polje rim functioning as swallow-holes at times of low water then act as springs and discharge water (*Photo 28*).

Another common experience is that the flooding of poljes is a much shorter process than the subsequent draining. The functioning of the openings serving alternately as springs and swallow-holes (katavothra, estavelles) is invariably characterized by the fact that the discharge in the

210

Photo 27. Temporary inundation of a polje near Metkovič (Yugoslavia)

Photo 28. A typical funnel-shaped katavothra alternately functioning as a spring or a swallow-hole depending on the position of the karst water table (on the alluvium of the Neretva, Yugoslavia)

14*   211

spring phase is much greater but of much shorter duration than the drainage during the swallow-hole phase.

The phenomenon is invariably due to a secondary obstruction of the katavothra funnel: this is the cause of the one-way-valve behaviour of the hole. The apertures partially or entirely obstructed by flood debris, streamload, silt, etc. are swept clean each time there is a surge of high-pressure flood water from the depths of the mountain, as the energy of the outrush of water can lift or eject the obstructions from the funnel. (The surge of water may often produce a water column rising 3 to 4 m above the katavothra level.) As soon as the surge ceases and the springs change into swallow-holes, however, the passage is immediately clogged again, since the external water pressure is now much less than required to force the huge amount of waste swept back to the swallow-hole through the underground passage.

It follows from the above considerations that in poljes flooded by katavothra, floods cannot altogether be prevented, but by suitable cleaning of the swallow-hole and katavothra inlets, by widening the constrictions in the funnels, it would be possible in almost every polje to shorten substantially the duration of floods; the slow drainage of the poljes is invariably due to the short-range obstruction of the swallow-hole inlets, which is relatively easy to eliminate, rather than to the insufficient drainage capacity of the swallow-hole throughout its length. That is, the suitable widening of the mouth of a katavothra, and the elimination of all obstacles to the flow of water in both directions, would not increase the discharge of the katavothra in times of flood, but it would vastly increase its drainage capacity. By such intervention it would be possible to prolong extensively the dry, unflooded periods in those areas that today are inaccessible to cultivation because of their prolonged inundation each year, and this would permit the crops to mature in the fields on the poljes (*Photo 29*).

The classic authors of karst research (Grund, Cvijić, Katzer, O. Lehmann, etc.) did not recognize this possibility of flood control in flooded poljes, and therefore accepted the spontaneous hydrological conditions as the manifestations of uncontrollable forces. The uncritical acceptance of their views has frustated any comprehensive organized measures towards flood control in polje areas. By contrast, we believe that this is one of the most important practical problems of karst research, as the removal of obstructions from the swallow-holes on the polje rims would surely permit extensive surfaces of land to be reclaimed for agriculture in just those barren karst areas where such land is most needed.

One example suffices to shed light upon the economic importance of such works of flood control. According to our calculations, in Yugoslavia alone more than 1000 sq. km of land, unproductive today, could be rendered fertile at low cost and within a very short time (cf. in this respect Fig. 34).

In Hungary, flood hazards in karst regions are much less significant, although the processes involved are the same as in the large karst poljes. Even in the Hungarian B-type karsts, after a large cloudburst or sudden snowmelt the clogged, obstructed inlets of the swallow-holes may be incapable of draining the floods fast enough. At such times, temporary lakes form in the area around and upstream of the swallow-hole, possibly covering roads, buildings, etc. for several days.

One of the memorable floods of the North Borsod Karst was that on 6 August, 1955: the Acheron swallow-hole was incapable of draining the vast amount of water discharged into it, and an extensive temporary lake formed on the surface around it (L. JAKUCS 1956/2). The length of the lake attained 1·5 km in a south-westerly direction, while its width exceeded 600 m at several places. The water was 3 m deep along the highway leading to the cavern entrance, and it took four days for the swallow-hole to drain the accumulated floodwaters (*Photos 30* and *31*).

On the Aggtelek karst, the swallow-hole inlets involved were opened up and/or cleaned some years ago, and flooding by waters dammed up by swallow-hole obstruction was thereby prevented. (The same could be achieved in any other karst region.) The inlet of the Acheron swallow-hole was later opened up to a depth of about 5 m by removing the rubble and boulders filling it, and the floods supplied by the extensive non-karstic drainage area since that time have an unhindered passage into the spacious tunnels of the Baradla Cavern.

Another point to be considered briefly here is the flood hazard near the spring outlets of B-type karsts. The vehemence of the flood once it has entered the cavern is not reduced or delayed: it will appear at the spring

Photo 29. Karst dwellers inhabiting the rim of the Fatničko Polje in Črna Gora, Yugoslavia, who can never be sure that their crops will ripen or be inundated before the harvest. Most peasant households own a boat: in the event of a flood, the boats are used immediately to harvest the crops, even if they are only half-ripe

Photos 30 and 31. Cavern Hostel, Aggtelek, and the extensive flood lake developed in front of it during the overloading of the Acheron swallow-hole on 6 August 1955

Photo 32. Jósvafő village inundated by a flood of B-type karst springs

with undiminished menace, as these springs are in essence the points of outflow to the surface of underground rivers.

Accordingly, if flood control considerations suggest the damming-up of the spring, thereby making its discharge uniform, this undertaking is unlikely to bring the desired result; even if it were possible temporarily to dam up the waters in the underground cavities, the hydrostatic and dynamic pressure of the underground river deprived of its free outflow would be liable, at times of really high floods, to burst the dam, and the impounded mass of water would rush out with an even greater vehemence and volume than in the case of free outflow.

This phenomenon too was convincingly illustrated by the flood of 6 August, 1955 on the Aggtelek Karst. Some decades before, a flood-level spring outlet, active only at times of high flood, draining the stream of the Baradla system at Jósvafő, had been obstructed by a highway fill of substantial mass. This fill could withstand the pressure of the flood in the cavern in the first few minutes, but as the pressure increased while the waters piled up in the cavern system, the plug of the spring outlet was ejected as if by an explosion, and in some minutes a crater some 20 m in diameter was washed out in its place (L. JAKUCS 1956/2, 1957/1). The unimpeded flood soon covered the streets of the village of Jósvafő to a considerable depth (*Photo 32*).

This example is a striking illustration of the fact that damage by high floods in the karst-spring area will be forestalled not by trying to prevent the outrush of the waters to the surface, or to constrict their outlet, but on the contrary, by making the outlet as wide and as unobstructed as possible. Floods caused by karst springs can at best be reduced by narrowing the swallow-hole inlets, at the expense of a longer and more extensive flood in the swallow-hole area. Flood control in a karst region where the spring area and the swallow-hole area are both threatened, involves of necessity the decision as to which is the more acceptable risk of the two. Depending on the decision, the required interference with the intake capacities of the swallow-holes can be projected and performed.

For an illustration of all this let us consider diagram I of *Figure 94*. The map sketch depicts two villages: A and B. Village A is situated in the drainage area, and part of it is inundated periodically by back-flooding from swallow-hole 3. Village B, in contrast, is in the spring-outlet area, but part of it is likewise inundated at times of flood. Our aim is to reduce the flood hazard in both villages. What should be done?

Opening up swallow-hole 3 and thereby ensuring a free passage to the flood waters discharged into it will solve the problem of A, but render the situation at B even worse (cf. diagram II of Fig. 94). The correct procedure, of course, is gradually to plug or to provide with adjustable gates both swallow-holes 1 and 2. By a temporary throttling of these two holes, that is, by letting the floods expand in their uninhabited areas (diagram III of Fig. 94), the peak discharge of the spring at B will be hardly more than the peak intake of the swallow-hole at A, and this discharge will no longer be sufficient to flood the inhabited areas of B. By letting the floods encroach upon the less valuable lands of the drainage areas 1 and 2, we have thus achieved simultaneous flood prevention in both villages.

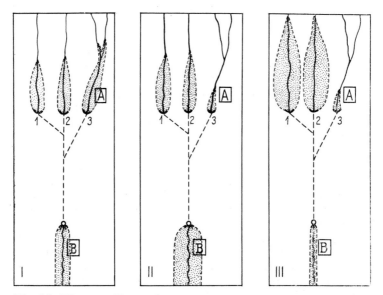

Fig. 94. Diagram illustrating measures taken to protect objects menaced by flood in the swallow-hole or spring sector (for explanation see text)

The problems to be solved are, of course, not always of this type. With an adequate knowledge of the caverns' hydrological systems and the interconnections between the related drainage areas, swallow-holes and springs, however, a karst morphologist will be able to suggest the most reasonable solution for almost every other real problem.

In our discussion so far we have analysed primarily the role of the plugging and reopening of swallow-holes in the context of their influence on flood characteristics, with social usefulness as the main criterion. We shall now briefly point out the consequences of human interference with swallow-holes as reflected by qualitative or quantitative changes in the intensity indicators of karstification.

One of the most important consequences of the activities in question is the intensification of linear erosion in the cavern. Floods in the outer non-karstic drainage areas are able to enter the caverns unimpeded and undelayed, bereft of any occasion to deposit their load, as opposed to the evened-out less extreme floods in the prior period of swallow-hole obstruction. The higher peak discharges in the cavern therefore primarily intensify linear erosion as compared with previous times. The basic consequence of this is that the underground stream incises itself into its own non-karstic or calcareous tufa deposits.

However, at the times of flood relevant to the intensity of streambed erosion, the throughput of water is greater in any cavern section, and thus the streambed section being sculptured is wider than the section cut in the previous phase. (In this connexion it was earlier found (L. Jakucs 1956/1) that the width of a cavern passage in a scour cavern always varies directly as the flood discharges of the stream sculpturing it and as the index of erosion characteristic of the region.)

The obstruction and subsequent clearing of swallow-holes is incidentally a phenomenon repeatedly occurring in scour caverns even without human intervention. This is documented by symmetric terrace grooves on the walls of scour-cavern passages (Photo 33), not to be confused with the asymmetric meandering terraces of opposite passage walls (Fig. 95).

Karst morphologist literature does not distinguish these two fundamental types of forms among the parallel rock grooves of cavern walls, attributing all terraces to the shiftings of the lines of lateral erosion of the streambed (Cholnoky 1917, Roglić 1956, Bögli 1956/1, Droppa 1957, Trimmel 1961, etc.) or to changes in discharge ascribed to changes in climate to explain them (Trombe 1952, Maksimovich 1957/1, Kyrle 1923, Cvijić 1926, Franke 1962, etc.).

Without denying the possible contributions of the above-mentioned causes, we have to point out that none of our investigations in cavern passages have so far revealed cavern rock terraces that could be ascribed beyond doubt to a climatic change. The principal argument against the terraces (even the symmetric ones due to changes in discharge) being due to changes in annual precipitation is that, even within one and the same cavern, the terraces of branches draining different swallow-holes cannot as a rule be made parallel. The non-synchronous development of these terraces in number, position and size is especially conspicuous where two cavern branches meet; if these forms were indeed climatogenetic, then land should

217

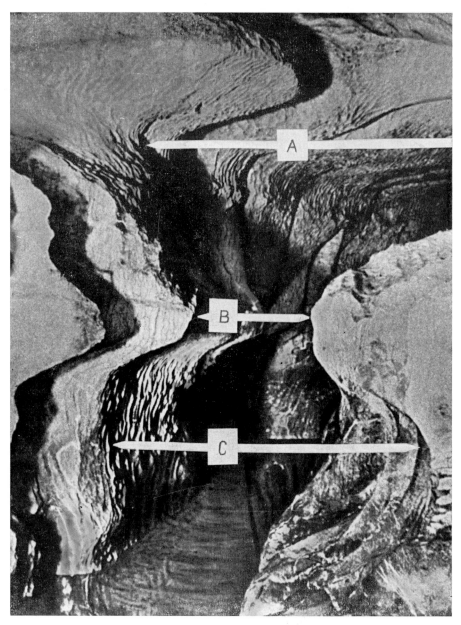

Photo 33. A construction of the passage profile, indicative of the increase and reduction of flood discharges by swallow-hole obstruction (at B) in the Fekete Cavern, Bihar Hill, Transylvania. The sections at A and C, where the streambed was much wider, reflect the fully-open state of the swallow-hole. The present active level of the stream is due to the throttling effect of a partial swallow-hole obstruction (photo by SERBAN)

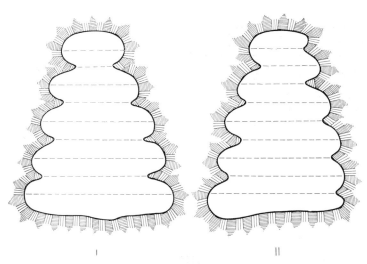

Fig. 95. Symmetrical or flood-discharge terraces reflecting changes in swallow-hole capacity (more seldom also climatic changes) (I) and covariant meander terraces sculptured by uniform maximum discharges (II)

correspond to land, and groove to groove. This is almost never the cause in nature, however (*Fig. 96*).

Naturally, the opening-up of an obstructed swallow-hole inlet also has other consequences for the karst process. Retreating erosion reaching out from the cavern to the surface, for instance, accelerates *the incision of the*

Fig. 96. Confluence of scour-cavern branches with symmetrical terraces: the mismatching at the confluence of the groove terraces indicates the individual, non-synchronous episodes of obstruction and liberation of the holes belonging to the two passages

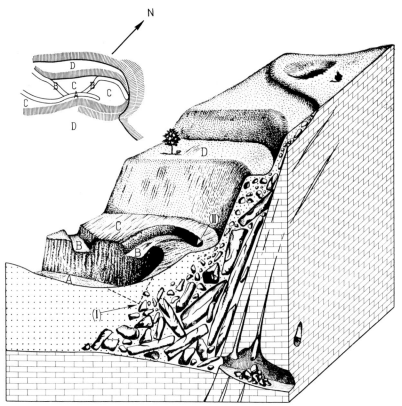

Fig. 97. Block diagram of the Nagy Valley swallow-hole of the Béke Cavern at Aggtelek (double vertical exaggeration). The inset is a ground-plan sketch A — D — terrace levels; I — present swallow-hole; II — flood-level swallow-hole

blind valley adjacent to the swallow-hole. Its bottom may develop degradation-type ravine-like gorges, deeply incised into the flat-surfaced river-laid alluvia deposited during the period of swallow-hole obstruction, thus initiating terrace sculpture in the blind valley.

As a matter of course, the spontaneous evolution of a swallow-hole is composed of repeated episodes of obstruction and reactivation. Hence, the surface valleys leading to the swallow-holes are of necessity terraced. The point to be kept in mind, however, is that these terraces may have no connexion whatever either with climatic changes, or with any other process of riverside terrace sculpture so abundantly discussed in the literature: on the contrary, they are due to a highly specific process accompanying the bathycapture phenomenon of the karst, and we are accordingly justified in regarding them as veritable karst phenomena.

We first recognized and described this special type of karst terrace sculpture in connexion with the Nagy Valley swallow-hole of the Béke Cavern (L. JAKUCS 1953/1), but we have encountered it since in a number of cases both in Hungary (Pénzpatak swallow-hole) and abroad (a fine example is the swallow-hole of the Nevesinje polje in Bosnia) (*Fig. 97*).

220

b) Influence upon the karst process of human interference with karst springs

Our studies have convinced us that interference with the natural outlets of B-type karst springs does not entail permanent changes in spring discharge. The traditional reluctance to develop or regulate such springs is therefore unfounded. Some of the discharge may escape into the surrounding alluvia only if the spring-outlet development involves building a weir and the weir is not cemented to that part of the solid limestone rock which constitutes the aperture of the underground channel.

In a weir-type development, however, when the water in the spring basin is dammed up to a level higher than before, this is likely to have the consequence that the streamload will start to build up natural obstructions in the near-surface syphon sections affected by the back-flooding of the underground streams; the formation of these obstructions takes various times, depending on the rate of coarse-load transport in the stream. This deposit gradually reaches farther and farther back into the mountain as time goes by; it may even plug up the cavern channel altogether, and considerably reduce the discharge capacity of the passage. This may result, especially at times of flood, in a substantial congestion of waters in the cavern portion next to the spring outlet. As a consequence, the higher parts of the cavern cross-section may undergo postgenetic scour and corrosion, with local phenomena of deformation in the surface micromorphology of the rock formations.

At times of flood, the hydrostatic pressure may attain high peak values in the cavern sections filled with the waters congested by the plugs of stream-laid deposits. This further increases the limestone- dissolving potential of the water. The intensified corrosion of the rock gives rise to a rough surface ornamented with sharp crenellations, jagged ridges and lapies microrills. This phenomenon is conspicuous in the portions called "Hell" in the Szabadság Cave at Égerszög, in the lowermost level of the Imre Vass Cavern at Jósvafő, in the Lower Cavern of the Baradla, etc. (*Photo 34*).

In a correctly conceived spring development, then, the weir to be installed must not impede the outflow of water by gravity by giving rise to an artificial syphon upstream from the point where the water emerges from the solid rock and where the weir is to be sited.

Another practicable means of spring development is to lower the outflow level of the spring outlet. In this case, the natural outlet of the emerging water is approached via a trench driven towards the outlet from a point downstream. This method is particularly helpful when the outlet in the solid rock is masked by a substantial volume of scree or other clayey products of mass wasting. The underground stream, entering the lowered open-channel section and matching itself to the new artificial baselevel of erosion, also deepens its underground bed by regressive erosion.

With luck, this activity can lead to the discovery of hitherto unknown caverns (*Fig. 98*). The caverns thus found include the spring cavern of Teresztenye (L. JAKUCS 1953/1, pp. 83—84) and the spring cavern of the Babot Well in the Kecső Valley in Hungary; and the Gombaszög cavern

Photo 34. Limestone roof of a scour channel, corroded by impounded floods ("Castle of Miracles" Cavern, Bihar Hills, Transylvania). The "root lapies" are postgenetic forms alien to the bas c process of passage sculpture (photo by SERBAN)

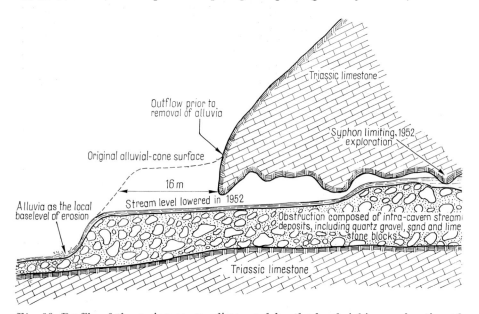

Fig. 98. Profile of the spring cavern discovered by the level-sinking exploration of the B-type karst spring at Teresztenye

222

Photo 35. Gyepü spring near Berzéte, Slovakia; the cavern entry visible in the photo was made accessible by constructing an attack trench that lowered the water table by about 3 metres (photo by ROZLOŽNIK)

(ROZLOŽNIK 1953, VINDIS 1955, L. JAKUCS 1961, pp. 189—193) and the cavern of the Gyepü spring near Berzéte (*Photo 35*) in Slovakia.

The consequences of interference with A-type karst springs are altogether different, as these springs are not as a rule the outflows of linear streams from a single underground channel; on the contrary, they drain the water reserve contained in the wide-ranging communicating rifts, fissures and passages of a three-dimensional rock horizon saturated with water (HORUSITZKY 1942, ALBEL 1950, PÁVAY-VAJNA 1950, SZÁDECZKY-KARDOSS 1957).

The waters tapping this type of karst reservoir in the Transdanubian Hills of Hungary (at Inota, Csór and Tata; and also the spontaneous and provoked inrushes of karst water in the coal and bauxite mines) reveal that in the majority of cases discharges can be augmented by opening up and widening passages, or by increasing the drawdown in the spring outflow area, whereas the reduction of the outflow cross-section (e.g. by cementation) or the elimination of the drawdown of natural springs by damming may

223

reduce or entirely dry up the discharge (KASSAI 1948, SZÁDECZKY-KARDOSS 1950, TAKÁCS 1950, SCHULHOF 1957).

In practice, the damming-up of the karst water table to a higher level by human interference is rather unusual: the opposite case is much more frequent, when a more or less substantial volume of water is drawn off from the karst for a protracted period, either for the purposes of water supply (from karst water shafts, drilled water wells, etc.), or as a catastrophe-prevention measure (pumping to prevent inrushes or to remove the inrush waters), faster than it is recharged by infiltrated precipitation (PÁLFFY 1920/1—2, KESSLER 1954, 1956, L. JAKUCS 1960/2, 1964). As a result, the A-type karst water table (the top boundary of the A-type lenticular zone) may subside in the karst by ten metres or more, entailing the earlier-discussed modifications in the process of erosion (*Fig. 99*).

It may be added that the short-term effects of these interferences with the karst process are restricted to qualitative and quantitative changes in the intensity of karstification in the individual horizons of the karst, and

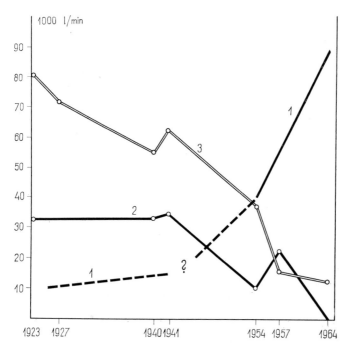

Fig. 99. Lowering of the karst water table in the lenticular zone of an A-type karst owing to pumping in excess of recharge by the long-term average infiltration. Influence of karst-water pumping in the Tatabánya Coal Mines upon the discharge of the Tata springs, 19 km away, between 1923 and 1964 (after WAGENHOFFER 1968)

1 (dashed line) — estimated pumping rates at the coal mines; 1 (full line) — idem, measured; 2 — discharge of Tükör spring at Tata; 3 — discharge of Fényes springs at Tata

possibly in the hydrographic network (such as the drying-up of the Tükör spring at Tata as a result of pumping in the coal mines); however, owing to their short duration on a geological time scale it is too early as yet to look for their morphological consequences.

c) Influence upon the karst process of the regulation of surface and underground stream channel sections

The usual river conservancy works of streambed dredging, the construction of flood-control levels, the cutting-through of meander necks, etc. are seldom applied to karst streams. However, other means of intervention are also frequently employed in the regulation of the drainage network in limestone regions. These include mainly smaller artifical weirs. The local population usually build them in the form of stone or stake dams (possibly combined with wickerwork) for the purposes of driving mills or utilizing water power in some other form.

These small local weirs are built primarily by the populations living along streams draining almost pure A-type karst water (the Korona River in Croatia, the Krka River near Šibenik, etc.) whereas karst rivers carrying B-type waters often lack such power-generating facilities; if there are any, the weirs are installed at the downstream end of a man-made channel (mill-race) branching off the natural streambed (e.g. on the Jósva Creek at Szin, on the river of the Planina Cavern in Slovenia, etc.) with no weir obstructing the river in its entire width (*Fig. 100*).

The logics of the two different approaches to water-power winning, reflected in the spontaneous activity of the local inhabitants, are that the water and streamload discharge features of A- and B-type karst streams are fundamentally different. True authigenic karst rivers draining a practically pure karst-type drainage area have no extreme fluctuations of yield, and almost no bottom load even at times of flood. Hence, bodies of water impounded by man-made dams are not silted up over long periods of time, similarly to the natural karst lakes formed by the rising of tufa weirs (e.g. the Plitvice lakes). A dam in a stream carrying hardly any erosion waste will be long-lived.

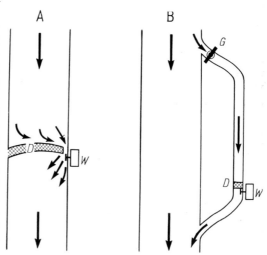

Fig. 100. Basic differences between the installation of power plants (mills, sawmills, etc.) on rivers of A and B-type karsts, respectively, matched to the water and sedimental discharge features of the two types of streams

D — dam or weir; W — installation exploiting water power; G — throughput control (gate)

On the other hand, a weir laid across the entire width of a B-type stream will not bring the desired results, as such a stream tends to exhibit extreme fluctuations and to produce devastating floods; in addition, it moves substantial amounts of load as suspended impurities. Deposited in the pond, this load will fill up the space behind the weir in a very short time.

The solution is provided by an artificial "mill-run" regulated by means of a gate. The gate can be closed at times of flooding to prevent damage by excessive flood erosion (or deposition, for that matter).

Concentrating now on the influence of these human activities upon erosion proper, it is easy to see that, expertly applied, the above measures will have no influence of any practical significance. In an A-type karst stream impounded by a dam, the distribution of calcium carbonate precipitation along the stream course may be displaced (the water overflowing the weir deposits more than the sluggish water in the deep pond behind the weir), but over the brief periods involved even this effect will lack any morphological consequences.

On the other hand, if the stream dammed up is of B-type, this will have a striking short-term consequence in the silting-up of the reservoir behind the dam. In the Baradla cavern of Aggtelek, for instance, or in the adjoining Domica, boating lakes formed by concrete weirs must be dredged at intervals of one or two years, during which periods mud deposits several decimetres thick are laid down by a B-type underground stream, a stream which deposits no sediment elsewhere in the cavern either upstream or downstream of the lakes.

As a surface example, let us mention the "Tengerszem" Lake at Jósvafő (Hungary). Its concrete dam keeps back tens of tons of silt and sand at each flood (*Photo 36*): consequently, the open water surface of the lake, dammed up in 1939, is today not more than one-third of the original. In this context it may be pointed out that a single flood (that of August 1955) was sufficient to advance the delta at the inflow into the lake by about 50 m, encroaching upon the open water by that amount.

It would clearly be unjustified from the above considerations to draw the conclusion that the discharge regulation by impounding B-type streams and the construction of reservoirs on such streams is invariably wrong, as it is precisely in the environs of allogenic rivers of widely fluctuating yield that the construction of large reservoirs is often a necessity. The point is, however, that in the knowledge of the silting-up process just outlined the size of the reservoirs in question should impound as a large a volume as possible compared to the volume of stream-laid deposit to be expected annually. It is in this way that the installation can be longest-lived and most economical.

The relevant calculations and the measurements and recordings on which they are based are beyond the scope of this book, but the problem already has an excellent literature (BOGÁRDI 1955, GAMS 1957, MOSONYI 1948, 1956, NÉMETH 1959, 1963, etc.).

As far as the regulation of streams in karst regions is concerned, another demand arising at times is the cutting of channels into the natural calcareous tufa dams (tetarates). The problem tends to arise in caverns, where

Photo 36. Example of the decay of an artificial lake constructed by damming up a B-type karst stream. The water overflowing the weir of the "Tengerszem" Lake at Jósvafő has left behind all its bottom load: the lake will fill up shortly

the deep lakes dammed up by tufa weirs make passage difficult (Padirac, Béke Cavern, etc.).

In our view, when intervention is considered, the protection of the environment and the preservation of natural values should invariably precede any arguments of expediency. Nevertheless, should intervention be considered imperative, it is necessary to reckon with some consequences concerning the karst process. Of these, the following are the most significant:

1. The slope of the streambed is increased, and so, in consequence, is the velocity of the water and the potential of erosion.

2. Owing to the faster passage of the water through the cavern, it has less time to deposit calcium carbonate, and hence the water is harder in the downstream sections than before regulation.

3. The discharge of the stream is slightly more fluctuating. (It is necessary to emphasize the word "slightly", as the naturally impounded lakes in karst caverns never possess the substantial discharge-regulating influence of a large surface lake (Lac Léman, Lake Balaton, etc.), because the karst lakes in question are valley lakes not wider than a few times the width of the stream discharging into them).

15*

d) Influence upon erosion of artificial dams

In the previous section we pointed out the influence of impounding water upon streamload deposition. In reservoirs constructed in mountainous areas, where dams are usually tall, this process may assume special importance if the streamload and its deposited portion contain a significant percentage of clayey colloidal grains. Infiltration of the water into the rock injects these into the fissures, clogging them in the bottom and flanks of the reservoir basin, thus providing self-insulation against the escape of water. The near-surface fissure network of the rock is thereby removed from the process of karst corrosion, and laid idle under an impermeable layer of silt (*Photo 37*).

The situation is altogether different with reservoirs where the streamload is dominantly coarse gravel and sand, unsuitable for lending impermeability to the reservoir bottom. This problem arises most frequently in mountain

Photo 37. The Rappbode Dam (430 m long and 106 m high) at Wendefurt in the Harz Mountains, capable of impounding 110 million cu. m of water. The streams (Rappbode and Hassel) supplying the reservoir, draining a wooded karst surface, empty substantial amounts of fine silt into the basin; this silt decreases the permeability of the bottom and sides of the basin

Photo 38. The impounded lake of the Grimsel in Switzerland (dammed-up water table at about 1900 m altitude). The streams supplying it, draining a barren high-mountain karst, deliver practically no clayey waste, so that the high-pressure aggressive waters (despite painstaking insulation) continually find new passages of escape through the basin bottom

reservoirs whose catchment area is barren with no plant or soil cover, whereas lower hilly regions with an all-over plant cover, indeed a forest vegetation, belong to the first-mentioned group.

This is precisely why in karstic mountains one of the fundamental tasks connected with the construction of reservoirs in regions where the catchment area is rocky and barren, is the artificial waterproofing of the joints and fissures prior to the filling of the basin, a task usually performed with much care. At the bottom of the basins behind the tall Alpine dams (*Photo 38*) the water may nevertheless find a way of escape through some hidden joint, which under the high hydrostatic pressure prevailing (the depth of water is often about 100 m!) is soon widened into a spacious channel by the increased aggressivity of the water. The rate of escape through this channel grows faster and faster, and in the end a B-type outlet of forced anthropogenic origin may come to exist.

The rock bottom of the reservoir at the same time exhibits signs of intensified corrosion under an active body of standing water. The rock surfaces become rough to the touch and, in keeping with the hidden lithologic and structural features, subsequently develop a set of forms of selective dissolution including pitting, sharp-bordered rills and serrated edges between

229

them. Finally, if the process has ample time to develop and is particularly intense, the limestone may be transformed into a skeleton of cellular-spongy texture.

It is impossible, of course, to formulate a scheme of general validity concerning these problems, and the consequences of any sort of intervention cannot always be accurately foretold. In a fair number of cases it is impossible at the start to assess the presence and distribution of hidden joints, their clogging or otherwise in the post-structural history of the rock, or the way in which they promote infiltration at any given point or instant, all these being a function of the erosional prehistory of the formation. In this context we quote NÉMETH (1959, p. 341): "Any river, and any drainage area or underground aquifer has a separate individuality, whose present is the consequence of a past that can be reconstructed after painstaking investigations. Lacking adequate knowledge of this past it is impossible to infer its future, let alone its reaction to various forms of human interference."

The above examples of anthropogenic intervention in the karst process should be regarded merely as special examples highlighting a few of the myriad lines of interaction between landscape and human activity. However, they do indicate the necessity of proceeding with further investigations into similar problems, and at the same time outline the perspectives of the evolution of our branch of science towards social and practical usefulness.

THEMATIC REVIEW OF THE THESES PUT FORWARD
IN THIS BOOK

The concept of karstification cannot be restricted merely to the erosion by *corrosion of limestone* and other rocks soluble without a residue, as is done in classical geomorphology. The set of karstic relief forms is invariably complex, and expressive of the interactions of the relative contributions and the respective durations of a variety of exogenous and endogenous landscape-forming agencies with the properties of the karstifying base material (the rock).

It is correct to speak of the karstification of any landscape element if the principal part in the sculpture of its set of erosion forms is played by *aqueous dissolution*. The difference between karst-type erosion and any other type or erosion is one of degree, depending on the proportions in which the individual agencies are involved, and hence any rigid delimitation of the karst as a landscape type apart is necessarily subjective. (Any rock, such as granite, sandstone, basalt, etc., may exhibit "classical karst forms", whereas innumerable limestone regions are known where the principal shaping agency was comminution by frost, insolation, wind erosion, etc. rather than corrosion; hence, from the geomorphological aspect, these regions can not be classified as karstic ones, either.)

The definition of the karst concept as a state of evolution (subject to certain conditions) of a mountain-size limestone mass by no means excludes the possibility of *the process of karst evolution* manifesting itself under similar influences and conditions in other rocks similar to limestone in certain respects.

The karst phenomena accessible to study are all merely the outward manifestations of an instantaneous state of a process of internal evolution. The *incessant evolution of the karst*, reflected in its geomorphological aspect, takes place not only on the surface and in the caverns accessible to investigation, but in the entire inaccessible three-dimensional mass of the karst rock; indeed, in four dimensions, with evolution in time as the fourth dimension.

Karstification in nature is an involved, complex process controlled by a multitude of agencies; in addition to aqueous dissolution, it receives contributions in varying proportions from the other agencies of exogenous denudation, but even the qualitative and quantitative parameters of the purely corrosive "classical" karst processes are controlled by several factors

231

each of which is variable in its own right. This broad range of possibilities constitutes the field of *variance of karst.*

Since the carbonate-dissolving potential of water in contact with a rock varies directly as its carbonic acidity, the most important thing to establish in interpreting the corrosion dynamism is the *set of conditions* controlling the absorption of CO_2 and its concentration in the water. Of these conditions, the abundance of CO_2 in the soil gas entering into contact with the water turns out to be the most important: infiltrating waters derived from precipitation, which by their dissolution of limestone essentially control the entire karst evolution, gain their carbon dioxide content (determining the dynamism of corrosion) almost everywhere and always in the top horizons of the soil.

The gas composition of the soil atmosphere reacts rapidly and sensitively to both macro- and microclimatic influences; it tends to exhibit significant differences even within one and the same test site (e.g. within one doline) depending on the type of plant cover supported by the soil, and even on the individual plant species making up the rhizosphere. That is, the rate of karst evolution by corrosion is determined not only by the abundance of precipitation, but primarily by the biological features and other processes of evolution of the soil mantles of varying thickness covering the rock.

Compared with the effects of fluctuation of the CO_2 partial pressure in the soil atmosphere, the temperature fluctuations occurring in nature affect the absorption of CO_2 much less, even in the most extreme cases. Hence, in the assessment of the thermal factors involved in karst development, the interpretation is indirectly a resultant of more intense pedological processes and a soil atmosphere richer in CO_2 due to the higher temperatures, as well as of intensified mass displacement (dissolution intensity) rather than that of the temperature levels typical of the individual terrestrial climatic zones in the direct sense of Schloesing and subsequently of Corbel. In other words, the fact that the *warm rain* of the tropics *can absorb much less CO_2 than the cold melt-waters* of the polar regions is outweighed many times over by the circumstance that the higher temperatures of the tropics *accelerate the dissolution process,* while the more intense inorganic and biogenic processes of soil evolution entail a much *more intense CO_2 production*: overall, therefore, the conditions for the water to be saturated with CO_2 are much more favourable in the tropics.

In a well-defined depth range within the karst, *a zone of high-pressure seeping karst water develops*; here, the water absorbs more and more CO_2 from the gas bubbles swept in by the waters of atmospheric origin: the CO_2 content of these bubbles is injected, so to speak, into the water. This enrichment in CO_2 under increased hydrostatic pressure is highly significant for karst evolution; it results in a sort of secondary aggressivity of karst water, and thereby marks out the vertical position of the zone of karst corrosion at depth (the zone of embryonic cavern formation).

As the pressure acting upon the water and the dissolved gas bubbles descending in the fissure system of the limestone mountain increases, the different absorption coefficients of the gases comprising the bubbles result in the comparatively fast absorption of CO_2, and higher pressure will be ineffective as far as further increases in the total CO_2 content of the solution are concerned. We are therefore convinced that *increase of the hydrocarbonate dissolution potential of karst water is effected essentially by the initial pressure increase* (from 1 to 10 atm, say), whereas higher pressures up to and above 100 atm acting upon the deep karst water will have a much lower influence per unit of pressure increase upon the direct intensification of dissolution. (The process tends to distort the original composition of the gas involved towards *pure nitrogen,* this being the least soluble component.)

Slight *differences in rock texture* within the larger classes of the petrographic system, insignificant from the petrographic aspect, may affect the dynamism and the qualitative consequences of corrosion much more than these larger classes.

It would be too difficult as yet to predict the influence upon limestone solubility of the mineralogical composition of the rock by purely theoretical calculations, probably because the basic types of chemical composition are modified by *elusive features of crystallinity and lattice structure* that may nevertheless significantly affect dissolution dynamism. For instance, compact homogeneous limestones having a soapstone-like appearance and exhibiting conchoidal fractures are much less soluble than the crystalline limestones of otherwise identical mineralogical composition.

Research so far suggests that *the magnesium content of limestone* retards the dissolution of the rock less if it is present not in the form of dolomite or magnesite but dispersed in the lattice of the calcite.

Karst corrosion of *strongly bedded limestones* with an easy parting along the bedding planes is slower than that of an unstratified thick-banked homogeneous limestone. Marked bedding promotes parting along the bedding planes and drainage along them, that is, infiltrating waters tend to contact the least pure surfaces of the rock, richest in pelitic components. In addition to impeding dissolution, this circumstance also entails the accumulation of dissolution residues and the clogging of passages.

If the composition of the rock differs even slightly from that of stoichiometrically pure dolomite, the karst corrosion of crystalline dolomites results in a *mineralic selectivity* as a natural consequence of the different solubilities of the minerals constituting the rock. Karst corrosion may in this case give rise to a peculiar end-product, dolomite rubble and pulverized dolomite. Hence, the comminution and pulverization of dolomite may be a karst phenomenon in the case of crystalline dolomites.

The forms of corrosion typical of limestone karsts are restricted under temperate climates to dolomite areas where either the rock is uncrystallized, or if it is crystalline, its $CaCO_3 : MgCO_3$ ratio is very close to that of pure dolomite. In areas where the dolomite is saccharoidal or even marble-like, there are hardly any dolines or lapies fields even on the most extensive surfaces, and relief forms are determined essentially by the typical alluvial cones of the comminuted rock and by relief elements recalling desert erosion.

Since *the quality of karst corrosion is highly sensitive to rock composition and texture,* the different geomorphological features of dolomite regions sculptured by corrosion are due to a considerable extent to differences in rock texture, finding expression in the macroforms of the relief.

The *dolomite rubble* resulting from karst corrosion is invariably closer in chemical composition to pure theoretical dolomite than to the parent rock of which it is the product.

Dolomite erosion under a warm humid climate excludes the intervention of weathering by comminution and the consequent formation of alluvial rubble cones; under such climates, even phanerocrystalline dolomites react to weathering by corrosion with forms similar to the karst forms of limestone. (Consider for example the forms of the dolomite relief underlying the Cretaceous bauxites of Transdanubia, Hungary.) This situation is due not only to the absence of frost comminution, but also to the circumstance that *the dolomite aggressivity of a warm solution is stronger than its limestone aggressivity,* so that selective corrosion so typical of colder climes is also absent.

The "karstification" of loess is largely a pseudokarstic process. In contrast to the textbook theories, the formation of loess dolines, for instance, is due not to the collapse of cavities in the loess, but to decalcification by corrosion of typical loess, accompanied by pedological alteration (formation of loam and clay) changing the consistency of the loess, and frequently also by local compaction due to phenomena of micro-solifluxion.

Structural preformation of the rock has a profound influence upon the efficiency and localization of *karst corrosion.* This influence is reflected not only in underground karstification but also in surface relief forms, and along the separate lines at that, since the large-scale structural features of a region determine the areal distribution of karst-form groups, and very often also affect the inherent proportions of the facies features of the individual form elements. In certain karst forms, poljes for instance, structural preformation may dominate the morphogeny so much that the poljes in question may not even be classified as karstogenic karst forms, but as structural features, drainageless basins frequently due to graben faulting or other intercolline, possibly folded structures, to which the process of karst erosion contributes only in preservation and further evolution rather than in origin.

Under a cold climate, the calcium carbonate carried in solution and suspension in the streams issuing from karst areas is nearly equal to the amount removed by corrosion. The non-aqueous content of the infiltrating precipitation is controlled by the influence of the *soil atmosphere* and its enriched CO_2 content (that is, the warmer the climate), however, the volume of precipitation influences the difference between the quantities of dissolved and removed material. This may reach the degree, largely typical of today's tropics, where the calcium carbonate removed in the streams is practically insignificant compared with the high-intensity erosion by karst corrosion.

Owing to the near-equality of the rates of corrosion and calcium carbonate removal in solution, cold-climate karsts develop into leached "skeletal karsts", whereas in a tropical karst the dissolved calcium carbonate is precipitated in the deeper horizons or almost at the site of dissolution, which turns these *karsts* into *compact, massive* ones. In these regions, calcium carbonate transportation is largely vertical, and inasmuch as if it is horizontal it is confined to a highly localized small domain.

Karsts of the temperate zones are intermediate between tropical and polar karsts not only in geographic latitude, but also morphogenetically, in the intensity and quality of products of the processes of karst corrosion.

The dynamism of karst corrosion is very different in the different climatic zones. Our calculations suggest the following approximate proportions: the intensity of tropical karstification exceeds that of desert karstification by a factor of 72; the corresponding factors are 6 for Mediterranean, 8 for temperate, and about 12 for high-mountain karstification, all referred to tropical karstification. Within this single parameter, the contributions of the individual genetic factors of karst corrosion vary over wide ranges. In temperate, Mediterranean and tropical karst corrosion, the biogenic CO_2 factor of the soil atmosphere is the most potent aggressive constituent of water. It is followed by the contribution of organic soil acids (humic, huminic acids and root liquor). The contributions of the remaining factors (atmospheric CO_2, CO_2 produced by weathering, inorganic acids) are subordinate in comparison. In high-mountain, periglacial and desert karst corrosion, on the other hand, the CO_2 of atmospheric origin in the solution plays the decisive role, and in the desert even the contribution of the inorganic acids is of significance.

Carbon dioxide of atmospheric origin does not play an important role in karst corrosion except in high mountains, periglacial regions and desert. In the tropical regions it is negligible in comparison with the other factors of karst corrosion. (In the tropics, for example, the biogenic CO_2 is about 100 times more effective than the atmospheric!)

Corrosion attributable to CO_2 produced by inorganic pedological processes and to other *inorganic compounds*, mostly acids, is 2 to 10 times more effective in calcium carbonate dissolution in the tropical zone than in any other zone; with the exception of the polar zone, it slightly exceeds the effectiveness of atmospheric CO_2.

The wide-ranging contributions to karst corrosion of *the biogenic CO_2 produced in the soil and of the soil organic acids* clearly indicate these factors to be highly climate-sensitive: as far as intensities are concerned, they are the essential carriers of karst corrosion over most of the earth's land surface. Their role becomes significant even in high-mountain and polar karsts as soon as the first lichen appears on the rock surface, or even the most languid bacterium in the soil. In the temperate and Mediterranean karst processes, on the other hand, they become the decisive factor of karstification, and as the biosphere (especially the plant cover) of the ground surface grows denser and its seasonally-controlled biological cycles attenuate, so their erosional efficiency grows.

Natural karst corrosion of limestone rocks over most of the earth's land area is simply the formal imprint upon the soluble parent rock of the phenomena of biological and chemical evolution of the soil covering the rock.

The dispersed calcium carbonate content of *soil ice in subpolar karsts* is less than that of the water from which the ice formed. The residual liquid is thus enriched in dissolved substances. In zones with a frequent alternation of freeze and thaw, this process may give rise to strikingly hard ground waters. Even these precipitate no calcium carbonate, however, since ionic diffusion in the solution is so slow at the prevailing near-frost temperatures that by the time the escape of gas could significantly upset the calcium carbonate equilibrium, the concentrated residual solution also freezes in most cases.

Thermokarst dolines are not formed by corrosion; they are temporary relief forms due to a special type of solifluxion accompanying the partial thawing of frozen ground in the summer. Genetically, this is at best a pseudokarst phenomenon. We consider the *sölle* of the North European *sandur surfaces* and the Canadian *pitted plains* to be longer-lived variants of these forms.

In high-mountain karsts, forms of classical karst corrosion visible on the surface are always scarcer than their actual rate of formation would justify, because other, more dynamic processes of erosion, more consistently operative in these regions, tend to efface the karst process.

Owing to intense *glacial erosion* in the Pleistocene, the underground karst phenomena of high-mountain karsts are as a rule older than the superficial phenomena, because they reflect the karst evolution of earlier periods.

Since *the rate of calcium carbonate dissolution varies inversely as the temperature*, the depth of rock sculptured by corrosion is larger in a temperate karst, let alone a tropical one than in a periglacial karst. This is why the formation of very deep corrosional shaft caverns (avens) is typical of subnival (high-mountain) karsts or, almost equivalent as regards the efficiency of karstification, of the karsts formed periglacially in low-mountain regions. That is, the origin of the inactive deep aven funnels of the Pyrenees, Dinaric Alps, Carpathians, Jailas, etc. must necessarily be dated to the episodes of Pleistocene glaciation.

Our studies into climatic karst morphogeny have revealed *the formal features* to be *closely dependent upon the quantitative parameters of the factors involved*. Climatic conditions directly or indirectly controlling the increase or decrease of pCO_2 determine the set of forms produced by the intermediary of corrosion dynamism. Surface temperatures, governing among other features the rates of absorption and dissolution reactions, influence the nature of the forms even in the depth of the karst mass. The duration of the karst process also plays a role in landform control, primarily by the intermediary of the total, integral volumes of the factors of erosion involved in the process.

The dominant feature of karst corrosion *in the temperate and Mediterranean zones* is a marked seasonal control of the nature and dynamism of the processes. It seems probable that the landform-controlling *role of microclimatic factors* is most efficient in the temperate zone. Owing to the climatic extremes typical of this zone, to the frequent alternation of freeze and thaw in the winter, producing large amounts of rubble lending considerable erosional efficiency to stream action, and to the frequent vehement floods outside the season of vegetation (in the Mediterranean zone), the formation of scour caverns is most intense in this zone of the earth's surface.

The local variance in *thickness of the humus-rich soil covering the tropical karsts* also contributes in a direct relation to the control of corrosion dynamism:

— In places where the humus is thicker, the biologically productive zone is more extensive vertically: the conditions of biogenic CO_2 production and accumulation are more favourable; further, the ground water is in more prolonged contact with the soil atmosphere.

— Thicker soil has a greater rain absorption and storage capacity, so that it can imbibe more of a sudden downpour than can a thin carpet of soil. Hence, a limestone surface underlying a thicker layer of soil is overall corroded by more water richer in CO_2; again, the release of water from the soil towards the rock is more uniform.

— At time of intense evaporation, a thin soil dries out sooner and hence more often than a thick one. Its phytedaphon in particular is therefore poorer in species, being essentially restricted to eurythermal ones resistant to fluctuations in humidity and the concomitant substantial fluctuations in temperature. To all this it must be added that drier soils are better aerated and hence less suited for CO_2 accumulation.

Within any given microspace, the corrosive karst process is invariably determined by the *microclimatological parameters* prevailing, and these of course do not depend only on the macroclimate of the area. The process of karst erosion in a region, then, should be interpreted as a statistic resultant of episodes of erosion in a mosaic of microspaces not necessarily similar in behaviour.

237

In karstification under a soil cover, where the processes of surface planation lending a subareal scope to any other type of erosion (erosion by wind,
water, etc.) cannot exert an influence, innumerable minute spots of different
erosion dynamics exist side by side even within the smallest landscape
unit. These may be of square metre, square centimetre or even square
millimetre size. Each of these microspaces, distinguished from its neighbours in corrosion dynamism, develops its appropriate set of microforms,
which give rise overall to the form types of traditional karst morphology
such as the lapies field, the doline, etc. The form and aspect of a karst
doline are thus to a substantial extent the formal products of the array of
its particular microclimatic spaces.

It would of course be entirely wrong to infer that the evolution, nature
and arrangement of macroforms in a karst is controlled exclusively by a
statistical summation of the partial processes in the microfacies. In reality,
there is a two-way interrelationship: it is the zonal macroclimate, the lithology,
topography, structure, hydrography, etc. of the region that determine the
features, proportions and distribution of the microclimatic spaces and their
associations. That is, the processes of erosion do take place in a microspace
mosaic, but this mosaic is determined by one or more higher systems, the
fundamental features of which are no longer composed by addition of
the partial features of the mosaic elements.

By the intermediary of the appropriate *microclimatic features of solar
irradiation,* temperature and soil humidity fluctuations, *differences of
exposure* according to the points of the compass of adjacent karst-surface
slopes entail significant differences in the life of their respective soil covers,
especially as regards the local factors controlling the CO_2 balance. And since
the CO_2 production and overall CO_2 concentration level of the soil is the
principal factor controlling both the aggressivity of precipitation seeping
through it and the local intensity of karst corrosion, exposure according to
the compass is in the final analysis an important quantitative regulator
of karst erosion. This is why the various flanks of a given doline differ in
rates of karstic erosion, the asymmetry of dolines being due primarily to
differences in microspace parameters rather than to lithologic factors
(notably the orientation of the strike and dip of the bedding), as assumed
by Cholnoky and his contemporaries. (This is why the axes of asymmetry
of dolines are parallel over entire mountain regions, quite independently of
the bedding orientation in various limestone sequences.)

Series of measurements aimed at exploring the features of CO_2 content in
adjacent karstic microspaces of different bio- and climatic specifications
have given the following *results*:
— In the exposures studied, at any depth down to the 20 cm limit
accessible to the equipment used the CO_2 content of the soil atmosphere
under a plant cover has at any point examined a specific daily course which,
under favourable conditions of soil moisture, is in a sensitive and approximately direct relationship to the course of the soil temperature graph.
— Fluctuations in the CO_2 content of the soil gas are more extreme in
southerly than in northerly exposures in the northern hemisphere.

238

— Even a slight breeze lowers the CO_2 concentration of the soil gas considerably, not by throttling CO_2 production in the soil but by promoting the aeration of the soil's pore space.

— Aeration by the wind is the slower and the less efficient, the more moist the soil.

— In the topsoil zone directly wetted by infiltrating rain, the rain absorbs the entire CO_2 content of the soil gas immediately on infiltration.

— In the deeper soil layers not affected by direct infiltration, the CO_2 content of the pore gas starts to increase abruptly directly after the rainfall, and the process may result in extremely high concentrations compared with the usual run of values. This inversion of the CO_2 content of the soil is presumably due to a strong swelling in the wetted topsoil, providing a seal which prevents the escape by natural aeration of the gaseous products of metabolism in the deeper soil layers.

— Under favourable conditions of soil humidity, the CO_2 concentration may be higher in the topsoil — especially in southerly exposures — than in the deeper soil layers.

— Simultaneous recordings of CO_2 production on slopes of easterly and westerly exposures almost invariably exhibit marked differences. On a day with sunshine throughout, the daily CO_2 turnover of the westerly facing slope of a doline is conspicuously retarded in comparison with the easterly slope.

— CO_2 gas levels in soils under a forest are almost always much higher than under a lawn association with no arborescent plants. This is to be attributed to the following principal circumstances: 1. Humidity in a forest soil is much more favourable and uniform than in soil under a steppe lawn. 2. The forest soil is protected from the wind by the foliage. 3. The forest soil is usually covered by a horizontally stratified layer of vegetal litter, which can impede soil aeration to a considerable extent. 4. The deep and extensive rhizosphere of arborescent plants appreciably increases the depth of the bioactive soil zone, most important for subcutaneous CO_2 production, as well as the edaphon number per unit surface.

— Soil gas most favourable for the promotion of the karst process is encountered on Hungarian karsts under oak and beech woods. Gas production under karst shrub woods is much less, and that under steppe lawns even poorer. The CO_2 content of the soil is much higher even under a pine forest than under a steppe vegetation. Somewhat surprisingly, peak CO_2 concentrations in the rhizosphere of a lawn association were encountered under *Nardus stricta*, a species partial to cool wet places, rather than under the species of *Festuca* and *Carex* studied in much more favourable exposures.

Depending on whether or not the drainage network of a karst carries waters flowing in from alien non-karstic areas, it is necessary to distinguish *B-type (allogenic) and A-type (authigenic) karsts*. In the hydrography of an authigenic karst, only the precipitation seeping in through the karst surface is available as a fundamental genetic factor, whereas in an allogenic karst linear streams of non-karstic surfaces also contribute to erosion.

In nature, only the authigenic hydrological character may appear as a *pure type*, the geomorphological facies of an allogenic karst invariably exhibiting hydrological and formal features of the A-type in addition to the B-type ones.

In a vertical profile of any authigenic karst, *four* functionally different depth *zones* can be distinguished. Uppermost of these is the *zone of infiltration*, where the waters are aggressive and effect limestone dissolution. The depth of this zone is seldom more than 20 m in the majority of European karsts. In the next zone below, the *gravity zone*, water in the fissure systems still filtrates downward, but having attained calcium carbonate–carbonic acid equilibrium it dissolves no more limestone. Arriving at either an *impermeable horizon* or a karst water table (the top boundary of the zone saturated with karst water, whose position is determined by the local base-level of erosion), the water moves on under the laws of hydrodynamics and drawdown governing its behaviour in a three-dimensional connected system of communicating vessels under hydrostatic pressure, rather than under the direct influence of gravity. Beneath the first two zones there is a *third zone* where water motion is horizontal in a statistical resultant, and directed towards the local baselevel of erosion. This zone is convex both upwards and (provided this is not prevented by an impermeable underlying formation) also downwards, and is consequently called the lenticular zone. Its thickness depends on the state of advance of karstification by corrosion, the horizontal extent of the karst mass, etc. In the *lenticular zone* water is under hydrostatic pressure: for this reason, and owing to mixing corrosion, it becomes aggressive once again. In the rock mass, if any, beneath the lenticular zone, the water stagnates and performs no dissolution. This zone is accordingly called the *inactive deep karst.*

Doline sculpture is restricted to the uppermost zone, the zone of infiltration; its component processes include surface corrosion of the rock, the substantial widening of its fissure grid, the subsidence of the ground surface by collapse and the repeated closing up of fissures as a result.

The zone of gravity does not affect the quality of karst erosion, but its height has a considerable influence on the duration of karst erosion up to complete denudation.

Secondary dissolution in *the lenticular zone*, especially near its upward-convex top boundary, gradually gives rise to a network of caves due to corrosion, filled throughout their period of activity with water under pressure.

A relative rise of the local baselevel of erosion during the process of karst erosion shortens the duration of the erosion period; it also displaces the network of caves in the former lenticular zone into the inactive deep karst. As a result, *zones of a high karst-water storage* capacity come about in the deep karst. Hitting these in the course of mining results in catastrophic *inrushes of water*. These hazardous horizons have already brought much

240

unforeseen damage in Hungarian coal mining. It would therefore be worth-while to carry out a karst morphological analysis in the mining regions thus afflicted, as this would permit an approximate assessment of the present position of the down-faulted former lenticular zones.

The relative subsidence of the baselevel of erosion during karstification pro-longs the time span required for the karst planation. The uplifting and inactivation of the former lenticular zone makes accessible the caves due to pressure and mixing corrosion.

The typical features of *caves due to secondary dissolution in the lenticular zone,* indicate the processes of their origin and are as follows.
— The entry to the cave (the former spring outlet) is higher than the rest of the cave passages, and access to the more or less horizontal passages requires climbing down the ancient spring tunnel.
— The caves are never of the transit ("through") type.
— The caves exhibit no streambeds, terraces due to erosion, or conspic-uous bottom or roof planes. Ground plans are labyrinthine, with narrower passages formed by corrosion connecting more spacious halls also due to corrosion. The bottom levels of the cavities do not fall into a well-defined surface.
— Structural preformation is reflected to a considerable extent in the cave's ground plan.
— Dripstone formation in the corrosional passages of authigenic karsts is always less intense than in the scour passages in the active lenticular zones of allogenic karsts.

In the first stage of evolution of an allogenic karst, streams penetrating the area from the non-karstic surroundings continue to incise valleys by linear erosion of the karst surface. Subsequently, once the three-dimensional system of water passages in the karst has developed, the surface valleys are tapped from below by *underground passages (bathycapture),* and from then on the linear valley sculpture by the stream is displaced underground, where it contributes to cavern sculpture.

If the karst mass is covered by an impermeable cover resistant to erosion, hindering to a great extent areal karstic infiltration and consequently also the formation of corrosion cavities, or if valley incision is too fast, the valleys epigenetically inherited from the non-karstic surface may even reach down to the karst water table prior to any occasion for bathycapture. Most of the deep rifts in karst areas are due to such a process rather than to cavern collapse.

When, subsequent to bathycapture, *allogenic waters* first *appear* in the passages of the lenticular zone, the further widening of the passages is taken in hand by upward scour, eroding the rocky roof of the confined stream up to a level where flow into a free water table is made possible by the relative position of the spring outlet and the flow conditions in the underground channels.

The evolution of scour channels in a karst results in the silting-up of the deeper-lying cavities of the lenticular zone. A-type karstification is thrown back thereby into an earlier stage of the denudation process. This necessitates the evolution of a new, more convex (B-type) lenticular zone whose axis of drawdown is already the allogenic scour channel.

Gravel terraces in allogenic caverns of the confined-karst type are relics of accumulations associated with the process of upward scour rather than with the deepening of the passage. In such channels, only the roof is a horizontal plane, whereas the bottom profile is irregular, a chaos of depressions and ridges buried in stream-laid sediment, and continuing downward in a network of labyrinthine passages towards the corrosional cavities of the former A-type lenticular zone.

The conspicuous presence of *aligned dolines* on a karst surface may indicate that the karst in question was more or less covered and confined at the beginning of its erosional process; the traces of the dolines usually follow the traces of former stream valleys caused by linear erosion, epigenetically inherited from the time when the karst was still buried. Structural preformation, if any, has determined the alignment only in so far as it controlled the drainage pattern in the non-karstic formation originally covering the karst mass.

Aligned dolines are invariably older and deeper-lying than individual dolines, and they are usually larger and better developed.

If the aligned dolines contain more voluminous non-karstic deposits than the individual ones, this is a sure sign that the arrangement of karst forms has been preformed by streambed erosion. At the bottoms of such dolines, the micromorphology of the limestone rock buried in the sediment often exhibits traces of scour by a linear watercourse (terraces, etc.).

Retreating underground evolution in the karst under a limestone valley carrying an allogenic stream may lead to repeated, retreating episodes of bathycapture. This converts the valley to a *multi-stage string of swallow-holes*. The process keeps on repeating itself until the youngest swallow-hole attains the limit of the karstic rock mass. Thereafter, retreating erosion reaching out to the surface from the deeper-lying cavern cuts down the non-karstic surface adjacent to the karst mass, resulting in time in its insular emergence as an island.

The cross-sections of scour cavern passages reflect the entire mechanism of evolution of the karst. Passages of triangular section are indicative of their having been active ever since the onset of karstification: accordingly, there are no aligned doline strings above them. On the other hand, aligned dolines appear as a rule above any passage of truncated, trapezoidal cross-section.

The general criteria of allogenic (B-type) *caverns are as follows.* Passages formed simultaneously are almost coplanar; they slope from the swallow-

242

hole towards the spring outlet gradually. Their ground plans most resemble the drainage pattern of a surface river: there are spacious main branches and less wide tributaries joining them. They invariably include a streambed, which may be active with a stream in it, or inactive. The cross-sections of the passages are uniform without abrupt extremes in the middle section of any given cavern branch, apart from local deformations due to collapses or differences in lithology. Side walls exhibit horizontal, parallel groove terraces, as well as conchoidal depressions due to cavitation. Kettles due to erosion are frequent. The rate of dripstone formation is much faster, especially in the juvenile phase of the cavern, than in those caves sculptured by corrosion in an authigenic karst. Their streambed fill is usually composed of waste different from the composition of the rock the passage has been cut in, and most often even of a non-karstic composition. Their tallest, widest halls are in the vicinity of the swallow-hole, as it is there that the abrupt drop in the steep streambed entails the most intense downward incision, and the underground branches of the swallow-holes of different periods join. If the baselevel of erosion subsided during cavern evolution, these branches exhibit a digitation (a three-dimensional delta) near the spring outlet. In such cases, there are also halls of extreme size where these passages diverge.

B-type (allogenic) karst erosion is simply the manifestation, with a number of special features, of a non-karstic process of relief sculpture, normal linear erosion, in the depth of the karst. The presence or otherwise of this process in a karst region is purely accidental, depending primarily on the relationship of the karst to its non-karstic environment, and it is not an inevitable stage in the evolution of any karst. The classical interpretation of karstification as the corrosive erosion of limestone did not take into account the possible manifestation of this influence of the environment, nor its morphogenetic consequences, but considered authigenic karstification solely. This is one of the reasons why *the classical definition of the karst concept* must be assessed as too narrow, and unsuited for the interpretation of the full range of phenomena, since by strictly adhering to this viewpoint it would be necessary to exclude from the karst concept the largest-scale and most majestic cavern formations encountered in the karst depths throughout the world.

The karst process can be most intensely affected by a *variety of human interferences and social activities*. However, their formal consequences are not always measurable, since their duration is too short on a geological time scale. They affect the trends of relief evolution fundamentally and recognizably by initiating a "cultural erosion" of an entirely new nature, which then results in a landscape different from any known result of spontaneous evolution.

Degradation resulting in the *barrenness of the karst* completely changes the set of forms of *lapies fields*. According to our observations, the phenomenon is so regular that this "lapies metamorphosis" in itself permits a fair estimate of the duration of degradation.

The drippings of water in caverns of a comparatively uniform yield all the year round invariably underlie forest-covered surfaces, whereas the stalactites whose yields fluctuate markedly underlie barren areas almost without exception. Another feature closely related to changes in the plant cover above caverns is the colour of dripstones. Degradation is usually accompanied by a considerable enrichment of clayey material in the dripstones and in the cavern deposits.

In cavern sections underlying forest, dripstone growth is usually many times faster than under a degraded plateau.

Under a karst in the process of degradation, *the discharges of karst springs* grow more and more irregular, and so also does the chemical composition of the water. Afforestation in the catchment areas of the karst springs used to supply habitations favourably affect this process.

A study of the hydrological features of regularly inundated poljes in Yugoslavia suggests that the observed prolonged floods are due to the *asymmetric valve action of the katavothra.* Hence, even though flooding cannot be completely eliminated, it would be possible to reduce the duration of the inundations with comparatively little effort. To do so, it would be sufficient to eliminate the assymetry in the operation of the katavothra, simply by removing the obstructions composed of driftwood, etc. in the katavothra apertures. In Yugoslavia alone, the measures proposed would render cultivable about 1000 sq. km of currently fallow land at a comparatively low cost.

By the *geomorphological variance of karstification* we mean the influence of the karst upon the process of its own karstification. The regressive action by which a set of karst forms, once sculptured, can affect the complex of processes operative in its further evolution are legion. Hence, karst forms, as well as the forms characteristic of any other type of relief, are not mere passive products of a set of processes, but highly active indirect factors of relief evolution. That is, the recent set of forms of the relief is not only a mirror reflecting the preceding sequence of landscape evolution, but also a dynamism-controlling factor affecting the events of present and future landscape evolution.

REFERENCES

ABEL, G. (1961/1): Die Erkundung, Befahrung und Vermessung von Höhlen. Österreich. *Hochschuhlzeitung*, Juli 1, Wien.

ABEL, G. (1961/2): Definitionen bei Konkretionen und Höhleneis. *Symp. Int. Spel.*, Varenna—Como.

ABSOLON, K. (1909): Problem podzemnich toku Punkvy y dejinném svém vyvoji . . . *Vestn. Klubu Prirodoved. v. Prostejove.*

ABSOLON, K. (1911): *Kras moravsky a jeho svet.* Praha.

ABSOLON, K. (1914): *Führer durch die Mazocha und die neuen Tropfsteingrotten Punkwaund Katharinenhöhle.* Brünn.

ABSOLON, K. (1970): *Moravsky Kras I—II.* Academia Praha.

Actes du Colloque International de Karstologie et de Spéléologie (Languedoc, Rouergue, Quercy, Périgord). 21—25 août 1971, *CRDP de Caen*, 126 p., 1973.

AGADZHANOV, A. M. (1947): *Gidrogeologiya i gidraulika podzemnykh vod.* Moscow.

ALBEL, F. (1950): Újabb elgondolások a karsztvízkérdéssel kapcsolatban (Recent ideas concerning the karst water problem). *Hidrológiai Közlöny*, Nos 11—12, Budapest.

ALLISON, V. C. (1923): The growth of stalagmites and stalactites. *Journ. of Geol.*, Vol. 31, Chicago.

AMBRUS, GY. (1965): Különböző expozíciójú lejtők talajhőmérsékleti vizsgálata egy középbérci töbörben (Soil temperature recordings on slopes of various exposures in a doline on Középbérc, Bükk Hills, Hungary). *B. Sc. thesis, manuscript.* Climatological Institute of A. József Univ., Szeged, Hungary.

ANELLI, F. (1957): *Castellana, arcano mondo sotteraneo in terra di Bari.* Puttignano.

ANELLI, F. (1958): Nomenclatura italiana dei fenomeni carsici. *Le Grotte d'Italia*, S. 3, II. Castellana–Grotte.

ANGERMAYER, E. (1959): *Die Eisriesenwelt im Tennengebirge.* Salzburg.

APRODOV, V. A. (1948): Some theoretical problems of karstification. *Izv. Akad. Nauk SSSR, Ser. Geol.–Geofiz.*, Vol. 12, Moskva.

AUBRECHT, K. (1963): Excentriken in Österreich und die Excentriqueshöhle bei Erlach. *Akten III. Int. Kongr. f. Speläologie*, Bd. II., Sekt. 1, Wien.

AUJESZKY—BERÉNYI—BÉLL (1951): *Mezőgazdasági meteorológia* (Agricultural meteorology). Budapest.

BACHINSKY—DUBLYANSKY—STENGELOV (1964): Krivchenskaya "Kristalnaya" peshchera v gipsakh Podolii. *Peshcheri*, No. 4, Perm.

BACSÓ, N. (1959): *Magyarország éghajlata* (The climate of Hungary). Budapest.

BACSÓ—ZÓLYOMI (1934): Mikroklíma és növényzet a Bükkfennsíkon (Microclimates and vegetation on the Bükk Plateau). *Időjárás*, Vol. X, pp. 177—196, Budapest.

BALÁZS, D. (1959/1): A jangsói Piljendung barlangjai (Caverns of the Piljendung in Yangsho). *Karszt- és Barlangkutatási Tájékoztató*, Dec., Budapest.

BALÁZS, D. (1959/2): A trópusi karszt terminológiai problémái (Problems of karst terminology in tropical regions). *Ibid.*, Nov., Budapest.

BALÁZS, D. (1960/1): Barlangi légáramlás napi járása nyáron (Daily fluctuations of the air current in a cavern in summer). *Ibid.*, Jan., Budapest.

BALÁZS, D. (1960/2): Földalatti folyók Dél-Kujcsouban (Underground rivers in southern Kweichow). *Ibid.*, July–Aug., Budapest.

BALÁZS, D. (1960/3): A Délkínai-karsztvidék vízrajza (Hydrography of the South China Karst). *Hidrológiai Közlöny*, No. 6, Budapest.

BALÁZS, D. (1961): A Délkínai-karsztvidék természeti földrajza (Physical geography of the South China Karst). *Földrajzi Közlemények*, Budapest.

245

BALÁZS, D. (1962/1): A karsztok elterjedésének azonális és zonális feltételei (Zonal and azonal conditions of the areal distribution of karsts). *Karszt és Barlang*, Jan., Budapest.

BALÁZS, D. (1962/2): Skandinávia karsztbarlangjai (Karst caverns of Scandinavia). *Ibid.*, Febr., Budapest.

BALÁZS, D. (1963/1): Karsztgenetikai problémák (Problems of karst genesis). *Földrajzi Értesítő*, No. 4, Budapest.

BALÁZS, D. (1963/2): A holttengeri tekercsek barlangjai (Caves of the Dead Sea Scrolls). *Karszt és Barlang*, Jan., Budapest.

BALÁZS, D. (1964): A vegetáció és karsztkorrózió kapcsolata (Relationship of plant cover to karst corrosion). *Ibid.*, Jan., Budapest.

BALÁZS, D. (1965): A karsztkorrózió általános vonatkozásai (General chemical relationships of karst corrosion). *Ibid.*, Jan., Budapest.

BALÁZS, D. (1966): A keveredési korrózió szerepe a karsztosodásban (Role of mixing corrosion in karstification). *Hidrológiai Közlöny*, No. 3, Budapest.

BALÁZS, D. (1968): Karst regions in Indonesia. *Karszt- és Barlangkutatás*, May, Budapest.

BALÁZS, D. (1973): Relief types of tropical areas. *IGU Symp. of Karst Morphogenesis*, Papers, Hungary, pp. 16–32.

BALKOV, V. A. (1964): Vliyaniye karsta na vodny balans i stokn (The influence of karst on the water budget and on flow). *Uch. Zap., Permsk. Gos. Univ.*, 112, Perm.

BALLENEGGER, R. (1953): *Talajvizsgálati módszerkönyv* (Textbook of soil testing methods). Budapest.

BALLENEGGER—DI GLÉRIA (1962): *Talaj- és trágyavizsgálati módszerek* (Methods of soil and manure testing). Budapest.

BALSAN, L. (1950): *Grottes et abîmes des Grands Causses*. Millau.

BARANOV, I. I. (1940): Beobachtungen über das Gefrieren des Wassers. *Ref. Neues Jahrb. f. Miner.*, II.

BARRÈRE, P. (1951): La morphologie karstique en Espagne. *Rev. Géogr. de Pyr. et du Sud-Ouest.*, XXII.

BARRÈRE, P. (1964): Le relief karstique dans l'ouest des Pyrénées centrales. *Rev. Belge de Géol.*, 88, pp. 9–62, Brussels.

BÁRTA, J. (1972): Jaskyna Certova pec pri Radosine. *Zbornik Múzea Slovenského Krasu*, Rocnik X, pp. 73–85.

BASKOV—KORNUTOVA (1959): Karstoviye yavleniya v Yuzhnoy Yakutii (Karst phenomena in southern Yakutsk). *Materialy Vses. Geol. Inst.*, Novaya Ser., Obshch. Ser., 24.

BAUER, F. (1953): Verkarstung und Bodenschwund im Dachsteingebiet. *Mitt. d. Höhlenkommission*, Jg. 1, Wien.

BAUER, F. (1958): Nacheiszeitliche Karstformen in den österreichischen Kalkhochalpen. *Actes du Congr. Int. de Spél.*, Bari–Lecce–Salerno, Vol. I., Sect. 1.

BAUER, F. (1964): Kalkabtragungmessungen in den österreichischen Kalkhochalpen. *Erdkunde*, Vol. 18, Bonn.

BÁRÁNY, I. (1967): Der Einfluss des Niveauunterschiedes und der Exposition auf die Lufttemperatur in einer Doline im Bükk-Gebirge. *Acta Climatologica Szegediensis.* Vol. VII., Szeged.

BECK, TH. (1968): *Mikrobiologie des Bodens*. München–Basel–Wien.

BEHREND, F. (1924): Über die Bildung von Eisen- und Manganerzen durch deren Hydroxidsole auf Verwitterungslagerstätten. *Journ. d. Prakt. Geol.*, 32.

BEKEY, I. G. (1914): A vecsembükki zsombolyok [The avens (doline wells) of Vecsembükk Hill (NE Hungary)]. *Turisták Lapja.*

BENICZKÝ, V. (1950): *Slovenské jaskyne*. Sv. Martine.

BERNASCONI, R. (1960): Contribution à l'étude du Mondmilch. *Part I: Stalactite*, No. 3, Sion, 1957. — *Part II: Rass. Spel. Ital.*, No. 2, 1959. — *Part III: Stalactite*, No. 4, Sion, 1960.

BERNASCONI, R. (1967): Il deposito chimico del carbonato di calcio in relazione con il fenomeno dello stillicidio. *Rass. Spel. Ital.*, Vol. XIX, Fasc. 1–2, Como.

BERTALAN, K. (1958): Magyarország nemkarsztos eredetű barlangjai (Non-karstic caves in Hungary). *Karszt- és Barlangkutatási Tájékoztató*, Jan.–June, Budapest.

BIESE, W. (1931): Über Höhlenbildung: Entstehung der Gipshöhlen am südlichen Harzrand und am Kyffhäuser. *Abh. Preuss. Geol. Landesanst.*, Berlin.

BIESE, W. (1956): Über Karstvorkommen in Chile. *Die Höhle*, No. 7, Vienna.
BILLINGS, M. P. (1942): *Structural geology*. New York.
BIROT, P. (1959): Problèmes de morphologie carstique. *Annal. de Géogr.*, Vol. 63, Paris.
BIROT, P. (1966): Le relief calcaire. *Centre de Documentation Universitaire*, p. 236, Paris.
BLEAHU—RUSU (1964): The karst of Rumania — brief outlook. *Rev. Roumaine Géol. Géophys. Géograph. Sér, Géogr.*, 12 (L), pp. 193–202.
BLÜTHGEN, J. (1964): *Allgemeine Klimageographie*. Berlin.
BOČEK, A. (1922): *Moravsky kras*. Praha.
BOGÁRDI, J. (1955): *A hordalékmozgás elmélete* (Theory of stream-deposit movement). Budapest.
BOGOMOLOV, G. V. (1951): *Osnovy gidrogeologii*. Moskva.
BORBÁS, I. (1934): A Szépvölgy és barlangjai morfológiája [Morphology of Szép Valley (Budapest) and its caverns]. *Barlangvilág*, Budapest.
BOROVYEV—YEGOROV—KISELYEV (1951): *Rukovodstvo k laboratorno-prakticheskim zanyatiyam po zemlevedenyu*. Chapters 1–4, Moskva.
BOSCOLO—MONTOVANI (1971): La Gruta de la querra. Efecto del carsismo en los Cerros Béricos. *L'Universo*, Vol. 51, No. 5, pp. 1195–1206, Firenze.
BOTS, S. G. (1957): *Formy reliefa morozno-merzlotnogo i termokarstogo proisozdeniya*. Moskva.
BOUTRY—DEVOS (1970): Vue générale de la grotte. *L'électron, Exploration Italo-Belge de la Grotte des Scogli neri*, 435 Li., pp. 11–20.
BÖGLI, A. (1951): Probleme der Karrenbildung. *Geographica Helvetica*, No. 3, Bern.
BÖGLI, A. (1954): Das Verhalten von Karbonaten in der Natur. *Die Höhle*, Nos 3–4, Wien.
BÖGLI, A. (1956/1): Grundformen von Karsthöhlenquerschnitten. *Stalaktit*, Vol. 6, No. 3.
BÖGLI, A. (1956/2): Der Chemismus der Lösungsprozesse und der Einfluß der Gesteinsbeschaffenheit auf die Entwicklung des Karstes. *Report of the Commission on Karst Phenomena, IGU*, New York.
BÖGLI, A. (1957): Die Phasen der Kalklösung. *Verh. Schweiz. Naturforsch. Ges.*, Neuenburg.
BÖGLI, A. (1960): Kalklösung und Karrenbildung. *Zeitschr. f. Geomorph.*, Suppl. 2, Berlin–Nikolassee.
BÖGLI, A. (1961/1): Entstehungsbedingungen von Kalkausscheidungen in Höhlen. *Symp. Int. di Speleologia*, Varenna–Como.
BÖGLI, A. (1961/2): Karrentische — ein Beitrag zur Karstmorphologie. *Zeitschr. f. Geomorphologie*, 5, Berlin.
BÖGLI, A. (1961/3): Der Höhlenlehm. *Mem. V della Rass. Spel. Ital.* Como.
BÖGLI, A. (1963/1): Beitrag zur Entstehung von Karsthöhlen. *Die Höhle*, No. 3, Wien.
BÖGLI, A. (1963/2): Höhlenkarren. *Akten III. Int. Kongr. f. Speläologie*, Bd. 2, Wien.
BÖGLI, A. (1963/3): Kalklösung und Karrenbildung. Abstract in *Karszt és Barlang*. Jan., Budapest. With a contribution by L. MARKÓ.
BÖGLI, A. (1964/1): Der Schichttreppenkarst als Beispiel eines Gletscherkomplexes. *Rev. Belge Géogr.*, Vol. 88, Nos 1–2, pp. 63–82, Bruxelles.
BÖGLI, A. (1964/2): Die Kalkkorrosion, das zentrale Problem der unterirdischen Verkarstung. *Steir. Beitr. zur Hydrogeologie*, Graz.
BÖGLI, A. (1964/3): Karst-hydrographische Untersuchungen im Muotatal Regio. *Brasiliensis*, Vol. 1, No. 2.
BÖGLI, A. (1964/4): Le Schichttreppenkarst. *Rev. Belge Géogr.*, Vol. 88, pp. 63–82, Bruxelles.
BÖGLI, A. (1964/5): Mischungskorrosion. *Erdkunde*, No. 2 Bonn.
BÖGLI, A. (1964/6): Mischungskorrosion — ein Beitrag zum Verkarstungsproblem. *Erdkunde*, Vol. 18, No. 2, pp. 83–92, Bonn.
BÖHM—KUNSKY (1941): Lednice, die Eishöhle von Silice. *Wiener Prähist. Zeitschrift*, Vol. 28.
BRUGGER, F. (1940): A budakörnyéki dolomitok kőzetkémiai vizsgálata (Petrochemical examination of dolomites from the environs of Budapest). *Matematikai és Természettudományi Értesítő*, Vol. LIX., Part. II, Budapest.

247

BUKOVINSKY, V. (1960): Beitrag zur Frage des Entstehens des Luftzugs in den Höhlen. *Slovenský Kras*, III.

BULLA, B. (1932): Morfológiai megfigyelések magyarországi löszös területeken (Morphological observations in loess regions of Hungary). *Földrajzi Közlemények*, Budapest.

BULLA, B. (1947): Tönkfelszínek (Peneplains). *Természettudomány*, Budapest.

BULLA, B. (1950): A természeti földrajz új útjai (New trends in physical geography). *Hidrológiai Közlöny*, Budapest.

BULLA, B. (1954/1): *Általános természeti földrajz* (General physical geography). Vol. II, Tankönyvkiadó, Budapest.

BULLA, B. (1954/2): A klimatikus morfológia területi rendszere (Regional system of climatic morphology). *MTA Társadalom- és Történettudományi Osztály Közleményei*, Nos 1–4, Budapest.

BURKE, A. R. (1967): Geomorphology and spelaeogenesis of vertical shafts in carboniferous limestone at Ystradfellte. *Breconshire Proc. Ann. Conf. Brit. Speleol. Assoc.*, 5, pp. 17–46.

BÜDEL, J. (1948): Das System der klimatischen Morphologie. *D. Geographentag*, München, 1948, Landshut, 1950 (2nd ed.).

BÜDEL, J. (1951): Fossiler Tropenkarst in der Schwäbischen Alp und den Ostalpen. *Erdkunde*, No. 5, Bonn.

BÜDEL, J. (1963): Klimagenetische Geomorphologie. *Geogr. Rundschau*, 15, Braunschweig.

BÜLOW, K. (1942): Karrenbildung in kristallinen Gesteinen? *Zeitschr. d. Deutschen Geol. Ges.*, Vol. 94.

CACHIA—DELABY (1970): L'expédition italo–belge de 1970. *L'électron, Exploration Italo–Belge de la Grotte des Scogli neri*, 435 Li., pp. 3–10.

CAILLEUX, A. (1971): Cas en ourson, cernes et thermokarst. *Cahiers de Géogr. de Québec*, Vol. 34, pp. 131–136.

CASTERET, N. (1955): *Sondeurs d'abîmes.* Paris.

CASTERET, N. (1957): *Geheimnisvolle Höhlenwelt.* Leipzig.

CASTERET, N. (1962): *Harminc év föld alatt* (Thirty years underground). Budapest.

CAUER, H. (1954): Chemisch–physikalische Untersuchungen der Klimaverhältnisse in der Kluterthöhle. *Archiv für Physikalische Therapie*, 1, Berlin.

CAUMARTIN—RENAULT (1958): La corrosion biochimique dans un réseau karstique et la genèse du mondmilch. *Notes Biospél.*, 13.

CAYEUX, L. (1935): *Roches, carbonates, calcaires et dolomites.* Paris.

CEBECAUER, I. (1970): Nové moznosti sledovania súvislosti podzemnyh tokov v krasovych územiach. *Zbornik Múzea Slovenského Krasu*, Rocnik VIII, pp. 110–111.

CEBECAUER—LISKA (1972): Prispevok k poznaniu krasovych foriem spisskych travertinov a ich krynovych zosuvov. *Zbornik Múzea Slovenského Krasu*, Rocnik X, pp. 47–61.

CHARLOT—ENSCHWILLER (1939): Géochimique Tab. *Bull. Soc. Chim. Franç.*, Ser. 5.

CHAUPPIS, P. A. (1947): *Spéléologie.* Basel.

CHIKISHEV, A. G. (1959): Karstoviye peshcheri SSSR. *Speleologiya i karstoved'eniye*, Moskva.

CHIKISHEV, A. G. (1965): *Tipy karsta Russkoy ravnini.* Nauka, Moskva.

CHIKISHEV, A. G. (1967): Rayonirovaniye podzemnykh karstovikh form Urala (Regionalization of subsurface karst features of the Urals). *Zmlevedeniye*, 7(47).

CHOLNOKY, J. (1916): Előzetes jelentés karszttanulmányaimról (Preliminary report on my karst studies). *Földrajzi Közlemények*, Budapest.

CHOLNOKY, J. (1917): Barlangtanulmányok (Cavern studies). *Barlangkutatás*, No. 5, Budapest.

CHOLNOKY, J. (1928): *A földfelszín formáinak ismerete* (Knowledge of earth relief forms). Budapest.

CHOLNOKY, J. (1932/1): Barlangok és folyóvölgyek összefüggése (Relationship of caverns to river valleys). *Barlangvilág*, Budapest.

CHOLNOKY, J. (1932/2): A mészkőhegységek földrajzi jellemvonása (Geographical features of limestone mountains). *Földgömb*, Budapest.

CHOLNOKY, J. (1936): A Budai-Várhegy barlangjai (Caves of Castle Hill in Budapest). *Barlangvilág*, No. 6, Budapest.

CHOLNOKY, J. (1939): A mészkővidék arculata (Aspect of limestone regions). *Barlangvilág*, Budapest.
CHOLNOKY, J. (1940): A mésztufa vagy travertino képződésről (On the formation of calcareous tufa or travertine). *Matematikai és Természettudományi Értesítő*, No. 3, Budapest.
CHOLNOKY, J. (1944): *A barlangokról (karsztjelenségek)* (On caverns [karst phenomena]). Budapest.
CHOPPY, J. (1965): Les types de cavités de Vercors. *Spelunca*, No. 4, pp. 50–56.
CHRAMUSHEV, A. C. (1941): Gidrogeologicheskaya klassifikaciya treshchinovatykh gornykhporod. *Sovietskaya Geol.*, No. 4.
CHROMY, J. (1934): *Zbrašovské aragonitové jeskyně*. Hranice.
CHURINOV, M. V. (1961): O karste gornogo Krima. *Sborn. Regionalnoye Karstoved'eniye*, Moskva.
CINCURA, J. (1973): Weathering crusts on the carbonatic rocks of the Western Carpathians and their relation to climate and relief. *Zbornik Múzea Slovenského Krasu*, Rocnik XI, pp. 23–39.
CLAYTON, K. M. (1966): The origin of the landforms of the Malham area. *Field Studies*, 2(3), pp. 359–384.
COMEL, A. (1937): *Elementi di pedologia climatica*. Udine.
CORBEL, J. (1951): Vitesse de l'érosion. *Zeitschr. f. Geomorph.*, No. 1, Berlin.
CORBEL, J. (1952/1): Traveaux russes sur le karst. *Annal. de Géogr.*, Paris.
CORBEL, J. (1952/2): Karsts et glaciers en Laponie. *Revue de Géogr. de Lyon*, 27, Lyon.
CORBEL, J. (1954/1): Karst de climat froid. *Erdkunde*, Vol. 8, Bonn.
CORBEL, J. (1954/2): Les phénomènes karstiques en climat froid. In: Das Karstphänomen in den verschiedenen Klimazonen. *Erdkunde*, Vol. 9, pp. 119–120, Bonn.
CORBEL, J. (1955): Note sur les karsts tropicaux. *Revue de Géogr. de Lyon*, 1, Lyon.
CORBEL, J. (1956): Les karsts proprement dit, étude morphologique. *Revue de Géogr. de Lyon*, 31, Lyon.
CORBEL, J. (1957): Les karsts du nord-ouest de l'Europe et de quelques régions de comparaison. *Inst. d'Étude Rhodaniennes de Lyon.*
CORBEL, J. (1959): Érosion en terrain calcaire. Vitesse d'érosion et morphologie. *Annal. de Géogr.*, Paris.
CORBEL, J. (1961/1): Sur la dissolution du calcaire. *Revue Géogr. de l'Est.*, No. 4.
CORBEL, J. (1961/2): Remplissages de grottes et climats. *Symp. Int. di Speleologia*, Varenna–Como.
CORBEL, J. (1963): Marmites de giants et microformes karstiques. *Norvais*, Poitiers, 10, 38, pp. 121–132.
CRAMER, H. (1933): Das Karstphänomen im Grundgips des fränkischen Keupers. *Mitt. über Höhlen- u. Karstforschung*, No. 4, Berlin.
CRAMER, H. (1935/1): Höhlenbildung und Karsthydrographie. *Zeitschr. f. Geomorph.*, No. 8, 1933/35.
CRAMER, H. (1935/2): Systematik der Karrenbildung. *Peterm. Mitt.*, Vol. 81, Gotha.
CRAMER, H. (1944): Die Systematik der Karstdolinen. *Neues Jahrb. Mineral. usw.*, Alt. B. Abh. 85, Stuttgart.
CRAMER, H. (1955): Die Karstgebiete der Britischen Inseln. *Peterm. Geogr. Mitt.*, Nos 3–4, Gotha.
CRICKMAY, C. H. (1953): The later stages of the cycle of erosion. *Geological Magazine*, Vol. 70. New York.
CROSE, D. (1964): Cryonival phenomena and karst in the plateau of the Sella Group. *Erdkunde*, No. 2, pp. 146–148, Bonn.
CSAJÁGHY—TOLNAY (1952): A víz összes keménységének, valamint Ca^{++} és Mg^{++} tartalmának helyszíni meghatározása (In situ determination of total hardness and Ca^{++} and Mg^{++} contents of water). *Hidrológiai Közlöny*, Budapest.
CSEKŐ, Á. (1957): A cseppkövek korának meghatározása radiokarbon módszerrel (Determination of radiocarbon age of dripstones). *Karszt- és Barlangkutatási Tájékoztató*, July–Dec., Budapest.
CVIJIĆ, J. (1893): Das Karstphänomen. *Geogr. Abh.*, 3.
CVIJIĆ, J. (1895): *Karst (Geographical monograph)*. Beograd.
CVIJIĆ, J. (1918): Hydrographie souterraine et évolution morphologique du Karst. *Trav. Inst. Géogr. Alpine*, Vol. IV, No. 4, Grenoble.
CVIJIĆ, J. (1923): Evolucija karsta u Moravskoj. *Glas. srp. Kral. Akad.*, Beograd.

CVIJIĆ, J. (1924/1): The evolution of lapies. A study in karst physiography. *Geogr. Reviews*, Washington.

CVIJIĆ, J. (1924/2): Types morphologiques des terrains calcaires. *Bull. Soc. de Géogr.*, Beograd.

CVIJIĆ, J. (1926): *Geomorfologija*, Chapter 5: Oblici karsna erozije i karsna hydrographija. Beograd.

CYPRIAN, V. (1949): Novějši theorie o vzniku terra rossi. *Sborn. Čs. spol. zemepisné*, 54, Praha.

CZÁJLIK, I. (1961): A Vass Imre-barlang részletes hidrológiai vizsgálatának újabb eredményei (Recent results of a detailed hydrographical survey in the Imre Vass Cavern). *Karszt- és Barlangkutatás*, March, Budapest.

CZÁJLIK—CSER (1963): Megjegyzések a hidrosztatikai nyomásváltozáson alapuló cseppkőképződési elmélethez (Remarks on the theory of dripstone formation by change in hydrographic pressure). *Karszt és Barlang*, Jan., Budapest.

CZÁJLIK—FEJÉRDY (1960): Cseppkövekről csepegő vizek vizsgálata a Vass Imre-barlangban (Analysis of water dripping from stalactites in the Imre Vass Cavern). *Karszt- és Barlangkutatás*, Jan., Budapest.

CZUDEK—DEMEK (1970): Thermokarst in Siberia and its influence on the development of lowland relief. *Quaternary Research*, Vol. 1, pp. 103–120.

DANES, J. V. (1914): Karststudien in Jamaica. *Vestn. Král. č. spol. nauk.*, Praha.

DANES, J. V. (1915): Das Karstgebiet des Goenoeng Sewoe auf Java. *Sitz. Ber. Kgl. Böhm. Ges. Wiss.*, Praha.

DANES, J. V. (1916): Karststudien in Australien. *Tamtéz*, Praha.

DAVIS, W. M. (1930): Origin of limestone caverns. *Bull. of the Geol. Soc. of America*, Vol. 41.

DE BUCHANANNE—RICHARDSON (1956): Groundwater resources of eastern Tennessee. *Tenn., Dept. Conserv., Div. Feol., Bull.*, 58(1), p. 393.

DE MARTONNE, E. (1940): *Traité de géographie physique*. Paris.

DÉNES, GY. (1973): Die Rolle der allmählich abgetragenen wasserundurchlässigen Decke in der morphologischen Entwicklung des Karstes. *IGU Symp. on Karst Morphogenesis*, Papers, Hungary, pp. 33–43.

DICKEN—BROWN (1938): Soil erosion in the karst lands of Kentucky. *U. S. Dept. Agr., Circ.*, 490, p. 61.

DI GLÉRIA, J. (1962): *Mezőgazdasági kémia* (Agricultural chemistry). Budapest.

DI GLÉRIA—KLIMES—SZMIK—DVORACSEK (1957): *Talajfizika és talajkolloidika* (Soil physics and soil colloids). Parts 4–9, Budapest.

DOBROVOLSKY, M. N. (1965): Kratkiye dannye o krupneyshikh peshcherakh Sredney Sibiri. *Peshcheri*, No. 5, Perm.

DOKUCHAEV, V. V. (1878): *Sposoby obrazovaniya rechnikh dolin Evropeyskoy Rossii*. St. Petersburg.

DOKUCHAEV, V. V. (1883): *The teaching of the zonality of nature*. St. Petersburg.

DOUGLAS, H. H. (1964): *Caves of Virginia*. Falls Church.

DROPPA, A. (1957): *Demanovské jaskyne. Krasové zkavy Demanoskej doliny*. Slov. Akad. Vied, Bratislava.

DROPPA, A. (1959): *Demänovká jaskyne*. Bratislava.

DROPPA, A. (1966): Characteristics of the karst region in the Carpathians. *Probl. Speleol. Res.*, No. 2, pp. 23–30.

DROPPA, A. (1972): Geomorfologické Pomery Demänovskey Doliny. *Zbornik Múzea Slovenského Krasu*, Rocnik X, pp. 9–47.

DROPPA—JAKUCS (1961): *Domica–Baradla*. Bratislava.

DUBLYANSKY, V. N. (1963): Die Bedeutung des Schnees für die Verkarstung und die Speisung von Karstgewässern. Translated from: *Izv. Akad. Nauk SSSR, Ser. Geogr.*, No. 2, pp. 69–75.

DUBLYANSKY, V. N. (1965): Novye dannye o glubinnom karste Gornogo Krima. *Peshcheri*, No. 5, Perm.

DUBLYANSKY, V. N. (1966): Karstovye peshcheri srednego pridnestrovya. *Voprosi izucheniya karsta Russkoy ravnini*, Moskva.

DUBLYANSKY—ILYUKHIN (1971): Vsled za Kapley vody. *Izd. Mysl.*, p. 205, Moskva.

DUBLYANSKY—SHUTOV (1966): Gazovy sostav vozdukha v karstovykh polostyakh Gornogo Krima. *Dokl. Akad. Nauk SSSR, Geol.*, Vol. 171, No. 2.

DUDICH, E. (1930): Az Aggteleki-barlang vizeiről (On the waters of the Aggtelek Cavern). *Hidrológiai Közlöny*, Budapest.

DUDICH, E. (1932): *Az Aggteleki-cseppkőbarlang és környéke* (The Aggtelek Stalactite Cavern and its environs). Budapest.

DÜRR, E. (1970): Kalkalpine Sturzhalden und Sturzschuttbildungen in den westlichen Dolomiten. *Tübinger Geogr. Studien*, No. 37, p. 128, Tübingen.

ECKERT, M. (1896): Das Karrenproblem. *Zeitschr. f. Naturwiss.*

ECKERT, M. (1898): Die Karren oder Schratten. *Peterm. Mitt.*, Vol. 44, Gotha.

EHRENBERG, K. (1960): Über Alter und Lebensdauer von Höhlen. *Die Höhle*, No. 11, Wien.

EHRENBERG, K. (1962): Über Grenzen und Gliederung der Speläologie. *Die Höhle*, No. 13, Wien.

ERNST, L. (1961): A karsztvizek telítettségéről (On the saturation of karst waters). *Karszt- és Barlangkutatás*, Jan., Budapest.

ERNST, L. (1964): Zur Frage der Mischungskorrosion. *Die Höhle*, No. 3, Wien.

ERNST, L. (1965): A keveredési korrózió kérdéséhez (On the problem of mixing corrosion). *Karszt és Barlang*, Febr., Budapest.

FEHÉR, D. (1954): *Talajbiológia* (Soil biology). Budapest.

FEKETE, Z. (1952): *Talajtan* (Pedology). Budapest.

FEKETE, Z. (1958): *Talajtan és trágyázástan* (Pedology and soil fertilization). Budapest.

FEKETE—HARGITAI—ZSOLDOS (1964): *Talajtan és agrokémia* (Pedology and agrochemistry). Budapest.

FIALA, F. (1930): Nekolik poznánek k morfologii Jihoslovenského krasu. *Vestnik St. Geol. Ust.*, No. 6, Praha.

FINDEISEN, W. (1939): Die Kondensationskerne, Entstehung, chemische Natur, Grösse und Anzahl. *Beitr. Phys. f. Atmosph.*, 25.

FIRBAS, F. (1949): *Waldgeschichte Mitteleuropas*. Jena.

FISCHER, J. J. (1963): Panamanian Caves. *National Speleological Society News*, 21, Washington.

FLATHE—PFEIFFER (1965): Grundzüge der Morphologie, Geologie und Hydrologie im Karstgebiet Gunung Sewu (Java, Indonesien). *Geol. Jahrb.*, 83, Hannover.

FORD, D. C. (1965): The origin of limestone caverns: a model from the Central Hills, England. *Bull. Nat. Speleol. Soc. Amer.*, 27(4), pp. 109–132.

FOURMARIER, P. (1939): *Géohydrologie*. Liège.

FOURNIER, E. (1928): *(A)* Phénomènes d'érosion et de corrosion spéciaux aux terrains calcaires. *(B)* Applications scientifiques et pratiques de la spéléologie et de l'hydrologie souterraine. Besançon.

FÖLDVÁRI, A. (1933): A Dunántúli Középhegység eocén előtti karsztja (A pre-Eocene karst in the Transdanubian Hills of Hungary). *Földtani Közlöny*, Nos 1–6, Budapest.

FRAIPONT, J. (1950): The dissolution of limestone and cave crystallization. *Cave Science*, 11.

FRANKE, H. (1956): Die Tropfsteinhöhle von Kiuyo (Korea). *Die Höhle*, No. 7, Wien.

FRANKE, H. (1962): Die Beziehungen zwischen Versinterung und Korrosion. *Die Höhle*, No. 4, Wien.

FRANKE, H. (1965): Mischungskorrosion an Haarrissen. *Die Höhle*, No. 3, Wien.

FRANKE, H. (1967): Bemerkungen zur Lösungsdynamik. *Kalk. Mitt. des Verbandes Deutscher Höhlen- u. Karstforscher*. Jahrg. 13, Munich.

FUCHS, F. (1970): Studien zur Karst- und Glazialmorphologie in der Monte-Cavallo-Gruppe/Venezianische Voralpen. *Frankfurter Geogr. Hefte*, 47, p. 113, Frankfurt am Main.

FULDA, E. (1912): Die Verbreitung und Entstehung der Schlotten in der Mansfelder Mulde. *Thesis, Preuss. Geol. Landesanstalt.*

FUTÓ, J. (1962): Mikroklimatikus mérések a Nagymezőn (Microclimatic recordings at Nagymező in the Bükk Hills, Hungary). *Földrajzi Értesítő*, No. 4, Budapest.

GAMS, I. (1957): Transporti material slovenskih rek. *Proteus*, Vol. XX, No. 2, Ljubljana.

GAMS, I. (1959): H geomorfologiji kraskega Globodola in okolice. *Porocila, Acta Cars.* II., Ljubljana.

251

GAMS, I. (1963): Der Einfluß der Schichtenlage auf die Richtung der Höhlengänge und auf die Querschnitte in der längsten Höhlen Sloweniens. *Akten d. III. Int. Kongr. f. Spel.*, Bd. II., Sekt. 1, Wien.

GAMS, I. (1965/1): On the types of tufa-depositing waters and on the corrosion intensity in the northwestern Dinaric. *Proc. Symp. on Hydrology in Fractured Rocks*, A.I.H.S.– UNESCO, 63 : 7, Dubrovnik.

GAMS, I. (1965/2): Types of accelerated corrosion. *Proc. Int. Speleol. Conf.*, 1964, pp. 133–139, Brno.

GAMS, I. (1967): Perspektive fizične geografije krasa. *Geogr. Obzornik*, Vol. 14, No. 2, pp. 47–50.

GAMS, I. (1973): A new method of determining the karstic soil erosion. *IGU Symp. on Karst Morphogenesis*, Papers, Hungary, pp. 44–51.

GAVAZZI, A. (1904): Die Seen des Karstes. *Abh. Geogr. Ges.*, 1903–04, 2, Wien.

GÁNTI, T. (1957): A barlangok keletkezésének kémiai vonatkozásai (Chemical aspects of the origin of caverns). *Hidrológiai Közlöny*, No. 3, Budapest.

GEIGER, R. (1961): Das Klima der bodennahen Luftschicht. Ein Lehrbuch der Mikroklimatologie. *Die Wissenschaft*, Bd. 78, No. 4. Auflage, Braunschweig.

GERSTENHAUER, A. (1960): Der tropische Kegelkarst in Tabasco (Mexiko). *Zeitschr. f. Geomorph.*, Supplementband 2, Göttingen.

GERSTENHAUER, A. (1966): Beiträge zur Geomorphologie des mittleren und nördlichen Chiapas (Mexiko) unter besonderer Berücksichtigung des Karstformenschatzes. *Frankfurter Geogr. Hefte*, 41, Frankfurt am Main.

GERSTENHAUER, A. (1969): Die Karstlandschaften Deutschlands. *Abh. zur Karst- u. Höhlenkunde*, Reihe A, Speläologie, No. 5, München.

GERSTENHAUER—PFEFFER (1966): Beiträge zur Frage der Lösungsfreudigkeit von Kalkgesteinen. *Abh. zur Karst- u. Höhlenkunde*, Heft 2, München.

GERSTENHAUER—SWEETING (1960): Zur Frage des absoluten Geschwindigkeit der Kalkkorrosion in verschiedenen Klimaten. *Zeitschr. f. Geomorph.*, Suppl. Bd. 2, Berlin.

GÈZE, B. (1947): Origine des eaux souterraines. *Annal. de Spél.*, Vol. II, Paris.

GÈZE, B. (1953): Genèse des gouffres. *I. Congr. Int. Spéléol.*, Vol. II, Paris.

GÈZE, B. (1965): La spéléologie scientifique. Paris.

GHIDINI, G. M. (1954): Uomini, caverne e abissi. Milano.

GLAZEK, J. (1971): Phases of karstification in the epi-Variscan Platform of Poland. *Bull. Acad. Polon. Sci.*, Sér. Sci. Géol. Géograph., 19.

GLENNIE, E. A. (1956): Caves in India and Pakistan. *Cave Res. Group. Newsletter*, Nos 30, 32, 33, 34, 35, 37, 58/59. (1950–56.)

GOLOVTSIN—ŠMOLNIKOV—DUBLYANSKY (1966): *Primeneniye geoelektricheskikh issledovaniy k resheniyu osnovikh problem karsta Gornovo Kryma*. Kiev.

GORBUNOVA, K. A. (1955): Karstovo-erozionnye dolini Usvinskogo rayona Kizelovskogo kamenougolnogo basseyna. *Uch. Zap. Molotovsk. Gos. Univ. im. A. M. Gorkogo*, IX. 1., Perm.

GORBUNOVA, K. A. (1965): Osobennosti gipsovogo karsta. Perm.

GÖMÖRI, I. (1967): Egy bükki töbör talajhőmérsékletének napi járása különböző expozíciókban (Daily fluctuation of soil temperatures in various exposures in a Bükk Hills doline). *Thesis manuscript*. Climatological Institute of A. József Univ. Szeged, Hungary.

GRIGORYEV, A. (1930): *Der ewige Frostboden und die diluviale Vereisung*. Leningrad.

GRIOSEL, Y. (1959): *Pyrénées souterraines*. Paris.

GRUND, A. (1903): Die Karsthydrographie. *Geogr. Abh.*, No. 7, Wien–Leipzig.

GRUND, A. (1912/1): Zur Frage des Grundwassers im Karst. *Mitt. d. Geogr. Ges. in Wien*, 53.

GRUND, A. (1912/2): Nochmals zur Morphologie und Hydrographie des Karstes. *Peterm. Geogr. Mitt.*, Gotha.

GRUND, A. (1914): Der geographische Zyklus im Karst. *Zeitschr. d. Ges. f. Erdkunde*, Berlin.

Grupo Espeleologico Vizcaino y diversos colaboradores, 1971, Morphologia del Karst de Itxina, Observaciones preliminares sobre el macizo Kárstico de Itxina, Macizo del Gorbea, Vizcaya, Kobie, 3, pp. 9–56, Grupo espeleologico vizcaino, Bilbao.

GUÉRIN, H. P. (1944): *Spéléologie*. Paris.

GUERNEE, R. H. (1959): The caves of Puerto Rico. *National Speleological Society News*, 17, Washington.

GÜLDALI, N. (1970): Karstmorphologische Studien im Gebiet des Poljetanzania. *Tübinger Geogr. Studien*, H. 40, p. 104, Tübingen.

GVOZDETSKY, N. A. (1947): Karstovaya konferenciya v g. Molotove. *Voprosi Geografii*, No. 4, Moskva.

GVOZDETSKY, N. A. (1949): Osobennosti landshaftov izvestnyakovikh karstovikh oblastey. *Voprosi Geografii*, No. 16, Moskva.

GVOZDETSKY, N. A. (1950): *Karst.* Moskva. (II. ed. 1954.)

GVOZDETSKY, N. A. (1958): *Regionalnoe karstovedeniye.* MOIP, Moskva.

GVOZDETSKY, N. A. (1959): *Speleology and studies in karst.* Moskva.

GVOZDETSKY, N. A. (1961): Nekotoriye nablyudeniya nad karstem Gotlenda. *Vestnik Moskovsk. Univ., Ser. V. Geogr.*, No. 3.

GVOZDETSKY, N. A. (1965): Novye dannye o krupneysikh peshcherakh SSSR. *Vestnik Moskovsk. Univ., Ser. V. Geogr.*, No. 3.

GVOZDETSKY, N. A. (1966): Novye materialy o karste russkoy ravnini i zadachi yego dalneysevo izucheniya. *Voprosi Izuch. Karsta Russkoy Ravnini*, Moskva.

GVOZDETSKY—CHIKISHEV (1966): Rayonirovaniye karsta russkoy ravnini. *Voprosi Izucheniya Karsta Russkoy Ravnini*, Moskva.

HAGEL, J. (1963): Die längsten Höhlensysteme der Erde. *Kosmos*, 59, Stuttgart.

HANSHAW—BACK—RUBIN (1968): Carbonate equilibria and radiocarbon distribution related to groundwater flow in the Floridan limestone aquifer, United States of America. In: Hydrol. of Fractured Rocks; *Proceedings of the Dubrovnik Symp.*, October, 1965 — *Int. Assoc. Sci. Hydrol., Bull.*, 2, pp. 601–614.

HARDIE, L. A. (1967): The gypsum-anhydrite equilibrium at one atmosphere pressure. *The American Mineralogist*, 52, pp. 171–200.

HARRASOWITZ, H. (1954): Chemische Einwirken des Niederschlages auf den Karst. Bericht von der Arbeitstagung d. Intern. Karstkomm. in Frankfurt/Main, vom 27–30. 12. 53, *Erdkunde*, No. 8, Bonn.

HASERODT, K. (1965): Untersuchungen zur Höhlen- und Altersgliederung der Karstformen in den Nördlichen Kalkalpen. *Münchner Geogr. Hefte*, No. 27, Regensburg.

HEIGEL, K. (1955): Exposition und Höhlenlage in ihrer Wirkung auf die Pflanzenentwicklung. *Meteorolog. Rundschau*, 8, Heidelberg.

HEIGEL, K. (1957): Die Bodenfeuchte in Abhängigkeit von Exposition. *Bodenart und Bewuchs. Wetter und Leben*, 9.

HERAK—STRINGFIELD (1972): *Karst, important karst regions of the Northern Hemisphere.* Elsevier Publishing Company, Amsterdam.

HERRMANN, A. (1966): Vergipsung und Oberflächenformung im Gipskarst. 3rd *Int. Congr. f. Speleol.*, Sect. C, pp. 99–108, Wien.

HERRMANN, A. (1969): Einführung in die Geologie, Morphologie und Hydrogeologie des Gipskarstgebietes am südwestlichen Harzland. *Jb. Karst- und Höhlenkunde*, No. 9, pp. 1–10.

HODGMAN, C. D. (1955): *Handbook of chemistry and physics.* Cleveland. (2nd ed. 1960.)

HOLLUTA, J. (1927): *Die Chemie und chemische Technologie des Wassers.* Stuttgart.

HORN, G. (1935): Über die Bildung von Karsthöhlen unter einem Gletscher. *Norsk Geografisk Tidsskrift*, Vol. 5, Oslo.

HORN, G. (1939): Über einige Karsthöhlen in Norwegen. *Mitt. ü. Höhlen- u. Karstforschung*, Berlin.

HORN, G. (1947): Karsthuler i Nordland. *Norsk Geologiske Undersokelse*, No. 165, Oslo.

HORUSITZKY, H. (1915): A barlangok rendszeres osztályozása (Systematic taxonomy of caverns). *Barlangkutatás*, No. 3, Budapest.

HORUSITZKY, H. (1923): Tata és Tóváros hévforrásainak hidrogeológiája és közgazdasági jövője (Hydrogeology and economic future of the thermal springs of Tata and Tóváros). *Földtani Intézet Évkönyve*, Budapest.

HORUSITZKY, F. (1942): A víz a Föld belsejében (Water in the earth's interior). *Hidrológiai Közlöny*, Budapest.

HORUSITZKY, F. (1953): A karsztvíz elhelyezkedése a Kárpátmedencében (Distribution of karst water in the Carpathian Basin). *MTA Műszaki Tudományok Osztályának Közleményei*, 1, Budapest.

HORVAT, I. (1953): Die Vegetation der Karstdolinen (Vegetacija Ponikova). *Geografski Glasnik*, Nos 14–15, Zagreb.

HOVEY, H. G. (1912): Mammoth caves of Kentucky. Louisville. (2nd ed.)

Höhl, G. (1963): Die Siegritz-Vorgendorfer Kuppenlandschaft. Ein Beitrag zur klimatisch-morphologischen Deutung einer Reliktlandschaft des Karstes aus feuchtwarmer Zeit in der nördlichen Frankenalb. *Mitt. Fränk. Geogr. Ges.*, 10, Erlangen. (Kärtchen.)

Jaag, O. (1945): Untersuchungen über die Vegetation und Biologie der Algen des nackten Gesteins in den Alpen, im Jura und im Schweizer Mittelland. *Beiträge zur Kryptogamenflora der Schweiz*, 9 : 3, Bern.

Jakál, J. (1973): Geneticheskiye tipy peshcher Slovakii i ikh svaz s reliefom, litologiey i tektonikoy. *Zbornik Múzea Slovenského Krasu*, Rocnik XI, pp. 3–13.

Jakucs, L. (1948): A hévforrásos barlangkeletkezés földtani alakulása (Geology of cavern formation by thermal-spring activity). *Hidrológiai Közlöny*, Nos 1–4, Budapest.

Jakucs, L. (1950): A dolomitporlódás kérdése a Budai-hegységben (Problem of dolomite pulverization in the Buda Mountains). *Földtani Közlöny*, Budapest.

Jakucs, L. (1951/1): Az Aggteleki-cseppkőbarlang szovjetrendszerű kutatásának eredményei (Results of cavern research on the Soviet pattern in the Aggtelek Cavern). *Természet és Technika*, Budapest.

Jakucs, L. (1951/2): Vízföldtani vizsgálatok a Gömöri-karszton (Hydrogeological studies in the Gömör Karst, NE Hungary). *Földtani Közlöny*, Budapest.

Jakucs, L. (1951/3): A Bükkhegység még feltáratlan, ismeretlen barlangrendszerei (Unexplored and unknown cavern systems in the Bükk Hills). *Földtani Közlöny*, Budapest.

Jakucs, L. (1952/1): *Az Aggteleki cseppkőbarlang* (The Aggtelek Stalactite Cavern). Budapest.

Jakucs, L. (1952/2): A vízföldtani tudomány fejlődése a Szovjetunióban (Evolution of hydrogeological science in the Soviet Union). *Földtani Közlöny*, Nos 4–6, Budapest.

Jakucs, L. (1953/1): *A Békebarlang felfedezése* (Discovery of the Béke Cavern). Budapest.

Jakucs, L. (1953/2): Jelentés az 1953. évi karsztvízfestési vizsgálatokról (Report on water-dyeing tests in the spring in 1953). *Állami Földtani Intézet Évi jelentése*, Budapest.

Jakucs, L. (1955): A barlangkutatás új irányai (New trends in cavern research). *Természetjárás*, Vol. X, Budapest.

Jakucs, L. (1956/1): Adatok az Aggteleki-hegység és barlangjainak morfogenetikájához (Contributions to the morphogeny of the Aggtelek Hills and their caverns). *Földrajzi Közlemények*, No. 2, Budapest.

Jakucs, L. (1956/2): A barlangi árvizekről (On floods in caverns). *Földrajzi Közlemények*, No. 4, Budapest.

Jakucs, L. (1957/1): Jelentés a Baradla alsó barlangjának feltárásáról (Report on the exploration of the Baradla Cavern's lower level). *Karszt- és Barlangkutatási Tájékoztató*, Jan.–June, Budapest.

Jakucs, L. (1957/2): *Aggtelek és vidéke útikalauz* (Travel guide to Aggtelek and environs). Budapest.

Jakucs, L. (1959/1): Neue Methoden der Höhlenforschung in Ungarn und ihre Ergebnisse. *Die Höhle*, No. 4, Wien.

Jakucs, L. (1959/2): *Felfedező utakon a föld alatt* (Travels of discovery underground). Budapest.

Jakucs, L. (1959/3): A Békebarlang gyógyhatásvizsgálatának első eredményei (First results of an investigation into the therapeutical effects of the Béke Cavern). *Természettudományi Közlöny*, Vol. 1, Budapest.

Jakucs, L. (1960/1): Az aggteleki barlangok genetikája a komplex forrásvizsgálatok tükrében (Genesis of the Aggtelek Caverns in the light of complex spring tests). *Karszt- és Barlangkutatás*, No. 1, Budapest.

Jakucs, L. (1960/2): Általános karsztgenetikai és hidrográfiai problémák vizsgálata az Aggteleki-karszton (A study of some general problems of karst genesis and hydrography on the Aggtelek Karst). *Candidate's Thesis*. Budapest.

Jakucs, L. (1960/3): Nuovi metodi de studio e risultati delle ricerche nelle grotte d'Ungheria. *Rass. Spel. Italiana*, Como.

Jakucs, L. (1961): *Aggtelek és környéke (Az Északborsodi Karsztvidék)* (Aggtelek and environs [The North Borsod Karst]). Budapest.

JAKUCS, L. (1962): Über die Färbung der Tropfsteine in den Höhlen. *Karszt- és Barlangkutatás*, Vol. 3, Budapest.

JAKUCS, L. (1964): Berechnung der Karstversickerungswerte im Aggteleker Karstgebiet. *Acta Geographica Szegediensis*, Vol. V, Szeged.

JAKUCS, L. (1965): Die Friedenshöhle in Ungarn, als klimatherapeutischer Kurort für Erkrankungen der Atmungsorgane. *Akten III. Int. Kongr. f. Speläologie*, Bd. 4, Wien.

JAKUCS, L. (1966): Untersuchungen über den Dynamismus und Chemismus der Tropfsteinbildung. *Acta Geographica Szegediensis*, Szeged.

JAKUCS, L. (1967): Eine neue Erklärung der Denudationsvorgänge und der Morphogenetik der Karstlandschaften. *Acta Geographica Szegediensis*, Vol. VII, Szeged.

JAKUCS, L. (1968/1): Szempontok a karsztos tájak denudációs folyamatainak és morfogenetikájának értelmezéséhez (Viewpoints on an interpretation of processes of erosion and morphogeny in karst regions). *Földrajzi Értesítő*, Vol. XVII, No. 1, Budapest.

JAKUCS, L. (1968/2): Offene Fragen der morphogenetischen Deutung nach Plateauniveaus des Karstformschatzes des Nord-Borsoder Karstes. *Acta Geographica Szegediensis*, Vol. VIII, Szeged.

JAKUCS, L. (1969): Voraussetzungen für die Epirovarianz der Verkarstung. *Acta Geographica Szegediensis*, Vol. IX, Nos 1–5, pp. 63–80, Szeged.

JAKUCS, L. (1971): Regulatoren der Karstkorrosion durch Petrovarianz. *Acta Geographica Szegediensis*, Vol. IX, Nos 1–7, pp. 1–26, Szeged.

JAKUCS, L. (1972): Die Deutung der Karstkorrosion der in der Natur vorkommenden Kalkgesteine in der Geomorphologie unserer Zeit. *Acta Geographica Szegediensis*, Vol. XII, Nos 1–7, pp. 3–36, Szeged.

JAKUCS, L. (1973/1): Differences of karst-formation processes in microareas. *Acta Geographica Szegediensis*, Vol. XIII, Nos 1–7, pp. 3–35, Szeged.

JAKUCS, L. (1973/2): Dynamische Unterschiede des Verkarstungsprozesses in den Mikroräumen. *IGU Symp. on Karst Morphogenesis*, Papers, Hungary, pp. 153–208.

JAKUCS, L. (1973/3): The karstic corrosion of naturally occurring limestone in the geomorphology of our age. *IGU Symp. on Karst Morphogenesis*, Papers, Hungary, pp. 52–121.

JAKUCS, L. (1973/4): The role of climate in the quantitative and qualitative control of karstic corrosion. *IGU Symp. on Karst Morphogenesis*, Papers, Hungary, pp. 122–152.

JAKUCS—KESSLER (1962): *A barlangok világa* (World of caverns). Budapest

JAKUCS, P. (1954): Mikroklímamérések a Tornai-karszton, tekintettel a fatömegprodukcióra és a karsztfásításra (Microclimate recording in the Torna Karst, NE Hungary, with a view to the mass production of timber and the afforestation of karst areas). *Annal. Hist. Nat. Musei Nationalis Hungarici*, Vol. V, Budapest.

JAKUCS, P. (1955): Geobotanische Untersuchungen und die Karstaufforstung in Nordungarn. *Acta Botan. Hung.*, Vol. II, Budapest.

JAKUCS, P. (1956): Karrosodás és növényzet (Lapies formation and plant cover). *Földrajzi Közlemények*, No. 3, Budapest.

JAKUCS, P. (1961/1): Az Északi-középhegység keleti felének növényzete (Plant cover in the eastern half of the Northern Hills of Hungary). *Földrajzi Értesítő*, No. 3, Budapest.

JAKUCS, P. (1961/2): *Die phytozönologischen Verhältnisse der Flaumeichen-Buschwälder Südosteuropas*. Budapest.

JAKUCS, P. (1962): A domborzat és a növényzet kapcsolatáról (On the relationship of relief to plant cover). *Földrajzi Értesítő*, No. 2, Budapest.

JASKÓ, S. (1935): Geomorfológiai megfigyelések és problémák az Aggteleki-karszton (Geomorphological observations and problems in the Aggtelek Karst). *Földrajzi Közlemények*, Budapest.

JEANNEL, R. (1947): *La spéléologie, science française*. Paris.

JENNINGS, J. N. (1971): *Karst*. The M.I.T. Press, Cambridge.

JULIVAN, M. (1967): Un petit karst alpine d'altitude. *Rev. Géogr. Alpine*, Vol. LV, pp. 325–336, Grenoble.

KACHURIN, S. P. (1940): Geomorphologische und Dauerfrostbodenbeobachtungen an, der Mündung des Anadyr-Flusses im Jahre 1935. *Ref. in Neues Jahrb. f. Miner.* Vol. II.

KADIĆ, O. (1936): Budapest, a barlangok városa (Budapest, city of caverns). *Földrajzi Értesítő*, Budapest.

KAREH, R. (1968): Les sources sous-marines de Chekka (Liban nord.). *Exploitation d'une nappe karstique captive à exetoires sous-marins* (II), Hannon (III), Besançon.

KAŠPAR—KUNSKY (1941): Geysirové krápniky ze Zbrašovskych aragonitovich jeskyň na severni Moravě. *Rozpr. II. tr. Čs. Akad.*, Praha.

KASSAI, F. (1948): Paleogén szénbányászatunk, a karsztvíz és a védekezés módjai (Hungarian Paleogene-coal mining, karst waters and how to fight them). *Hidrológiai Közlöny*, Nos 1–4, Budapest.

KASSAI, F. (1953): A karsztvíznívó és ezzel kapcsolatos problémák (The karst water table and related problems). *MTA Műszaki Tudományok Oszt. Közleményei*, 1, Budapest.

KATZER, F. (1909/1): *Karst und Karsthydrographie*. Sarajevo.

KATZER, F. (1909/2): *Zur Kunde des Balkanhalbinsel*. Sarajevo.

KATZER, F. (1912): Zur Morphologie des Dinarischen Gebirges. *Peterm. Mitt.*, Gotha.

KAYSER, K. (1934): Morphologische Studien in Westmontenegro. *Zeitschr. Ges. Erdkunde*, Berlin.

KAYSER, K. (1955): Karstrandebene und Poljeboden. *Erdkunde*, Vol. 9, Bonn.

KÁDÁR, L. (1954): Az eróziós folyamatok dialektikája (Dialectics of the processes of erosion). *Földrajzi Közlemények*, Budapest.

KÁDÁR, L. (1955): Das Problem der Flußmäander. *Acta of L. Kossuth University*, Debrecen.

KÁDÁR, L. (1960): Hordalékmozgás és folyószakaszjelleg (Stream-load motion and river grades). *Földrajzi Értesítő*, No. 3, Budapest.

KÁDÁR, L. (1966): A földfelszíni formák természetes rendszere (Natural system of earth relief forms). Duplicated manuscript. *Publ. Inst. Geogr. L. Kossuth Univ.*, Debrecen.

KEILHACK, K. (1935): *Lehrbuch der Grundwasser- und Quellenkunde*. Berlin.

KEMPE, ST. (1970): Beiträge zum Problem der Speläogenese im Gips unter besonderer Berücksichtigung der Unterwasserphase. *Die Höhle*, Vol. 21, No. 3, p. 126, Wien.

KEREKES, J. (1941): *A budakörnyéki hévforrásos barlangokról* (On hot-spring caves in the Buda region). Földrajzi Zsebkönyv, Budapest.

KESSLER, H. (1932): A zsombolyok keletkezéséről (On the formation of avens [doline wells]). *Barlangvilág*, Nos 3–4, Budapest.

KESSLER, H. (1938): Az aggteleki barlangrendszer hidrográfiája (Hydrography of the Aggtelek cavern system). *Földrajzi Közlemények*, Budapest.

KESSLER, H. (1954): A beszivárgási százalék és a tartósan kitermelhető vízmennyiség megállapítása karsztvidéken (Establishing the infiltration ratio and the assured water yield in a karst region). *Vízügyi Közlöny*, No. 2, Budapest.

KESSLER, H. (1956): Karsztvidékek lefolyására és beszivárgására vonatkozó újabb vizsgálatok (Recent investigations into runoff and infiltration in karst regions). *Beszámoló a VITUKI 1956. évi munkájáról*, Budapest.

KESSLER, H. (1957): *Az örök éjszaka világában* (The world of eternal night). Budapest.

KESSLER, H. (1960): A barlangkutatás módszerei és az eredmények tudományos felhasználása (Methods of speleology and the scientific utilization of its achievements). *Karszt- és Barlangkutatási Tájékoztató*, Dec., Budapest.

KESSLER—MEGAY (1961): *Lillafüred barlangjai* (The caverns of Lillafüred). Miskolc.

KETTNER, R. (1959): *Allgemeine Geologie*. Berlin.

KÉZ, A. (1959): A mészkőfelszín pusztulása (Weathering of limestone surfaces). *Földrajzi Értesítő*, No. 4, Budapest.

KÉZ, A. (1960): A trópusi karszt (kúpkarszt) (The tropical karst [cone karst]). Review of a paper by H. LEHMANN (1960). *Földrajzi Értesítő*, Budapest.

KÉZ, A. (1963): A Föld klimatikus geomorfológiai területei (Climato-geomorphologic regions of the earth). *Földrajzi Értesítő*, Budapest.

KILINSKI, E. (1958): *Lehrbuch der Luftelektrizität*. Leipzig.

KINZL, H. (1951): Karsterscheinungen in den peruanischen Anden. *Geographische Studien* (Festschrift J. SÖLCH), Wien.

KLIMASZEWSKI, M. (1958): Neue Ansichten über die Entwicklung des Karstes. *Przeglad Geogr.*, Vol. XXX, No. 3, Warszawa.

256

KLIMASZEWSKI, M. (1964): The karst relief of the Kweilin area (South China). *Geogr. Polonia.*

KNEBEL, W. (1906): *Höhlenkunde mit Berücksichtigung der Karstphänomene.* Braunschweig.

KOCH, F. (1955): Beszámoló a Szovjetunió Össz-szövetségi Földrajzi Társaságának II. Földrajzi Kongresszusáról (Report on the Second Geographical Conference of the Soviet Union's All-Union Geographical Society). N. A. Gvozdetsky's lecture on problems of karst research, *Földrajzi Értesítő,* No. 2, Budapest.

KOCKERT, W. (1968): Mögliche Typen der im Salzbergbau der DDR zusitzenden Wasser und Salzlösungen. *Bergakademie,* Vol. 20, No. 5, pp. 284–288, Leipzig.

KOCKERT, W. (1972): Höhlenbildungen im Zechstein der DDR und einige grundsätzliche Bemerkungen zur Karsthydrologie der Zechsteinschichten. *Berichte Deutsch. Ges. Geol. Wiss. Geologie-Paläontologie,* No. 2, pp. 261–272, Berlin.

KOROZHYEV, S. S. (1965): *Karst Yakutii* (The karst of Yakutsk). In: Tipy Karste v SSSR (In: Types of karst in the USSR). Nauka, Moskva.

KOSACK, H. P. (1952): Die Verbreitung der Karst- und Pseudokarsterscheinungen über die Erde. *Peterm. Geogr. Mitt.,* No. 1, Gotha.

KOWALSKI, K. (1953): *Jaskinie Polski.* Vols I–III, 1951–53, Warszawa.

KÖHN, M. (1948): Über den Einfluß einer Schneedecke auf die Bodentemperaturen. *Wetter und Klima,* No. 1.

KREBS, N. (1904): Morphologische Skizzen aus Istrien. 34. *Jahresbericht K. K. Staatsrealschule,* Trieste.

KREBS, N. (1907): Die Halbinsel Istrien. *Pencks Geogr. Abhandl.,* Vol. 9, No. 2.

KREBS, N. (1910): Offene Fragen der Karstkunde. *Geogr. Zeitschr.*

KREBS, N. (1928): Zur Geomorphologie von Hochkroatien und Unterkrain. *Zeitschr. Ges. Erdkunde* (Jubileums-Sonderband).

KREBS, N. (1929): Ebenheiten und Inselberge im Kroatischen Karst. *Zeitschr. d. Ges. f. Erdkunde,* Berlin.

KREJČI, J. (1960): Zur Frage der Existenz des Karstzyklus. *Sbornik Čs. spol. zemepisné,* 65, Praha.

KRIEG, W. (1964): Gedanken zur Theorie des glazialen Karstes in Salzburg. *Die Höhle,* No. 3, pp. 57–64, Wien.

KRUBER, A. A. (1913): *Gidrographiya karsta.* Moskva.

KRUBER, A. A. (1922): Karstovaya oblast Kryma. *Zemlevedeniye,* 22, Moskva.

KUBINY, D. (1970): Geologické a Speleologické krasového územia v okoli Srncej Priepasti na Trangoske. *Zbornik Múzea Slovenského Krasu,* Rocnik VIII, pp. 99–102.

KUDELIN, B. I. (Editor), (1966): Podzemnyy stok na Territorii SSSR (Underground flow in the USSR). *Mosk. Gos. Univ.,* Moskva.

KUKLA, J. (1958): Jeskyně na Cejlone. *Československy Kras,* 11, Praha.

KUKLA—LOŽEK (1958): Zum Problem der Höhlenfüllungen. *Čs. Kras,* Vol. XI., Praha.

KUNAVER, J. (1973): The high mountainous karst of the Julian Alps in the system of alpine karsts. *IGU Symp. on Karst Morphogenesis,* Papers, Hungary, pp. 209–226.

KUNSKY, J. (1941): Zur Altersfrage der Tropfsteine. *Vestn. Stát. geol. ust.,* 17, Praha.

KUNSKY, J. (1950): *Kras a jeskyne.* Praha.

KUNSKY, J. (1954): *Reise in die Unterwelt.* Praha.

KUNSKY, J. (1957): Thermomineral karst and caves of Zbrasov. *Sborn. Čs. spol. zemepisné,* 4, Praha.

KURZ—ZWITTKOVITZ (1963): Zum Problem der Karrenbildung in den nördlichen Kalkalpen. *Anzeiger d. math.-naturw. Klasse d. österr. Akad. d. Wiss.,* No. 3.

KUZNETSOVA, L. S. (1965): Kizelovskaya Medvezhya peshchera. *Peshcheri,* Nos 5–6, Perm.

KÜHNELT, W. (1950): *Bodenbiologie.* Wien.

KYRLE, G. (1923): *Grundriß der theoretischen Speläologie.* Wien.

LAIS, R. (1941): Über Höhlensediments. *Quartär.,* No. 3.

LANDOLT—BÖRNSTEIN (1936): *Physikalisch-chemische Tabellen.* 5. Auflage, Berlin.

LAPTEV, F. F. (1939): *Agressivnoe deystviye vody na karbonatnye porody, gipsy i betony.* Leningrad–Moskva.

LAPTEV—PRIKLONSKY (1949): *Fizicheskiye svoistva i khimicheskiy sostav podzemnikh vod.* Moskva. (Hungarian ed.: Budapest, 1952.)

LAUTENSACH, H. (1931): Die chemischen Methoden der Untersuchung des Karrenphänomens (a contribution to a paper by H. G. Linder). *Peterm. Mitt.*, Gotha.

LAUTENSACH, H. (1945): *Korea.* Leipzig.

LAUTENSACH, H. (1950): Granitische Abtragungsformen auf der Iberischen Halbinsel und in Korea (ein Vergleich). *Peterm. Mitt.*, Gotha.

LÁNG, S. (1937): Felvidéki karsztok (Karsts of Northern Hungary). *Földrajzi Közlemények*, Nos 6–7, Budapest.

LÁNG, S. (1942): Karsztforrásokra vonatkozó mérések 1940–42-ben (Measurements on karst springs). *Hidrológiai Közlöny*, Budapest.

LÁNG, S. (1943): Geomorfológiai és hidrológiai tanulmányok Gömörben (Geomorphological and hydrographical studies in Gömör). *Hidrológiai Közlöny*, Budapest.

LÁNG, S. (1948): Karszttanulmányok a Dunántúli-középhegységben (Karst studies in the Transdanubian Hills). *Hidrológiai Közlöny*, Budapest.

LÁNG, S. (1952): Geomorfológiai-karsztmorfológiai kérdések (Geomorphological-karstmorphological questions). *Földrajzi Értesítő*, No. 1, Budapest.

LÁNG, S. (1953): A Pilis geomorfológiája (Geomorphology of the Pilis Hills). *Földrajzi Értesítő*, Budapest.

LÁNG, S. (1954): Hidrológiai és morfológiai tanulmányok a Bükkben (Hydrological and morphological studies in the Bükk Hills). *Hidrológiai Közlöny*, Budapest.

LÁNG, S. (1955): Geomorfológiai tanulmányok az aggteleki karsztvidéken (Geomorphological studies in the Aggtelek karst region). *Földrajzi Értesítő*, Budapest.

LÁNG, S. (1956): A hidrogeográfiai kutatások módszertani kérdései (Methodological problems of hydrogeographical research). *Földrajzi Értesítő*, No. 4, Budapest.

LÁNG, S. (1958): A Bakony geomorfológiai képe (karsztos tönkösödés) (Geomorphological aspect of the Bakony Hills [karst peneplanation]). *Földrajzi Közlemények*, No. 4, Budapest.

LÁNG, S. (1964): A Bükk geomorfológiai vázlata (A geomorphological outline of the Bükk Hills). *Karszt- és Barlangkutatási Tájékoztató*, Nos 5–6, Budapest.

LÁNG, S. (1966): A víz szerepéről hazánk természeti földrajzi környezetében (On the role of water in the physico-geographical environment of Hungary). *Földrajzi Közlemények*, No. 1, Budapest.

LÁNG, S. (1973): Quelques questions de la dénudation des karsts et de leur entourage en Hongrie. *IGU Symp. on Karst Morphogenesis*, Papers, Hungary, pp. 227–232.

LEBEDEV, A. B. (1963): *Metodi izucheniya gruntovikh vod.* Moskva.

LEEL-ŐSSY, S. (1952/1): Karrosodás és karros formák (Lapies origin and forms). *Hidrológiai Közlöny*, Budapest.

LEEL-ŐSSY, S. (1952/2): A barlangok osztályozása (Classification of caverns). *Földrajzi Értesítő*, Budapest.

LEEL-ŐSSY, S. (1954): A Magas-Bükk geomorfológiája (Geomorphology of the High Bükk). *Földrajzi Értesítő*, Budapest.

LEEL-ŐSSY, S. (1955): Magyarország karsztmorfológiája (Karst morphology of Hungary). *Candidate's thesis.* Budapest.

LEEL-ŐSSY, S. (1957): A Budai-hegység barlangjai (Caverns of the Buda Hills). *Földrajzi Értesítő*, Budapest.

LEEL-ŐSSY, S. (1958): A Kevély-csoport karsztmorfológiája és barlangjai (Karst morphology and caverns of the Kevély Group). *Földrajzi Értesítő*, Budapest.

LEEL-ŐSSY, S. (1959): A Bükk víznyelőinek és víznyelőbarlangjainak tanulmányozása (Study of sinkholes and sinkhole caverns in the Bükk Hills). *Földrajzi Értesítő*, No. 2, Budapest.

LEEL-ŐSSY, S. (1960/1): Magyarország karsztvidékei (Karst regions of Hungary). *Karszt- és Barlangkutatás*, Jan., Budapest.

LEEL-ŐSSY, S. (1960/2): A tinnyei hévizes barlang (Kissomlyói aragonitbarlang) (The hot-spring cave of Tinnye, the Kissomlyó aragonite cave). *Karszt- és Barlangkutatási Tájékoztató*, July–Aug., Budapest.

LEHMANN, H. (1936): Morphologische Studien auf Java. *Geogr. Abh.*, Stuttgart.

LEHMANN, H. (1948): Der tropische Kegelkarst auf den Grossen Antillen. *Die Erde*, No. 2, Berlin.

LEHMANN, H. (1954/1): Das Karstphänomen in den verschiedenen Klimazonen. *Erdkunde*, Bd. VIII, Bonn.

258

LEHMANN, H. (1954/2): Der tropische Kegelkarst auf den Grossen Antillen. *Erdkunde*, Bd. VIII, No. 2, Bonn.

LEHMANN, H. (1955): Der tropische Kegelkarst in West-Indien. *Tagungsbericht des Deutschen Geogr.-Tages in Essen*, Wiesbaden.

LEHMANN, H. (1956): Der Einfluß des Klimas auf die morphologische Entwicklung des Karstes. *Rep. of the Comp. on Karst Phenomena. Int. Geographical Society*, New York.

LEHMANN, H. (1959): Studien über Poljen in den Venezianischen Voralpen und im Hochappennin. *Erdkunde*, No. 13, Bonn.

LEHMANN, H. (1960): La terminologie classique du karst sous l'aspect critique de la morphologie climatique moderne. *Revue de Géogr. de Lyon*, Vol. XXXV, No. 1., Lyon.

LEHMANN, H. (1962): *Karstmorfologie* (Westermanns Lexikon der Geographie). Braunschweig.

LEHMANN, H. (1964): Stand und Aufgaben der Erforschung der Karstphänomene. *Erdkunde*, No. 18, pp. 81–83, Bonn.

LEHMANN—KRÖMMELBEIN—LÖTSCHET (1956): Karstmorphologische, geologische und botanische Studien in der Sierra de los Organos auf Cuba. *Erdkunde*, Bonn.

LEHMANN, O. (1927): Das Tote Gebirge als Hochkarst. *Mitt. Geogr. Ges.*, 70, Wien.

LEHMANN, O. (1931): Über die Karstdolinen. *Mitt. Geol. Ethnogr. Ges.*, 31, Zürich.

LEHMANN, O. (1932): Die Hydrographie des Karstes. *Enzykl. d. Erdkunde*, Wien–Leipzig.

LINDNER, G. (1930): Das Karrenphänomen. *Peterm. Mitt. Ergänzungsheft*, Gotha.

LINDBERG, K. (1956): Grottes et spéléologie en Suède. *Rass. Speleol. Ital.*, Nos 3–4, Como.

LINK—OTTEMANN (1968): Zur Frage des Einbaues von Strontium in Gips. *Jb. Geologischen Landesamt Baden-Württ.*, No. 10, pp. 175–178.

LLOPIS-LLADO, N. (1953): Karst holofossile et mérofossile. *Comm. I. Congr. Int. de Spéléol.*, Paris.

LOBECK, A. K. (1939): *Geomorphology*. New York.

LÓCZY, I., sen. (1886): *A Kinai-birodalom természeti viszonyainak a leírása* (A description of natural conditions in the Chinese Empire). Budapest.

LOUIS, H. (1956/1): Das Problem der Karst-Niveaus. *Rep. of the Comm. on Karst Phenomena, XVIII. Int. Geogr. Congr.*, Rio de Janeiro.

LOUIS, H. (1956/2): Die Entstehung der Poljen und ihre Stellung in der Karstabtragung. *Erdkunde*, Vol. X, Bonn.

LOUIS, H. (1964): *Allgemeine Geomorfologie*. Berlin. (2nd ed.)

LUKASHOV—SIMONOV (1971): Geomorfologicheskiy analiz pri izuchenii endogennikh poley vosztochnogo Zabaikalya. *Vestnik Moskovs. Univ.*, No. 4, pp. 35–41, Moskva.

LUNDEGARDH, H. (1954): *Klima und Boden*. (4th ed.) Jena.

MACHATSCHEK, F. (1934): *Geomorphologie*. Leipzig–Berlin.

MAKSIMOVICH, G. A. (1947): Tipy karstovikh javleniy. *Tezisi dokl. Molotovs. Karst. konf.*

MAKSIMOVICH, G. A. (1957/1): Korreláciya rechnik teras i gorizontalnikh karstovikh peshcher. *Tr. kom. po izuch. chetver. perioda*, 13, Moskva.

MAKSIMOVICH, G. A. (1957/2): Osnovnye tipy gidrodinamicheskoy profiley oblastey karsta karbonatnykh i sulphatnykh otlozheniy. *Dokl. Akad. Nauk SSSR*, Vol. 112, No. 3, Moskva.

MAKSIMOVICH, G. A. (1958): *Karst Permskoy oblasti*. Perm.

MAKSIMOVICH, G. A. (1959): Osnovnye tipy i modul' podzemnogo stoka karstovykh oblastey. *Dokl. Akad. Nauk SSSR*, Vol. 128, No. 5, Moskva.

MAKSIMOVICH, G. A. (1962/1): *Karst Japonii. Gidrogeologiya i karstovedeniye*. (1st ed.) Perm.

MAKSIMOVICH, G. A. (1962/2): Osnovnye stadii razvitiya mnogoetazhnykh gorizon. talnykh karstovykh peshcher v izvestnyakakh i gipsakh. *Peshcheri*, No. 2, Perm-

MAKSIMOVICH, G. A. (1962/3): Karst gipsov i angidritov zemnogo mira. *Obshchiye voprosi karstovedeniya*, Moskva.

MAKSIMOVICH, G. A. (1963/1): *Osnovi karstovedeniya, Voprosy Morfologii, Speleologii i Gidrogeologii Karsta, I* (Principles of the study of karst, problems of the morphology, speleology, and hydrogeology of karst, I). Nauka, Perm.

MAKSIMOVICH, G. A. (1963/2): *Osnovi karstovedeniya*. Perm.

MAKSIMOVICH, G. A. (1963/3): Jestestvenniye tonneli, mosti i arki karstovykh rayonov. *Peshcheri*, No. 3, Perm.

MAKSIMOVICH, G. A. (1964/1): Karst Afriki. *Gidrogeologiya i karstovedeniye* (2nd ed.) Perm.

MAKSIMOVICH, G. A. (1964/2): *Gidrogeochimicheskiye zony platform*. Khimicheskaya geografya i gidrogeokhimiya (3rd ed.), Perm.

MAKSIMOVICH, G. A. (1965): Geneticheskiy ryad natechnikh otlozheniy peshcher. *Peshcheri*, Nos 5–6, Perm.

MAKSIMOVICH, G. A. (1969): *Osnovy karstovedeniya*. Vol. I. Perm, Vol. II. Perm.

MAKSIMOVICH—GORBUNOVA (1965): *Tipy karsta Urala. Tipy karsta SSSR*. Moskva.

MARKÓ, L. (1961): Kalciumkarbonát és magnéziumkarbonát elegyek oldhatósága. vízben, széndioxid jelenlétében (Solubility in water of calcium and magnesium carbonate mixtures in the presence of carbonic acid). *Karszt- és Barlangkutató*, 1, Budapest.

MARKÓ, L. (1962): A barlangi légáramlás szerepe a karsztbarlangok képződésénél (The role of air currents in the evolution of karst caverns). *Karszt és Barlang*, 1, Budapest.

MARKÓ—JAKUCS, L. (1955): A barlangi légáramlás keletkezése (On the origin of air currents in caverns). *Hidrológiai Közlöny*, Budapest.

MAROSI, S. (1962): A contribution to the discussion of L. Jakucs' candidate's thesis (Jakucs, L. 1960/2). *Földrajzi Értesítő*, No. 2, Budapest.

MAROSI—PÉCSI—SZILÁRD (1958): *Budapest természeti képe* (Nature in and around Budapest). Budapest.

MAROSI—SZILÁRD (1963): A természeti földrajzi tájértékelés elvi-módszertani kérdéseiről (Principles and methods of landscape assessment in physical geography). *Földrajzi Értesítő*, No. 3, Budapest.

MARTEL, E. A. (1900): *La spéléologie*. Paris.

MARTEL, E. A. (1908): *L'évolution souterraine*. Paris.

MARTEL, E. A. (1921): *Nouveau traité des eaux souterraines*. Paris.

MARTEL, E. A. (1933): *La France ignorée*. Paris.

MAUCHA, L. (1959): Beszámoló az ÉKME ... (Report on the activity of the Spelaeological Research Group of the Budapest School of Engineering, October 1957 to March 1959). *Karszt- és Barlangkutatási Tájékoztató*, Sept., Budapest.

MAUCHA, L. (1960/1): Az ÉKME Jósvafői Kutatóállomásának 1959/60. évi munkájáról (On the activity of the Budapest School of Engineering's Research Station at Jósvafő, 1959–60). *Karszt- és Barlangkutatási Tájékoztató*, June, Budapest.

MAUCHA, L. (1960/2): Die Nachweisen von Höhlensystem. *Karszt- és Barlangkutatás*, I, Budapest.

MAUCHA, L. (1968): Ausweis der Gezeiten-Erscheinungen des Karstwasserspiegels. *Karszt- és Barlangkutatás*, V, Budapest.

MAUCHA, R. (1930): Az aggteleki barlang vizeinek kémiai vizsgálata (Chemical testing of waters from the Aggtelek Cavern). *Hidrológiai Közlöny*, Budapest.

MAULL, O. (1940): Vergleichende Karstländerstudien. *Jahrb. Univ. Graz*, Graz.

MAULL, O. (1958): *Geomorfologie*. Wien.

MÁNDY, T. (1954): Mészkövek és dolomitok oldási vizsgálata (Dissolution study on limestones and dolomites). *Hidrológiai Közlöny*, Nos 11–12, Budapest.

MÁTHÉ, I. (1954): *A növényföldrajz alapjai* (Fundamentals of phytogeography). Budapest.

MELIK, A. (1955): *Kraska polja Slovenija v Pleistocenu*. Ljubljana.

MERCK, E. (1956): *Komplexometrische Bestimmungsmethoden mit Titriplex*. (3rd ed.) Darmstadt.

MEYERHOFF, H. A. (1938): The texture of karst topography in Cuba and Puerto Rico. *Journ. of Geomorph.*, No. 1.

MIHÁLTZ, I. (1938): *A Bihar-hegység barlangjai és a hegyszerkezet* (Caverns of the Bihar Hills and mountain building). Kolozsvár.

MILLER, I. P. (1952): A portion of the system $CaCO_3$–CO_2–H_2O with geological implications. *Amer. Journ. of Sci.*, Vol. 250, No. 16.

MIOTKE, F.-D. (1968): Karstmorphologische Studien in der glazial-überformten Höhenstufe der "Picos de Europa", Nordspanien. *Jb. der Geogr. Ges. zu Hannover*, Sonderheft 4, p. 161, Hannover.

MIOTKE, F.-D. (1971): Die Naturlandschaft an der Porta Westfalica. In: *Jahrbuch der Geogr. Ges. zu Hannover* für 1968, p. 265, Hannover.

MORTENSEN, H. (1949): Über die morphologische Härte des Granits. *Att. Congr. Int. Géogr.*, Lisbonne.

MOSONYI, E. (1948): Hegyvidéki nagyobb víztároló medencék hidrológiai méretezése (Hydrological dimensioning of larger water reservoirs in hilly regions). *Vizügyi Közlemények*, No. 1, Budapest.

MOSONYI, E. (1956): *Wasserkraftwerke*. Budapest.

MOSONYI—PAPP (1959): *Műszaki földtan* (Engineering geology). Budapest.

MRKOS, H. (1959): Hydrographische Forschungen in Albaniens Karstgebieten. *Höhlenkund. Mitt.*, No. 15.

MUNCK, S. (1963): Über Höhlen in Grönland. *Akten III. Int. Kongr. f. Speläologie*, Vol. II, Sect. 1, Wien.

MURRAY, J. E. (1954): The deposition of calcite and aragonite in caves. *Journ. of Geol.*, 62, Chicago.

MÜLLER, G. O. (1962): *Praktikum der quantitativen chemischen Analyse*. Leipzig.

MÜLLER—SÁRVÁRY (1973): Pure corrosive model of the development of vertical karst shafts. *IGU Symp. on Karst Morphogenesis*, Papers, Hungary, pp. 233–245.

NAUM, T. (1973): Le volcano-karst du massif des Calimani. *IGU Symp. on Karst Morphogenesis*, Papers, Hungary, pp. 246–257.

NÉMETH, E. (1959): *Hidrológia és hidrometria* (Hydrology and hydrometry). (2nd ed.) Budapest.

NÉMETH, E. (1963): *Hidromechanika* (Hydraulics). Budapest.

NESVARA, J. (1972): O pruchodu zvétralin pres zkrajovatélé vápence. *Zbornik Múzea Slovenského Krasu*, Rocnik X, pp. 87–89.

NICOD, J. (1965): Karst du gypse dans les Alpes et en Provence. *Actes Congr. Natl., Soc. Savantes*, Nice, Sect. Géogr., pp. 87–104.

NIKOLAEV, N. I. (1946): Ob evolutsionnom razvitii karstovikh form i znachenii strukturno-tektonicheskogo faktora. *Sovyetskaya Geologiya*, 10.

NUÑEZ, J. A. (1963): *Geografia de Cuba*. La Havana.

NUÑEZ, J. A. (1964): *Geologia de Cuba*. La Havana.

OERTLI, H. (1953): Karbonathärte von Karstgewässern. *Stalaktite*, III, 4, Sion.

OVCHINNIKOV, A. M. (1938): K metodike izucheniya treshchinovatosti. *Razvedka nedr.*, Nos 4–5.

OVCHINNIKOV, A. M. (1949): *Obshchaya gidrogeologiya*. Moskva.

OZORAY, GY. (1960): Nemkarsztos üregek genetikája magyarországi példák alapján (Origin of non-karstic cavities: Hungarian examples). *Karszt- és Barlangkutatási Tájékoztató*, Jan.–Feb., Budapest.

OZORAY, GY. (1963/1): Einige genetische Probleme der Höhlen in Karstgesteinen (an Beispielen aus Ungarn). *III. Int. Kongr. f. Speläologie*, Vol. 2, Sect. 1, Wien.

OZORAY, GY. (1963/2): Új kősószakadék Parajdon (A recent rift in the rock salt of Parajd). *Földrajzi Értesítő*, No. 2, Budapest.

PÁLFFY, M. (1920/1): Tengeralatti forráslerakódások a budapesti triászkorú képződményekben (Submarine spring deposits in the Triassic of Budapest). *Földtani Közlöny*, Budapest.

PÁLFFY, M. (1920/2): Adatok Pécs környékének hidrogeológiájához (Contributions to the hydrogeology of the environs of Pécs). *Hidrológiai Közlöny*, Budapest.

PALMER, H. S. (1927): Karrenbildungen in den Basaltgesteinen der Hawaiischen Inseln. *Mitt. d. Geogr. Ges. in Wien*, 70, Wien.

PANOŠ, V. (1955): Jeskyné Severomoravského krasu. *Hranicky kras*, Praha.

PAPP, F. (1953): A karsztvizek mennyiségi és minőségi viszonyairól (On the quantity and quality parameters of karst waters). *MTA Közleményei*, Budapest.

PAPP, SZ. (1954): A hidrológiai kutatás kémiai vonatkozásai (Chemical aspects of hydrogeological research). *Mérnöki Továbbképző Int. kiadv.*, Budapest.

PAPP, SZ. (1956): *A víz kémiája* (Water chemistry). Budapest.

PAPP—VÁRY, Á. (1959): A szoplaki Ördöglyuk-barlang morfológiája és genezise (Morphology and origin of the Devil's Hole on Szoplak Hill). *Karszt- és Barlangkutatási Tájékoztató*, Nov., Budapest.

PARMUZIN, J. P. (1954): Landshaftobrazuyushchiye znacheniye karsta Sibiri. *Geogr. Izd. Moskovsk. Univ.*, Moskva.

261

PASSARGE, S. (1916): Morphologie der Klimazonen oder Morphologie der Landschaftsgürtel? *Peterm. Mitt.*, Gotha.

PASTORINO, M. V. (1970): Notes pour une étude biospéléologique de la Grotte des "Scogli neri". 435 Li., pp. 20–30.

PÁVAY-VAJNA, F. (1930): A forró oldatok és gőzök-gázok szerepe a barlangképződésnél (Role of hot solutions, vapours and gases in cavern sculpture). *Hidrológiai Közlöny*, Budapest.

PÁVAY-VAJNA, F. (1950): A "karsztvíz" és a "karsztvíztérképek" ("Karst water" and "karst water maps"). *Hidrológiai Közlöny*, Budapest.

PENCK, A. (1904): Über das Karstphänomen. *Schr. d. Ver. z. Verbreitung nat. w. Kenntnisse in Wien*, 44, Wien.

PENCK, A. (1913): Die Formen der Landoberfläche und Verschiebungen der Klimagürtel. *Sitz. Ber. d. Preuss. Akad. d. Wiss.*, 4.

PENCK, A. (1924): *Das unterirdische Karstphänomen*. CVIJIĆ-Festschrift, Beograd.

PÉCSI, M. (1961): A periglaciális talajfagyjelenségek főbb típusai Magyarországon (Main types of a periglacial ground frost phenomena in Hungary). *Földrajzi Értesítő*, Budapest.

PÉCSI, M. (1964): A magyar középhegységek geomorfológiai kutatásának újabb kérdései (Recent problems of geomorphological research in the Hungarian hills). *Földrajzi Értesítő*, No. 1, Budapest.

PÉCSI, M. (1967): A földfelszíni külső (exogén) folyamatok osztályozása és nevezéktani értelmezése (Classification and terminological interpretation of the exogenous processes of the earth's surface). *Földrajzi Közlemények*, No. 3, Budapest.

PFEFFER, D. (1963): Die geschichtliche Entwicklung der Anschauungen über das Karstgrundwasser. *Geol. Jahrbuch*, Beihefte 57, Hannover.

PIA, J. (1933): *Die rezenten Kalksteine*. Berlin.

PIA, J. (1953): Theorien über die Löslichkeit des kohlensauren Kalkes. *Mitt. Geol. Ges.*, Wien.

PITTY, A. F. (1970): An approach to the study of karst water. *Univ. of Hull Publ.*, Occasional papers in Geography, No. 5.

POLOVINKINA, N. (1948): *Struktury gornykh porod*. Vol. 2. Moskva–Leningrad.

PRIESNITZ, K. (1967): Zur Frage der Lösungsfreudigkeit von Kalkgesteinen in Abhängigkeit von der Lösungsfläche und ihrem Gehalt an Magnesiumkarbonat. Sonderdruck aus: *Annal. de Géomorph.*, Neue Folge, Bd. 11, No. 4, pp. 491–498, Berlin.

PRIESNITZ, K. (1969/1): Das Nixseebecken, ein Polje im Gipskarst des südwestlichen Harzvorlandes. *Jb. Karst- und Höhlenkunde*, No. 9, pp. 73–82.

PRIESNITZ, K. (1969/2): Kurze Übersicht über den Karstformenschatz des südwestlichen Harzlandes. *Jb. Karst- und Höhlenkunde*, No. 9, pp. 11–23.

PRIESNITZ, K. (1969/3): Über die Vergleichbarkeit von Lösungsformen auf Chlorid-, Sulfat- und Karbonatgestein, Überlegungen zur Fragen und Methodik der Karstmorphologie. *Geol. Rundschau*, Vol. 58, No. 2, pp. 427–438.

PRIESNITZ, K. (1972/1): Formen, Prozesse und Faktoren der Verkarstung und Mineralumbildung im Ausstrich salinarer Serien. *Göttinger Geogr. Abh.*, No. 60, Sonderdruck, pp. 317–339, Göttingen.

PRIESNITZ, K. (1972/2): *Methods of isolating and quantifying solution factors in the laboratory*. Göttingen.

RADINJA, D. (1973): Caractéristiques fondamentales de la karstification en Slovénie. *IGU Symp. on Karst Morphogenesis*, Papers, Hungary, pp. 258–270.

RAJMAN—RODA (1972/1): Vyskum Pricin destruccie sintrového materiálu v jaskyni Domica. *Zbornik Múzea Slovenského Krasu*, Rocnik X, pp. 63–71.

RAJMAN—RODA (1972/2): Zmeny mikroklimy a ich následky v Ochtinskej aragonitovej jaskyni. *Zbornik Múzea Slovenského Krasu*, Rocnik X, pp. 90–93.

RASMUSSON, G. (1958): Kleinkegelkarst in Nordschweden. *Wiss. Zeitschr. der Ernst-Moritz-Arndt-Universität*, Greifswald 1957/58, Mat.-Naturwiss., R., Nos 1–2.

RASMUSSON, G. (1959): Karstformen im Granit des Fichtelgebirges. *Die Höhle*, 10, Wien.

RATHJENS, C. (1951): Der Hochkarst im System der klimatischen Morphologie. *Erdkunde*, Bonn.

RATHJENS, C. (1954/1): Zur Frage der Karstrandebene im Dinarischen Karst. *Erdkunde*, No. 8, Bonn.

Rathjens, C. (1954/2): Karsterscheinungen in der klimatisch-morphologischen Vertikalgliederung des Gebirges. *Erdkunde*, Bonn.

Reinboth, F. (1967): Die Waldschmiede bei Walkenried eingestürzt. *Mitt. d. Verb. Deutsch. Höhlen- und Karstforscher*, Nos 3–4, München.

Reinboth, F. (1968): Beiträge zur Theorie der Gipshöhlenbildung. *Die Höhle*, Vol. 19, No. 3, pp. 75–83, Wien.

Reiter, R. (1960): *Meteorobiologie und Elektrizität der Atmosphere*. Leipzig.

Renault, P. (1959): Processus morphogénétiques des karsts équatoriaux. *Bulletin A.G.F.*

Renault, P. (1967): Contributions à l'étude des actions mécaniques et sédimentologiques dans la spéléogenèse. *Annal. Spéléol.*, 22(1), pp. 1–16.

Reuter—Molek (1971): Beziehungen zwischen Gebirgsfestigkeit und Karsterscheinungen im Salzkarst der DDR. *Neue Bergbautechnik*, No. 1, pp. 14–19, Leipzig.

Richter, E. (1908): Beiträge zur Landeskunde Bosniens und der Herzegowina. *Wiss. Mitt. a. Bosnien u. d. Herzegowina*, Vol. X.

Rizikov, D. V. (1954): Priroda karsta i osnovnye zakonomernosty yego razvitiya (na primere Urala). *Trudy Gornogeol. Inst.*, Moskva.

Robertson, C. E. (1964): Carbonate equilibria in selected natural waters. *Amer. Journ. of Science*, 262 (1), pp. 56–65.

Robinson, E. (1967): Submarine slides in white limestone group, Jamaica. *Bull. Amer. Assoc. Petrol. Geologists*, 51(4), pp. 569–578.

Roglić, J. (1956): Karstprozess und fluviatile Erosion. Rep. of the Comm. on Karst Phenomena. *17th Int. Geogr. Congr.*, Rio de Janeiro.

Roglić, J. (1957): Quelques problèmes fondamentaux du karst. *L'information Géogr.*, No. 1, Paris.

Roglić, J. (1960): Das Verhältnis der Flußerosion zum Karstprozess. *Zeitschr. f. Geomorph.*, Vol. IV, No. 2, Göttingen.

Roglić, J. (1961): Korrosionsformen in bedeckten Karst, *Glasnik Srpskog geografskog drustva*, 41, pp. 7–13, Beograd.

Roglić, J. (1963): Glaciation of the Dinaric Mountains and its effects on the karst. *6th Intern. Congr. Quaternary*, 1961, Rept., 3, pp. 293–299, Warszawa.

Roglić, J. (1965/1): The delimitations and morphological types of the Dinaric karst. *Naše Jame*, 7/1/2, pp. 12–20.

Roglić, J. (1965/2): The depth of the fissure circulation of water and the evolution of subterranean cavities in the Dinaric karst. Problems of the Speleological Research. — *Int. Speleol. Conf.*, Brno, 1964, pp. 25–35.

Rohdenburg—Meyer (1963): Rezente Mikroformung in Kalkgebieten durch inneren Abtrag und die Rolle der periglazialen Gesteinverwitterung. *Zeitschr. f. Geomorph.*, No. 7, Berlin.

Rose, P. V. (1966): Caves and caving in Australia. *Proc. of the Brit. Speleol. Association*, 4.

Rosszinszkij—Kuzmin (1956): A mederalakulás törvényszerűségei (Laws of streambed sculpture). *MTA VI. Oszt. Közleményei*, Vol. 19, No. 4, Budapest.

Rozložnik, V. (1953): Objavy a problémy jaskýň Čiernej vyvieračky v Slovenskom krase. *Geogr. časopis*, 5, Bratislava.

Russell, W. H. (1960): Distribution of caves in Texas. *National Speleol. Soc. News*, 18, Washington.

Russell, W. H. (1964): The caves of Mexico. *National Speleol. Soc. News*, 22, Washington.

Sachs, J. (1865): *Handbuch der experimental Physiologie*. Leipzig.

Saint-Ours, J. (1959): Les phénomènes karstiques à Madagascar. *Annal. Spéléol.*, Nos 3–4.

Santoyo, A. L. (1973): A remarkable lapies topography in the South of Central Mexico. *IGU Symp. on Karst Morphogenesis*, Papers, Hungary, pp. 271–274.

Sapper, K. (1914): Über Abtragungsvorgänge in den regenfeuchten Tropen und ihre morphologischen Wirkungen. *Geogr. Zeitschr.*, Wiesbaden.

Savnik—Gantar (1959): Le karst souterrain dans la région d'Idrija. Porocila. *Acta Karstolog.*, 2, Ljubljana.

Sawicki, L. (1909): Beiträge zum geographischen Zyklus im Karste. *Geogr. Zeitschr.*, 15, Wiesbaden.

SCHAUENBERGER, O. (1951): Höhlen in Norwegen und ihre Bedeutung für die Morphologie der norwegischen Landschaft. *Protokoll d. 6. ord. Vollvers. d. Höhlenkommission.*

SCHAUENBERGER, O. (1955): Über die vertikale Verbreitung der nordalpinen Karsthöhlen. *Mitt. d. Höhlenkommission,* No. 1.

SCHERF, E. (1922): Hévforrások okozta kőzetelváltozások a Budai-hegységben (Rock alteration due to thermal springs in the Buda Hills). *Hidrológiai Közlöny,* Budapest.

SCHEUER—SCHWEITZER (1970): Az édesvízi mészkövek csoportosítása (Classification of freshwater limestones). *Földrajzi Értesítő,* Vol. XIX, pp. 356–360, Budapest.

SCHEUER—SCHWEITZER (1971): A negyedkori fagyaprózódási folyamatok hatása a karsztforrásokra (Influence of Quaternary-frost comminution upon karst springs). *Földrajzi Értesítő,* Vol. XX, No. 4, pp. 465–468, Budapest.

SCHMIDT, E. R. (1944): Barlang-, dolina- és poljeképződés (Origin of caverns, dolines and poljes). *Bányászati és Koh. Lapok,* Budapest.

SCHMIDT, E. R. (1953): Karsztvízjáratok kialakulásának geomechanikája (Geomechanics of karst water channel evolution). *MTA Közleményei,* Vol. 8, No. 1, Budapest.

SCHMIDT, E. R. (1954): A geomechanikai szemlélet szerepe a karsztvízkutatásban és a karsztvíz elleni védekezésben (Role of the geomechanical viewpoint in karst water prospecting and in karst water hazard prevention). *Bányászati Lapok,* Budapest.

SCHMIDT, E. R. (1957): *Geomechanika* (Geomechanics). Budapest.

SCHMIDT-THOMÉ, P. (1943): Karrenbildung in kristallinem Gestein. *Zeitschr. d. Deutsch. Geol. Ges.,* 95.

SCHOELLER, H. (1956): Géochimie des eaux souterraines. *Soc. des Edit. Techn.,* Paris.

SCHOKLITSCH, A. (1950): *Handbuch des Wasserbaues.* Wien.

SCHULHOF, Ö. (1957): *Magyarország ásvány- és gyógyvizei* (Mineral and medicinal waters of Hungary). Budapest.

SERBAN—VIEHMANN—COMAN (1961): *Romanian caverns.* Bucharest.

SERKO—MICHLER (1953): *Die Grotte von Postojna und sonstige Sehenswürdigkeiten des Karstes.* Ljubljana.

SHCHEPETOV—VOLOSHENKO—EMELYANOV—RIZHKOV—LOBANOV (1965): Krupnaya peshchera na yuzhnom Urale. *Peshcheri,* Nos 5–6, Perm.

SHOSTAKOVICH, A. (1927): Der ewig gefrorene Boden Sibiriens. *Zeitschr. d. Ges. f. Erdkunde,* Berlin.

SHVETSOV, M. C. (1948): *Petrografiya osadochnikh porod.* Moskva–Leningrad.

SKRIVANEK, F. (1960): Karst und Karsthöhlen der Tschechoslowakei und ihre Untersuchung. *Die Höhle,* No. 11, Wien.

SMITH, J. G. (1963): A short note on the karst area of Papua. *National Speleol. Soc. News,* 21, Washington.

SMYK—DRYZAL (1964): Untersuchungen über den Einfluß von Mikroorganismen auf das Phänomen der Karstbildung. *Erdkunde,* No. 18, Bonn.

SMYKATZ-KLOSS, W. (1966): Sedimentpetrographische und geochemische Untersuchungen am Karbonatgestein des Zechsteins. *Contr. Mineral. and Petrol.,* 13, pp. 207–268.

SOKOLOV, N. I. (1960): Tipologicheskaya klassifikatsiya karsta (Typological classification of karst). *Materialy Komiss. Izuch. Geol. Geograf. Karsta,* Inform. Sb., 1.

SOKOLOV, D. S. (1962): *Osnovniye usloviya razvitiya karsta* (Fundamental conditions for the development of karst). Gosgeoltekhizdat, Moskva.

SOÓ, R. (1953): *Növényföldrajz* (Plant geography). Budapest.

SPECHT, R. L. (1958): Micro-environment (soil) of a natural plant community. *Proc. Canberra Symp.* 1956, Unesco, Paris.

STEFANOVITS, P. (1959/1): A magyarországi erdőtalajok genetikus talajföldrajzi osztályozása (Genetic pedogeographic classification of Hungarian forest soils). *Agrokémia és Talajtan,* Budapest.

STEFANOVITS, P. (1959/2): A talajföldrajz eredményei és feladatai Magyarországon (Achievements and tasks of pedogeography in Hungary). *Földrajzi Közlemények,* Budapest.

STEFANOVITS, P. (1963): *Magyarország talajai* (The soils of Hungary). (1st ed.) 1956, (2nd ed.) 1963, Budapest.

Stirn, A. (1964): Kalktuffvorkommen und Kalktufftypen der Schwäbischen Alb. *Abh. zur Karst- und Höhlenkunde*, Reihe E, Botanik, No. 1.

Stoklasa—Doerell (1926): *Biochemische und biophysikalische Erforschung des Bodens*. Berlin.

Stoklasa—Ernest (1922): Über den Ursprung etc. des CO_2 im Boden. *Chemisch. Zeitung*, No. 6.

Strömpl, G. (1927): A Gömör-Tornai karszt hidrológiája (Hydrology of the Gömör-Torna karst). *Hidrológiai Közlöny*, Budapest.

Strötker—Reinboth (1968): Das Kalktufflager und die darin befindliche Horststeinhöhle in Valdorf bei Vlotho/Weser. *Der Minden-Ravensberger Heimatkalender*, Jg. 40, Bielefeld.

Stupishin, A. V. (1967): Ravninny karst i zakonomernosti ego razvitiya na primere Srednego Povolzh'ya (Plains karst and the mechanisms of its formation, with the example of the Central Povolzh'ye). *Kazanskogo Univ.*, Kazan.

Stupishin, A. V. (1973): Plain karst and the basic laws of its development. *IGU Symp. on Karst Morphogenesis*, Papers, Hungary, pp. 275–287.

Sunartadirdja—Lehmann (1960): Der tropische Karst von Maros und Nord-Bone in SW-Celebes (Sulawesi). Int. Beiträge zur Karstmorphologie. *Zeitschr. f. Geomorph.*, Suppl. Bd. 2.

Sweeting, G. S.—Sweeting, M. M. (1969): Some aspects of the carboniferous limestone in relation to its landforms. *Méditerranée*, No. 7, pp. 201–209.

Sweeting, M. M. (1958): The karstlands of Jamaica. *Geogr. Journ.*, 124, pp. 184–199, London.

Szabados, A. (1950): A földalatti harmat talajtani és talajbiológiai szerepe (Pedological and pedobiological role of underground dew). *Mezőgazdasági Tudományos Közlöny*, Budapest.

Szabó, J. (1883): *Geológia kiváló tekintettel a petrográfiára, vulkánosságra és hidrográfiára* (Geology with special regard to petrography, volcanism and hydrography). Budapest.

Szabó, P. Z. (1953): A Mecsek karsztvízrendszere (The karst hydrography of the Mecsek Hills). *Hidrológiai Közlöny*, July–Aug., Budapest.

Szabó, P. Z. (1955): A karsztkutatás népgazdasági jelentősége (Economic importance of karst research). *Dunántúli Tud. Gyűjtemény*, Pécs.

Szabó, P. Z. (1956): Magyarországi karsztformák klímatörténeti vonatkozásai (Climato-historic implications of karst forms in Hungary). *Ibid.*, Pécs.

Szabó, P. Z. (1957): A karszt, mint klimatikus morfológiai probléma (The karst as a problem of climatic morphology). *Ibid.*, Pécs.

Szabó, P. Z. (1963/1): A vízföldrajz jelentősége (The importance of hydrogeography). *Földrajzi Közlemények*, No. 3, Budapest.

Szabó, P. Z. (1963/2): A hidrodinamika és a karsztalaktan néhány összefüggése Magyarországon (On certain connexions of hydrodynamics with karst morphology in Hungary). *Dunántúli Tud. Gyűjtemény*, Pécs.

Szabó, P. Z. (1964): Neue Daten und Beobachtungen zur Kenntnis der Paläokarsterscheinungen in Ungarn. *Erdkunde*, Vol. 18, No. 2, Bonn.

Szabó, P. Z. (1966): Újabb adatok és megfigyelések a magyarországi őskarsztjelenségek ismeretéhez (New data and observations concerning paleokarst phenomena in Hungary). *Dunántúli Tud. Gyűjtemény*, Pécs.

Szabó, P. Z. (1968): A magyarországi karsztosodás fejlődéstörténeti vázlata (Outline evolution history of karst in Hungary). *Ibid.*

Szádeczky-Kardoss, E. (1950): Karsztvíztérkép és preventív védekezés (Karst water maps and prevention of the karst water hazard). *Hidrológiai Közlöny*, Nos 5–6, Budapest.

Szádeczky-Kardoss, E. (1953): Karsztvíztérkép-problémák és karszttípusok (Problems of karst water maps and various types of karst). *MTA Műszaki Tudományok Oszt. Közl.*, No. 1, Budapest.

Szádeczky-Kardoss, E. (1957): A Dunántúli-középhegység karsztvíztérképe (Karst water map of the Transdanubian Hills). *Hidrológiai Közlöny*, 28, Budapest.

Szádeczky-Kardoss, E. (1963): *Geokémia* (Geochemistry). Budapest.

Szelényi, F. (1953): Laboratóriumi vizsgálati módszer a talajok levegő- és vízgazdálkodásának meghatározására (Laboratory method for recording air and water households of soils). *Agrokémia és Talajtan*, Vol. 3, Budapest.

SZÉKELY, A. (1953): Az ágasvári Csörgőlyuk-barlang (Csörgőlyuk Cave on Ágasvár Peak, Mátra Hills, Hungary). *Földrajzi Értesítő*, No. 1, Budapest.

TAKÁCS, P. (1950): A dorogi karsztszén és a bányavíz kölcsönhatása (Interaction between karst coal and water inflows in mines). *Hidrológiai Közlöny*, Nos 11–12, Budapest.

TATARINOV, K. A. (1965): *Karstovye peshcheri Srednogo Pridnestrovya.* Tipy karsta v SSSR, Moskva.

TELL, L. (1961): The rate of erosion with special reference to the caves of Lumelunda. *Arch. of Swedish Speleology*, Norrköping.

TELL, L. (1962): Die Höhlentypen Schwedens. *Arch. of Swedish Speleology*, 2, Norrköping.

TERZAGHI, K. (1913): Beiträge zur Hydrographie und Morphologie des Kroatischen Karstes. *Földtani Intézet Évi Jelentése*, Budapest.

THOM—HUMFELD (1932): Notes on the association of microorganisms and roots. *Journ. of Bacteriology*, 23.

THORNBURY, W. D. (1956): *Principles of geomorphology.* New York–London.

TILLMANNS, J. (1932): *Die chemische Untersuchung von Wasser und Abwasser.* Halle.

TILLMANNS—BÖMER—JUCKENAK (1940): *Handbuch der Lebensmittelchemie* (Vol. 8: Wasser und Luft). Berlin.

TILLMANNS—HIRSCH—LURMANN (1931): Nouveau procédé de désadification de l'eau. *Gas- u. Wasserfach*, Nos 48–52.

TÓTH, A. (1931): *Adatok a gránit morfológiájához* (On granite morphology). Budapest.

TRIMMEL, H. (1956): Tektonik und Höhlenbildung. *XX. Int. Congr. Geol.*, Resumenes, Mexico.

TRIMMEL, H. (1957): Die Probleme der alpinen Karst- und Höhlenforschung. *Festschr. z. Hundertjahrfeier d. Geogr. Ges.*, Wien.

TRIMMEL, H. (1961): Höhlenausfüllung, Höhlenentwicklung und die Frage der Höhlenbildungszyklen. *Rass. Spel. Italiana*, Memoria 5, Como.

TRIMMEL, H. (1968): *Höhlenkunde.* Braunschweig.

TROLL, C. (1944/1): Diluvialgeologie und Klima. *Geol. Rundschau*, 34, Stuttgart.

TROLL, C. (1944/2): Strukturböden, Solifluktion und die Frostklimate der Erde. *Geol. Rundschau*, 34, Stuttgart.

TROLL C. (1953): Die Klimatypen an der Schneegrenze. *Act. IV. Cong. INQUA* Rome.

TROMBE, F. (1951/1): *Les eaux souterraines.* Paris.

TROMBE, F. (1951/2): Quelques aspects des phénomènes chimiques souterrains. *Annal. de Spéléol.*

TROMBE, F. (1952): *Traité de spéléologie.* Paris.

TROMBE, F. (1956): *La spéléologie.* Paris.

TROMBE, F. (1962): Sédiments d'origine chimique dans les grottes. *Paper presented to the Int. Speleol. Symp.*, Varenna. Duplicated copy, Paris.

TUĆÁN, F. (1933): *Pogledi na geokemiju Dinarskoga krsa.* Zagreb.

VACHRUSHEV, G. V. (1965): Lyodyanye peshcheri Bashkirii v gipsach i angidritach. *Peshcheri*, Nos 5–6, Perm.

VADÁSZ, E. (1940): A Dunántúl karsztvizei (Karst waters of Transdanubia). *Hidrológiai Közlöny*, Budapest.

VADÁSZ, E. (1946): A magyar bauxitelőfordulások földtani alkata (Geological structure of the Hungarian bauxite deposits). *Földtani Intézet Évkönyve*, 2, Budapest.

VADÁSZ, E. (1951/1): *Bauxitföldtan* (Bauxite geology). Budapest.

VADÁSZ, E. (1951/2): Adatok a laterites mállás kérdéséhez (Data on lateritic weathering). *Földtani Közlöny*, Nos 10–12, Budapest.

VADÁSZ, E. (1955): *Elemző földtan* (Analytical geology). Budapest.

VADÁSZ, E. (1957): *Földtörténet és földfejlődés* (Earth's history and evolution). Budapest.

VADÁSZ, E. (1960): *Magyarország földtana* (The geology of Hungary). (2nd ed.) Budapest.

VASILYEV, B. V. (1962): Karstovye peshcheri v Oktyabrskom rayone Bashkirskoy SSSR. *Peshcheri*, No. 2, Perm.

VENKOVITS, I. (1949/1): Leszivárgó csapadékvizek vegyi összetételének változásai (Changes in chemical composition in descending atmospheric waters). *Földtani Intézet Évi Jelentése*, Budapest.

266

VENKOVITS, I. (1949/2): Dorogi vízvizsgálatok (Hydrological studies at Dorog). *Hidrológiai Közlöny*, Budapest.

VENKOVITS, I. (1949/3): Adatok a dorogi mezozoos alaphegység . . . (On cavities and water passages connected with structure in the Mesozoic bedrock at Dorog). *Hidrológiai Közlöny*, Budapest.

VENKOVITS, I. (1952): A barlangok fejlődésének dialektikája (Dialectics of cavern evolution). *Hidrológiai Közlöny*, Nos 5–6, Budapest.

VENKOVITS, I. (1953): Újabb megfigyelés a karsztvízkérdéssel kapcsolatban (A recent observation concerning the karst water problem). *MTA Műszaki Tudományok Oszt. Közl.*, No. 1, Budapest.

VENKOVITS, I. (1960/1): Karsztnevezéktani vita (A discussion of karst terminology). *Karszt- és Barlangkutatás*, I, Budapest.

VENKOVITS, I. (1960/2): A karszt fogalmi meghatározása (A definition of the karst concept). *Karszt- és Barlangkutatási Tájékoztató*, Oct., Budapest.

VERNADSKY, V. J. (1929/1): O klassifikatsii i khimicheskom sostave prirodnykh vod. *Priroda*, No. 9.

VERNADSKY, V. J. (1929/2): *La biosphère*. Paris.

VERSTAPPEN, H. TH. (1964): Karst morphology of the Star Mountains (Central New Guinea) and its relation to lithology and climate. *Zeitschr. f. Geomorph.*, No. 8, Berlin.

VIEHMANN—SERBAN (1961): Über die Entstehung der flachen und horizontalen Höhlendecken. *Akten des III. Int. Kongr. f. Speläologie*, Vol. A, Wien.

VILJAMSZ, V. R. (1950): *Talajtan* (Pedology). Budapest.

VINDIS, I. (1955): *Jaskyna Gombasek, sprievodca*. Bratislava.

VINOGRADSKY, S. (1892): Recherches sur les organismes de la nitrification. *Arch. Sci. Biol.*, 1, Petersburg.

VITÁLIS, S. (1941): A vízkutatás és bányászata (Prospecting and winning of water). *Bányászati és Kohászati Lapok*, Budapest.

VITÁSEK, F. (1940): Der Rhythmus im Wachstum der Tropfsteine und die Demänová-Höhlen. *Zeitschr. f. Geomorph.*, Berlin.

WAGENHOFFER, V. (1968): A Gerecse természeti földrajza (Physical geography of the Gerecse Hills, Hungary). *Ph. D. thesis, manuscript*. Library of Physico-Geographic Institute, A. József University, Szeged.

WAGNER, R. (1953): A táj és a légkör (Landscape and atmosphere). *Időjárás*, Nos 7–8, Budapest.

WAGNER, R. (1954): Fluktuáló töbörköd (Fluctuating mist in a doline). *Időjárás*, Nos 7–8, Budapest.

WAGNER, R. (1955/1): A mikroklímák földrajzi elrendeződése Hosszúbércen (Geographical distribution of microclimates on Hosszúbérc Ridge, Bükk Hills, Hungary). *Időjárás*, Budapest.

WAGNER, R. (1955/2): A mikroklíma fogalma és kutatási módszere a természeti földrajzi kutatásokban (Concept of microclimate and methods of its investigation in physical-geographical studies). *Földrajzi Értesítő*, Budapest.

WAGNER, R. (1956): Mikroklímatérségek és térképezésük (Microclimatic spaces and their mapping). *Földrajzi Közlemények*, No. 2, Budapest.

WAGNER, R. (1960): *Egy bükki töbör felmelegedése és lehűlése* (Warming and cooling in a doline of the Bükk Hills). A Magyar Meteorológiai Társulat 5. vándorgyűlésének előadásai és tanulmányútjai (28–30. Aug. 1959. Eger), Budapest.

WAGNER, R. (1963): Der Tagesgang der Lufttemperatur einer Doline im Bükk-Gebirge. *Acta Climat. Szegediensis*, Vols 2–3, Szeged.

WAGNER, R. (1964): Lufttemperaturmessungen in einer Doline des Bükk-Gebirges. *Zeitschr. f. angew. Meteorologie*, Vol. 5, Nos 3–4.

WARWICK, G. T. (1953): *Cave formations and deposits*. British Caving, London.

WATSON, R. A. (1966): Central Kentucky karst hydrology. *Natl. Speleol. Soc. Bull.*, 28(3), pp. 159–166.

WAYLAND, E. J. (1934): Peneplains and some erosional platforms. *Geol. Survey*, Uganda.

WEIR, G. G. (1960): An Iranian Gypsum Cave. *Nat. Speleol. Soc. News*, 18, Washington.

WENDELBERGER, G. (1961): Verkarstung und Pflanzendecke. *Österreichische Hochschulzeitung*, July 1.

WHITE, W. B. (1962): Further notes on Jamaican caving. *Nat. Speleol. Soc. News,* 20, Washington.

WHITE, W. B. (1963): Cavern and karst development in the Swago Creek area, West Virginia, USA. *Akten III. Int. Kongr. f. Speläologie,* Vol. 2, Sect. 1, Wien.

WISSMANN, H. (1954): Der Karst der humiden-heissen und sommerheissen Gebiete Ostasiens. *Erdkunde,* No. 2, Bonn.

WISSMANN, H. (1957): Karsterscheinungen in Hadramaut. Ein Beitrag zur Morphologie der semiariden und ariden Tropen. *Geomorph. Studien, Peterm. Mitt.,* Erg. H., Gotha.

ZÁMBÓ, L. (1973): The effect of terra rossa type sediments on dolina morphogenesis. *IGU Symp. on Karst Morphogenesis,* Papers, Hungary, pp. 288–304.

ZEHENDER—STUMM—FISCHER (1956): Freie Kohlensäure und pH von Wasser im Calciumkarbonat-Lösungsgleichgewicht. *Schweizer ver. von Gas- und Wasserfachmännern,* H. 11.

ZHUKOVSKY, S. YA. (1962): Karstovye yavleniya v srednem techenii r. Onegi. *Bull. MOIP, Otdel' Geol.,* Vol. 37, No. 4.

ZÖTL, J. (1957): Neue Ergebnisse der Karsthydrographie. *Erdkunde,* No. 2, Bonn.

ZÖTL, J. (1958): Beitrag zu den Problemen der Karsthydrographie mit besonderer Berücksichtigung der Frage des Erosionsniveaus. *Mitt. d. Geogr. Ges.,* Wien.

ZÖTL, J. (1960): Zur Frage der Niveaugebundenheit von Karstquellen und Höhlen. *Zeitschr. f. Geomorph.* Suppl. Bd. 2, Berlin.

ZUBASHCHENKO, M. A. (1947): Opit rayonirovanya karsta Vostochno-Evropeyskoy ravnini. *Eezisi dokl.* Molotovsk. Karst. Konf., No. 6.

ZWITTKOVITZ, F. (1966/1): Die Karstformen in Wadi Garawi (Arabische Wüste-Ägypten). *Mitt. d. Österr. Geogr. Ges.,* Vol. 108, Nos II/III, Wien.

ZWITTKOVITZ, F. (1966/2): Klimabedingte Karstformen in den Alpen, den Dinariden und im Taurus. *Mitt. d. Österr. Geogr. Ges.,* Vol. 108, No. 1, Wien.

INDEX OF NAMES

Absolon 8, 9
Agajanov 118
Albel 35, 174, 223
Ambrus 143
Aprodov 103, 121

Bachinsky 95
Bacsó 142
Balázs 9, 45—47, 108, 115, 117, 118, 129, 135, 137, 139, 165
Ballenegger 152, 153
Baranov 118, 121
Bárány 142
Bauer 26, 30, 47, 118, 120, 121, 123
Beaumont 51
Beck 52, 145, 151
Beniczký 125, 188, 189
Biese 79
Billings 86
Birot 9, 104
Blanck 56
Bogárdi 226
Borbás 93
Boroviev 152
Bots 16, 103, 118, 121
Boussingault 32
Bögli 9, 26, 27, 30, 34, 39, 42, 45, 47, 48, 55, 168, 217
Brugger 72, 73, 77
Bulla 9, 16, 20, 54, 71, 72, 77, 82, 84, 108, 129
Büdel 25, 103, 104, 108

Casteret 9
Cauer 30
Cayeux 69, 72
Chikishev 104, 118, 121
Cholnoky 8, 28, 33, 103, 195, 217
Chramushev 39
Clarke 56
Corbel 9, 16, 34, 104—108, 111, 118—121, 233
Cramer 104
Cvijič 8, 96, 103, 195, 212, 217
Czájlik 30, 45, 128

Danes 103, 129
Davis 9
Di Gléria 152
Dobrov 56
Dobrovolsky 118
Doerell 149
Dokuchaev 9, 34, 103, 108
Douglas 104
Droppa 217
Dryzal 152
Dublyansky 87, 89, 95
Dudich, sen. 15, 32, 103
Dvoracsek 152

Eckert 8, 103
Ernest 151
Ernst 9, 42, 45, 47

Fehér 33, 49, 128, 142, 145, 148, 151, 153
Feitknecht 48
Fejérdy 128
Fekete 151
Findeisen 50
Fodor 32
Franke 26, 27, 45, 47, 217
Frear 48
Fulda 80
Futó 142

Gams 226
Gánti 45, 47, 56
Gedeon 56
Geiger 149, 151
Gerstenhauer 27, 48, 57—63, 66, 67, 104, 118
Glennie 104
Gorbunov 152
Gömöri 143, 144
Grigoriev 121
Grund 8, 54, 71, 96, 103, 169, 195, 212
Gvozdetsky 16, 34, 103, 104, 117, 118, 121

Hargitai 151
Harrasowitz 26, 50
Heublein 38
Hollenzer 202

Holluta 37
Horn 118, 121
Horusitzky 168, 223
Horvát 149
Humboldt 9
Humfeld 150

Jakucs, L. 19, 25, 30, 35, 56, 62, 66, 67, 72, 75, 76, 93, 128, 166, 168, 170, 179, 181, 206—208, 213, 215, 217, 220, 221, 223, 224
Jakucs, P. 16, 142, 149, 150, 201, 207
Jäckly 33
Johnston 48

Kachurin 118, 121
Kadić 15, 103
Kassai 68, 147, 224
Katzer 8, 103, 212
Kerekes 93
Kessler 15, 16, 168, 203, 224
Kettner 54, 86
Kéz 108
Kilinski 50
Kiselyev 152
Klimaszewski 104
Klimes 152
Knebel 32
Kosack 9, 25, 104, 116, 117, 129
Köhn 199
Krebs 8, 103
Krömmelbein 168
Kruber 8
Kukla 55, 104
Kunsky 97
Kuznetsova 95, 99
Kyrle 28, 217

Lais 55
Land 33
Laptev 39, 42
Lautensach 82
Láng 178

Leel-Őssy 85
Lehmann, H. 9, 16, 26, 29, 30, 34, 77, 103, 104, 109, 118, 129, 130, 134, 136, 139, 168
Lehmann, O. 8, 212
Lévy 32
Lindberg 118
Lomonosov 9
Louis 54, 72, 109, 168
Ložek 55
Lötschet 168

Maksimovich 16, 72, 101, 102—104, 118, 121, 129, 217
Markó 9, 27, 47, 56, 72
Martel 8, 9, 68, 103
Maucha 45, 128
Maull 54
Mándy 47, 56, 57, 59, 72, 74, 75
Merck 27
Meyer 107, 118, 120
Meyerhoff 103
Michler 100
Miller 9, 26, 47
Mortensen 82
Mosonyi 226
Munck 118, 120
Müller 27

Németh 168, 226, 230
Nikolaev 95

Ovchinnikov 71

Papp 39
Parmuzin 118, 121
Parrot 33
Pasa 95, 98
Pálffy 72, 224
Pávay-Vajna 223
Penck 9, 103, 108
Pécsi 16, 20

Pfeffer 27, 48, 57—63, 66, 67
Pia 37, 69
Polovinkina 68, 69
Pustovalyov 73

Rasmusson 82, 118, 120, 121
Rathjens 9, 103, 118, 120, 121, 123
Reinboth 80
Reiter 50
Renault 77, 104
Richthofen 9
Roglić 25, 217
Rohdenburg 107, 118, 120
Rose 104
Rozložnik 223
Russel 145, 148

Sachs 49
Saint-Ours 77, 104
Samolyov 73
Savchin Miron 87, 90
Schauenberger 118, 120
Scherf 72, 75
Schloesing 29, 30, 32, 46, 233
Schmidt 69, 86, 102, 168, 174
Schoeller 26, 72
Schulhof 224
Serban 218, 222
Serko 100
Shchepetov 95, 100
Shostakovich 121
Shvetsov 56, 73
Smirnov 73
Smith 104
Smyk 152
Sokolov 95, 118
Sommer 33
Specht 150
Stefanovits 151

Stoklasa 149, 151
Sunartadirdja 104
Sweeting 104, 118

Szabó, J. 72
Szabó, P. Z. 9, 16, 77, 104
Szádeczky-Kardoss 223, 224
Székely 91
Szmik 152

Takács 224
Tatarinov 95
Tell 47, 107, 118, 120
Thom 150
Thornbury 54
Tillmanns 26, 28, 38, 39, 41
Tóth 82
Trimmel 89, 95, 123, 217
Troll 118, 121
Trombe 9, 33, 34, 39, 72, 79, 105, 152, 168, 217
Tućan 39

Vadász 72, 77
Vass 33
Venkovits 16, 39, 168
Verstappen 104
Vindis 223
Vinogradsky 50

Wagenhoffer 224
Wagner 141—143, 146, 148
Weisse 56
White 77, 104
Wissmann 16, 34, 104
Wollny 32

Zólyomi 142
Zubashchenko 9
Zsoldos 151

Yegorov 152

SUBJECT INDEX

ablation 71
absence of water in agricultural land 200
absorption coefficient 29, 36, 233
abundance of karsts 116
accumulated sediment 97
accumulation of alluvia 136
acetic acid 49
Acheron (Baradla, Hungary) 185
Acheron swallow-hole 213, 214
Achromatium 49
Aconitum 149
aeration of the soil 159
aerobic
— conditions 49
— decay 48, 49
— process 160
— soil (tropical) 130
afforestation 244
— of karst surfaces 205
Africa 82
aggressive
— solution 42, 51
— water 40, 41
aggressivity 130, 139, 142, 163, 229, 240
— of dolomite 77, 234
— of water 40, 75, 107
—, secondary 36, 232
Aggtelek, Aggtelek Cavern (Hungary) 183, 187, 188, 202, 206, 207, 214, 220, 226
Aggtelek Hills (Hungary) 56, 187, 202
Aggtelek Karst (Hungary) 185, 213, 215
air 174
Alaska 118, 120
Albanian karst 47
allogenic (B-type) karst 166, 167, 175—177, 180, 182, 183, 186, 193, 208, 212, 213, 239, 241
— cavern 180, 188, 189, 193, 242
— — channel 181
— channel 186
—, covered 182
— denudation 186
— erosion 177, 193, 243
— karstification 188
— lenticular zone 191, 208, 242
— river 226
— scour channel 242
— spring 215, 221, 222

allogenic (B-type) karst
— stream 225, 226, 242
— —, linear 239
— —, underground 226
— water 179, 182, 186, 241
— water table 181, 182, 208
—, equilibrium of 180
— —, two-stage 185
alluvial
— cone 234
— fan 74, 77
Alpine dams 229
aluminium sulphate 52
American Great Salt Lake 72
ammonia 50
ammonium
— carbonate 51
— phosphate 51
— sulphate 52
anaerobic
— decay 48
— substances 49
andesite 81, 114
anhydrite 76, 78, 79, 80, 81, 87
— deposit 79, 81
annual periodicity 128
Antarctica 117
anthropogenic
— effects 200
— influence 25, 205, 229
— interference 207
— intervention in the karst 230
anthropovariance 200, 201
— of karstification 200
anticlinal 89, 102
— flank 102
Antri di Corchia cavern (Italy) 126
aqueous dissolution 231
aragonite 26, 76
archeospeleology 22
areal
— karstic infiltration 241
— selectivity 131
artificial
— dam 228
— mill-run 226
— waterproofing of the joints 229
— weir 225
association of tall weeds 149

271

atmospheric
— CO_2 105, 111—114, 235
— convection 161
A-type karst (see authigenic karst)
Australian
— grassland 150
— regions 197
authigenic (A-type) karst 166—172, 174
    174—176, 178, 179, 181, 183, 186,
    193, 239, 241, 243
— cavern 188
— erosion 168, 170
— karstification 177—179, 181, 193, 243
— lenticular zone 180, 183, 197, 224, 242
— plateau 167
— spring 203, 223
— stream 225, 226
— water 225
— water table 181
aven 124, 126, 127, 236
— funnel 236
azonality 20
a-zone (see infiltration zone)
axes of symmetry of dolines 163

bacterial
— abundance in the soil 145
— contamination 203
— symbiosis 151
bacteriochlorophyll 50
bacterioerythrin 50
Bakony Hill (Hungary) 154
Banksia 150
Baradla Cavern (Aggtelek, Hungary)
    90, 187, 188, 190, 191, 202, 204, 213,
    215, 221, 226
barren karst 126, 202—205, 207, 212, 244
barrenness of the karst 243
basalt 54, 82, 231
baselevel of erosion 80, 86, 97, 117, 132,
    133—135, 168, 169, 172, 173, 174,
    176, 179, 181, 185, 186, 191, 241,
    243
—, artificial 221
bathycapture 178, 179, 184—186, 220,
    242
—, multistage 185
bauxite 77, 223
Bear Cave (USSR) 96
Beggiatoa 49
Bermudas 56
Béke (Peace) Cavern (Aggtelek, Hungary)
    175, 181, 191, 202, 204, 206, 207, 220,
    227
Bihar Hill (Transylvania, Romania) 218,
    222
Binnetal (Switzerland) 74
bioactive soil zone 164, 239
bioactivity 146—148
biocarbonate dissolution 26
biochemical corrosion 137

biogenic
— CO_2 109—111, 113, 114, 130, 131,
    235, 237
— karst 138
— process 232
biogeography 20
biological
— activity of edaphon 159, 160
— cycle 113, 236
— equilibrium 201
biologically productive horizon 131
biospeleology 22
biosphere 130, 236
bitumen 55
Bochil (Chiapas, Mexico) 58
Borsod Karst (Hungary) 97, 145, 149,
    154, 163, 164, 195, 205, 213
Bosnia (Yugoslavia) 220
bottom
— level 191
— of the cavern 180
— of the karst 178
— profile 242
Boyle—Mariotte gas law 35
Brenner (Tyrol) 74
British Columbia 105
brittle deformation 88
Bryansk area (USSR) 56
B-type karst (see allogenic karst)
Buda Hills (Budapest, Hungary) 74, 76
Budaörs Hills (Hungary) 93, 94
butte 20
Bükk Hill (Hungary) 97, 149, 154, 161,
    162, 163, 164, 167, 174, 175, 187, 195
Bükk Plateau (Hungary) 143, 155, 196
b-zone (see infiltration zone)

$CaCO_3$—CO_2 equilibrium 39
$CaCO_3$ in secondary dissolution 45
Cadisha source (Lebanon) 47
calcareous
— oozes 28
— tufa 28, 69, 71, 107, 126—128, 136,
    140, 170, 217, 226
calcification 21
calcite 26, 51, 52, 55, 63, 68, 72, 75, 76
calcium
— bicarbonate 28
— diphosphate 50
— hydrocarbonate 38, 112
— hydrophosphate 50
— phosphate 52
— sulphate 52 78, 79
calcium carbonate 52, 53
— aggressivity 131
— — formation 128
— dissolution 130, 170, 176
—, removal of 107
— solution 175
— transportation 41, 107, 235
— —, vertical 107, 235

calcium carbonate—carbonic acid 39
— equilibrium 240
calcium-magnesium hydrocarbonate 40
Campo di Rovere (Abruzzi) 58
Campo Felize (Abruzzi) 58
Campo Saline (Abruzzi) 58
Canada 121
Canon (Chiapas, Mexico) 58
canyon 84, 134, 138
capacity of
— absorption 48
— diffusion 48
carbon dioxide
—, accessory 41, 42, 44
—, aggressive 40, 42—44
—, bound 31, 40—42, 44
— content in soil 152, 157
— production in the soil 142, 151
— saturation 28
carbonate
— dissolution 21, 26, 47
— hardness 40, 42, 53
carbonate—carbonic acid 46
— equilibrium 169
carbonic acid 38, 39, 49
—, accessory 38, 39, 41, 42, 44, 46, 53
—, aggressive 39
—, bound 39
— corrosion 105
— saturation 128
Carex species 164, 239
Carex humilis 164
Carpathians 236
Carrara (Apuane Alps) 58
cascade 48
Castellani Cavern (Italy) 183
catchment area 244
cave 93, 139, 174—176, 241
— bottom 175
—, corrosional 82
—, entry of the 174, 241
— formation 36
—, ice 79
— network 240
— passage 95, 96, 134
cave-roof collapse 174
cavern 17, 21, 34, 37, 41, 71, 81, 107, 108,
    118, 120, 121, 124, 125, 127, 129, 134,
    140, 171, 175, 181, 186, 193, 213, 217,
    231, 243
— branch 189, 243
— channel 221
— collapse 135, 241
—, corrosional 171
— deposit 244
—, erosional 80, 124
— evolution 182, 191, 243
— formation 118, 194, 243
—, hydrothermal 176
— map 95
—, non-structural 81

cavern
— of mountain karst 124
— of tectonic origin 90
— passage 45, 90, 99, 180, 182, 183, 210
— roof 182
— sculpture 241
— section 203, 207, 217
—, shaft 125, 126
—, structural 81
— system 124, 181, 191
—, tropical 140
— tunnel 208
—, underground 125
— water 45
cavity 84, 183
—, collapse of 91
—, corrosional 171, 173
— destruction 93
—, diameter of the 71
—, erosional 174
—, inactive 172
—, silting up of the 242
Central and Eastern European karsts 168
Cepovani Valley (Slovenia, Yugoslavia) 99
changes in the natural plant of a karst
    region 201
changing colour of dripstones in caverns
    205, 206
channel due to corrosion 175
Chatyr-Dagh Mountain (Crimean Pen-
    insula, USSR) 198
Chélif (near Orleansville) 105
chemical
— composition of rainwater 30
— decomposition 48, 81
— weathering 21
chemosynthetic assimilation 50
chert nodes 51
"classical" karst process 231
clay 54, 81, 139
—, intrastalactic 206
—, washing of 207
clay minerals 55
climate
—, cold 104, 234
—, warm 104
climatic
— conditions 82
— karst morphogeny 34, 37
— karst morphology 103, 126
— variance 103
— variance of karstification 104
— zonality 34, 82, 105, 115
— zones 111, 232
— zones of karsts 108
— zones of karst morphology 110
climatic-morphologic-regional system of
    karsts 16
climatogenetic terrace 217
climato-morphology 130
climatovariance 25

CO_2 bound in the hydrocarbonate 41
CO_2 concentration 105
— of the soil 232, 239
CO_2 content of the
— air 29
— soil atmosphere 159, 161, 239
— water 28
CO_2 gas levels in soils under a forest 239
CO_2 of
— atmospheric origin 110, 235
— biogenetic origin 107
— inorganic origin 109, 111
CO_2 partial pressure 232
CO_2 production
— in the soil 29, 146, 149, 152, 163, 198,
    232, 238, 239
— of the rhizospheres 154
— of various agricultural crops and soil
    bacteria 149
cockpit karst 134
cold
— climate 234
— karst 107
— water solution 198
complete cycle of erosion 187
conchoidal
— depression 191, 192, 243
— fracture 67
cone karst (region) 132, 133
confined karst acquifer 117
Congo 124
consequent orientation 123
convergence 191
Copoya (Chiapas, Mexico) 58
corrosion 21, 25, 45, 66, 81, 84, 93, 95,
    114, 121, 135, 174, 178, 193, 194,
    231
— dynamism 68, 113, 126, 131, 232, 233,
    237
—, mixing 42, 45, 170, 176, 179, 241
— of dolomite regions 74
— of granite 82
— of inorganic acids 49
— of water flow 176
—, postgenetic 221
—, selective 77
—, spatial 166
—, subareal 166
—, thermal 77
—, vertical depth of 127
—, vertical zones of 127
corrosion-sculptured funnel 175
corrosional passage 241
corrosive
— effect 71
— erosion 77
— karst erosion 110
Corylus avellana 149
covered karst 116, 183, 184, 186
crenic acid 49
Crimean Peninsula (USSR) 98

crystal
— formation 21
— structure 62
— water 80
crystallinity 56, 67, 233
Cueva del Indio (Cuba) 130
cultural denudation 201
cumulative effects 133

Dachstein (Austria) 124
dam 215
Danube—Tisza Interfluve (Hungary) 123
decalcification 84, 172, 234
deep karst
—, inactive 170—173, 181, 240
deflated tableland 20
deflation 119, 129
deforestation 181, 201, 204
—, age of 204
degradation 205, 243
—, duration of 243
— of karst soil 202
degraded
— planina 203
— plateau 244
denudation 54, 104, 135, 240, 242
—, allogenic (B-type) 177
—, authigenic (A-type) 177
—, dynamism of 54
— forms 54
—, measure of 107
—, rate of 127
denudational features 54
depression 169
desert
— erosion 234
— weathering 113
dessication crack 91
Devaux cave 79
diaclase 69, 88
diagenesis 68, 84
Diamond Mountains (near Seoul), South
    Korea) 82
Dinaric Alps 236
Dinaric Karst 96, 103, 210
Dinarids 15, 98
dip and strike of strata 99
discharge capacity 208
—, genetic 208
discharge in the spring phase 210
disintegration 71
dislocation 87
dissociation 32
dissolution
—, cold 75
— dynamism 233
—, intensity of 124
— potential 104
— process 232
— residue 71, 171, 233

dissolution
—, secondary 170, 241
—, selective 74, 75, 81, 82, 229
— —, activation of the 170
—, warm 75
dissolved residue 55
dissolving power 28
doline 17, 21, 33, 74, 82, 96, 102, 120,
    121, 127, 131, 132, 140, 143, 145, 147,
    149, 151, 158, 162—164, 171, 175,
    183, 184, 195—197, 232, 234, 239
—, aligned 127, 183, 184, 187, 242
—, asymmetry of 195, 196, 238
—, clogged 171
— development 171
—, erosional 241
— evolution 171
— formation 99, 127, 174, 176, 186, 207
—, funnel-shaped 120
— hollow 183
—, lone 183, 184, 242
— series 184
— sculpture 240
— string 96—98, 183
— well 125, 134
dolomite 54, 55, 57, 63, 65, 68, 72, 74, 77,
    78, 81, 82, 93, 233
— aggressivity 77, 234
— corrosion 71, 74, 75
—, crystalline 233
—, debris 72, 75
—, holocrystalline 72, 74, 77
— grain 75
—, mineralogically pure 72
—, normal 72
—, phanerocrystalline 234
— powder 71
— pulverization 93, 94, 233
—, pulverulent 72, 76
— relief 234
—, rigidity of 72
— rubble 234
dolomitization 51
Domica Cavern (Slovak section of the
    Aggtelek Cavern, CSSR) 188, 189, 226
dominant wind 145
double
— carbonate 52, 77
— salt 72
downstream 208
drainage
— area 107, 179, 181
— coefficient 106
— network 239
drippings of water in cavern 244
dripstone 107, 121, 127, 128, 140, 175,
    181, 205, 206, 244
—, chemical composition of 205
— colour 205
— formation 126, 139, 140, 176, 181,
    193, 203, 243

dripstone
— in cavern 128
—, intensity of 127
—, mineralogical composition of 205
—, structure of 205
— under barren karst 206
duration of
— diffusion 48
— sunshine 144
dynamic
— pressure 215
— soil layer 132
dynamism of
— dissolution 24, 47, 52, 56
— karst corrosion 63, 174, 235
— karst erosion 102, 134, 166
— karstification 32, 86, 104, 217

edaphic production of carbon dioxide 150
edaphon 130, 151, 164, 239
electrical discharges in the tropics 50
eluvium 71
embryonic
— cave formation 36, 232
— phases of valley sculpture 97
enlargement of passage 179
epeirogenic
— deformation 86
— movements 86, 93, 172
epeirovariance 25, 95, 166
epigenetic valley 177, 178, 184, 185
equilibrium of
— absorption 107
— carbonic acid 38, 39
— concentration of CO_2 46
— diffusion 107
— dissolution 37
equilibrium free carbonic acid 40
eroded karst 203
erosion 93, 96, 120, 121, 132, 135, 201,
    236, 237, 241, 242
—, areal 114, 119, 129, 133
—, cultural 243
— dynamics 237
—, efficiency of 129, 237
—, glacial 124, 236
—, hydraulic 182
—, lateral 132, 209, 217
— — scour 182
— — streambed 131
—, linear 114, 120, 129, 130, 166, 175,
    177, 178, 186, 217, 241—243
— of dolomite relief 77
— potential of the stream 179
—, retreating 242
—, streambed 129
—, type of 238
—, wind 129, 238
erosional
— valley 98
— variance 25, 166

Esparros sinkhole (Pyrenees) 79
estavelle 210
etching
— of rocks 65
— pits 67
Eube (German Mountains) 58
eurythermic species 131, 237
evaporation 146, 237
evapotranspiration 106
excavation 95
exchange reaction 51, 76
— by a decrease of volume 51
exposure 142, 144—146, 159—163, 195, 238, 239
—, differences of 238
extrazonality 141

facing 143—145, 149
factor K_t 41
factors of erosion 20
fan-shaped arrangement of tension 102
fault 80, 86, 93
— breccia 90
— plane 173
— — striation 90
fauna in the soil 165
ferric oxide 51
ferrous carbonate 51
Festuca ovina 149, 164
Festuca species 239
Festuca sulcata 149, 162, 164
Festucetum sulcatae 149
Fichtel Mountains (FRG) 82
filled soil 202
filling cavern 55
fissuration 68
—, structural 70
fissure 69, 80, 93, 140
—, cave 91
— —, tectonic 93
— cavern 90
—, hairline 69
— —, syngenetic 87
— network 168, 169
— —, primary 169
—, structural 70, 81
— system 202
— —, primary 178
—, tectonic 93
flexure 88
flood 213, 215, 244
—, duration of 212
—, frequency of 237
— prevention 210
flood-control level 225
flood-discharge terrace 219
flood-level spring 215
flow rate 75
fluvial transport 21
Forelian stratification 120
forest-covered surface 244

forest fire 206
formaldehyde 50
free water table 176
freeze-and-thaw 124
freezing water 119
frost 72, 77
— comminution 119, 123
— karst 103, 109, 122
frozen
— climate 103
— ground 121
fulvic acid 49
funnel 125
furrow
— karst 138
—, tecto-orientated 127
furrow-rill 201
Fusshöhlen 139

gas absorption 112
gas microanalyzer using a calibrated capillary 156
Gellért Hill (Budapest, Hungary) 75
geographic
— biologism 200
— determinism 200
geological age 69, 70, 243
"geological organ pipes" 171
geomorphological
— feature 198
— variance 25, 195, 198
— — in karstification 198
geospeleology 22
geostatic pressure 86
geothite 51
Gerecse Hill (Hungary) 56, 154
German degree of hardness 40
Gladiolus 149
glauconite 51
Glattalp (Swiss Alps) 58
Gouffre Berger Cavern (France) 126
graben faulting 234
granite 54, 81, 82, 114, 231
granulation 74
grassland 164
gravel 182, 228
— terrace 182, 242
gravity zone 240
Greece 201
Greenland 117, 118, 120
Grimsel (Switzerland) 229
ground
— isotherms 199
— surface area 164
— temperature 143
ground water 119
—, hard 236
Grönligrotten Cavern (Sweden) 120
gypsum 54, 76, 78, 79
— cave 81
— cavern 87, 93

gypsum
— deposit 79
—, formation of 79
- karst 80, 81, 87
— swelling 80

Hagengebirge (Austria) 124
hairline crack 138
hardness 119
— of water 165
Harz Mountains (GDR) 79, 228
Hauptdolomite 56, 57
heat exchange by convection 34
hematite 51
hemisphere 238
Henry's law 36
Henry—Dalton law of gas 29, 111
hiatus in deposition 68
high-mountain karst 47, 107, 116, 125,
    235, 236
high strength of the limestone 93
hill karst 126
hillfoot
— cave 139
— cavern 135, 136
hilly region 170
hogback 134
holocrystalline texture 67
hollow depression 63
horizontal
— karst-water flow zones 35
— passage 171
hot-spring cavern 93, 94
human
— activity 226
— interference 217, 221, 243
— intervention 217
humic acid 41, 49, 82, 110, 114, 235
huminic acid 49, 110, 114, 235
humus 131
— concentration 151
humus-rich soil 168, 176, 237
hydration 79
hydrocarbonate 39, 40, 47
— concentration 42, 47
— dissolution 21, 28, 30, 38, 47, 48, 52,
    113, 233
— solution 40, 42, 48
hydrogen sulphide 50
hydrogeography 20
hydrographic cycle 170
hydrostatic pressure 29, 35, 48, 68, 117,
    169, 170, 173, 181, 209, 215, 221, 229,
    232, 240
hydrothermal
— effect 93
— pulverization of dolomite 76
— solution 72

ice formation 21
Iceland 121

impermeable
— bedrock 121, 172
— cover 241
— formation 169, 177
— horizon 240
— rock 167
Imre Vass Cavern (Baradla, Hungary)
    181, 191, 221
inactive
— cavern 124
— valley 96, 127
incision of the blind valley 219
index of erosion 217
indicator 27
infiltrating water 168
infiltration zone 41, 107, 112, 239, 240
—, by gravity (a-zone) 171, 172, 174—
    176, 180
—, b-zone 171, 172, 175
influence of relief 191
— upon the karst process 195
inland ice
—, buried mass of 123
inorganic acid 111, 235
inselberg karst 134, 135, 166
—, tower-shaped 134
insolation 72, 149, 231
intensity of
— CO_2 production 232
— dissolution 34
intercolline basin 96, 210, 234
intermontane
— basin 132
— depression 132
— karst 136
— plain 133—136, 139
intrazonality 141
inundation by dammed-up floods 208
inverse zonality 149
inversion of the CO_2 content 161
ionic diffusion 27, 119
—, rate of 236
iron
— carbonate 51
— oxide 55
— sulphate 51, 76, 77
irreversible dilute solutions 49
István Cave (Bükk Hill, Hungary) 174,
    175
Ivanovo-Voznesensk area (USSR) 56

jagged ridge 138, 221
Jamaica 135
joint(ing) 69, 80, 88, 102, 124, 170, 178,
    197
—, structural 71, 101
— system 168
Jósvafő (Hungary) 172, 183, 184, 187,
    215, 221
Julian Alps 15

K_1 index 26
Karlovac (Yugoslavia) 158, 172
karst
— à pitons 134
— à tourelles 135
— brush wood associations 16
— concept 231, 243
— cone 132, 135, 137
— corrosion 21, 25, 26, 63, 67, 68, 74, 93,
95, 96, 104, 109—111, 113, 117, 118,
120, 124, 129, 143, 147, 157, 197, 228,
233, 235—238
— — agency 110—112, 114
— —, intensity of 108
— —, selective 77
— —, superficial 93
— —, surface of 195
— —, tropical 235
— denudation 109
— — by corrosion 33
— doline 101
— dynamism 141, 145
— erosion 114, 128, 169, 171—173, 176,
234, 237, 240
— —, baselevel of 169, 172, 173, 182
— evolution 46, 172, 232, 236
— —, azonal view of 103
— form 77, 95, 96, 121, 124, 233, 234, 244
— —, corrosive 82
— —, hydrothermal 93
— hydrography 166, 167
— inselberg 133
— island sea 137
— marginal plain 136
— mass 169, 170, 173, 174, 176, 178,
186, 193, 197, 237, 241
— —, size of the 197
— morphogenic analysis 173
— morphological analysis 241
—, of suspended type 169
— passage 179
— peneplains 9, 172
— phenomenon 10, 17, 231, 233
— planina 96, 98, 163, 172
— plateau 131, 134, 167, 172, 175, 198,
200
— process 141, 197, 231
— region 9, 115, 128, 142, 197, 207, 241
— —, denuded 47
— relief 74, 77, 131, 197, 231
— river 225
— shrub woods 164, 239
— spring 127, 164, 172, 182, 205, 221,
244
— —, discharge of 244
— —, hardness of 165
— — level 171
— stream 128
— surface 130
— topography upon karstification 198
— tower 132—135

karst
—, underground 236
— valley 97, 177, 186
—, variance of 232
— water 32, 35, 41, 42, 44—46, 53, 55,
117, 119, 166, 169, 170, 173, 175, 179,
224, 233
— —, cold 175
— —, inrushes of 173, 223, 224, 240
— — lens 179
— — saturation 169
— — shaft 224
— — storage capacity 173
— — —, zone of a high 240
karst water table 25, 34, 68, 97, 168—171,
176, 178, 210, 224, 241
karst
— biology 18
— geochemistry 18
— geology 18
— hydrology 18
— morphogenetics 10, 18—20, 198
— morphology 18, 19, 21, 107
— petrography 18
karst in
— desert zone 109, 116, 118, 129
— Mediterranean zone 109, 113, 114,
120, 122, 127—129, 236, 237
— savannah zone 130
— semidesert steppe 109
— subnival regions 109
— temperate zone 109, 116, 127, 129,
140, 164, 165, 233, 235—237
— tjäle zone 16, 109
— tropics 109
— tundra regions 109
karst regions in
— Albania 201
— China 135, 197
— Croatia (Yugoslavia)   15, 158, 159,
163, 201
— Cuba 130, 132, 135—137, 197
— Dalmatia (Yugoslavia) 201, 203
— Italy 197
— Serbia (Yugoslavia) 200
— Slovakia (ČSSR) 97
— Slovenia (Yugoslavia)
187, 203, 209
— Yugoslavia 197, 204
karst-type
— erosion 231
— denudation 201
karstic
— drainage area 217
— relief forms 231
— surface 178
karstification 16, 17, 25, 70, 86, 104, 107,
118, 126, 127, 142, 162, 172, 174, 176,
186, 193, 197, 234, 236, 240—242
—, concept of 194, 231
—, corrosive 80

karstification
—, dynamism of 127
—, evolution of 200
—, geomorphological variance of 244
—, hydrothermal 93
—, intensity of 163, 224
— of loess 234
—, tropical 103
— under soil 149, 238
karstogenic karst forms 234
Karstrandebene 136
katavothra 139, 210—212, 244
Kegelstkarst 134
kettle hole 123
kettles due to erosion 243
Kissimmee (Florida) 104—106, 108
Kizel river (Perm region, USSR) 96
Korea 82
Kornet es Saouda (in Lebanon) 47
Krain, Istria 15
Kristalnaya Peshchera (Crystal Cavern, USSR) 89
Kyffhäuser Mountains 79

La Causses 103
Lac Léman (Switzerland) 227
laccolith
—, hydro 122
—, ice 122
lactic acid 49
Lake Balaton (Hungary) 227
landscape evolution 244
lapies 17, 63, 74, 96, 101, 102, 120, 123, 127, 128, 138, 139, 175, 201, 204, 207, 221
—, barren 203
—, cavern 125
—, embryonic 127
— field 74, 102, 151, 205, 234, 238, 243
— formation 127
— formed under soil cover 123
— furrow (channel) 68, 102, 123, 125, 128
— —, protogenic 127
—, metamorphism of 201
— metamorphosis 243
—, micro 65
— rhizosphere 128
— ridge 139
— rill 27
—, root 68, 127, 137, 150, 202, 222
—, underground 124
lapies-like forms 82
Lapland 105
lateral conglomerate terrace 182
lattice structure 56, 233
leaching of calcium carbonate 84
lenticular zone 169—174, 176, 179, 180, 241
—, equilibrium position of 170
—, fossil 174
Les Sognettes (Jura) 58

limestone 54, 55, 60, 68, 186, 193
— aggressivity 234
—, bedded 233
—, cherty 55
—, composition of 55, 56, 58, 59
— —, textural feature in 64
—, corallian 116
— corrosion 231
— —, non-karstic 48, 53
—, crystalline 67
—, dolomitic 55
— erosion 117
—, holocrystalline 68
—, fresh-water 69
—, lithology of 68
—, meadow 69
— plateau 186
—, Sarmatian 69
— solubility 233
—, structure of 68
—, tropical 137
lithological conditions 129
lithomorphology 20
loess 16, 54, 82, 84, 85, 100, 234
—, cavity in 234
— corrosion 84, 85
— doline 83—85, 234
— plateau 83, 84
— sinkhole 84
"loess dolls" 84
loess karst doline 123
Longarone (Piave Valley, Italy) 58
long-term average infiltration 224
low-hill karst 168
low-mountain region 236
lower cavern 185
Lulletjarro Cavern (Sweden) 120, 192
Lumelunda Cavern (Sweden) 120
Lundegardh device 153

Mackenzie (Alaska) 105, 118
macroclimate 141, 152, 238
macroclimatic
— changes 33
— influence 232
macroflora 149
macroforms 114, 151
macrostructural elements 102
Macuspana (Tabasco, Mexico) 58
magnesian calcite 65
magnesite 55, 63, 65, 68, 72, 233
magnesium 63, 233
— carbonate 59, 60, 67, 72
— calcite 63
— chloride 51, 52
— solution 84
Maksimovich Cavern (Ural, USSR) 96, 100
Malay Peninsula 134
man-made dam 225
map of the climatic zones of karst regions 116

marginal sinkhole 186
marl 55
mass
— of debris 81
— wasting 102, 119
Matapo Hills (South Africa) 82
mean
— annual rainfall 134
— temperature 106
— —, annual 134
mechanical stress acting on a rock 87
mechanism of evaluation 118
Mecsek Hill (Hungary) 97, 154
melting ground ice 117
mesophile hill lawns 149
meteorological rhythms 128
method of selective staining 63
microclimate 197
microclimatic
— changes 33
— conditions 128, 129
— factors 163
— —, role of 237
— features of solar irradiation 238
— influences 232
— parameters 141, 149, 237
— zones 143
microfissure 69
microforms 114, 128, 193, 238
— of dissolution 68
microorganism 49, 142, 145, 147, 150
microrelief 65
micro-solifluxion 85
microspace 141, 151, 157, 237
microstructural preformation 123
mineralic
— differentiation 74
— selectivity 233
mineralogical
— heterogeneity 74
— selection 72
mining area 173, 241
mixing corrosion (see corrosion)
modifications in the natural plant cover 201
mogote 134
molar volume 51
monogenous sedimentary deposits 81
monomineralic rocks 55
monsoon region
—, tropical 130
—, subtropical 130
Monte Cavallo (Venetian Prealps) 58
Montenegro (Yugoslavia) 200
Moravian Karst (CSSR) 98, 183, 193
Morelia (Chiapas, Mexico) 58
morphogenetic analysis 81
morphometric analysis 126
Moscow Basin (USSR) 56, 73
mound 140

mountain
— karst 103, 109, 113, 123—125, 166
— reservoir 229
mountain's structure 96
mylonitic breccia 91
Nagykevély Hill (Budapest, Hungary) 73
Nardus stricta 149, 150, 164, 239
narrowing
— of the swallow-hole passage 208
— passage 179
natural
— hydrology of a karst 207
— succession 207
Neubrandenburg (GDR) 122
New Guinea 134
nitric acid 49, 50
nitrification 50
nitrous acid 50
non-carbonate
— contaminants 60
— contaminating substances 206
non-karstic
— cavern 91
— deposit 182
— drainage area 182, 186
— environment 208, 243
— formation 177, 178, 182, 242
— nature 193
— process of relief sculpture 243
— region 25
— surface 166, 167, 173, 176, 177, 186, 239, 241, 242
— valley 187
non-synchronous development of the terrace 217
North German—Polish lake districts 123
Norway 105
nunatak 117

obstruction 217, 221
— in cavern 209
open passage 93
Optimisticheskaya Peshchera (Optimist's Cavern, USSR) 87
organic
— processes of soil evolution 34
— soil acids 111, 113, 130, 236
orientation of the
— bedding 238
— strike 238
orogenic
— belts 115
— deformation 86, 90
Orsat stack-gas analyser 152, 154, 155
overburden pressure 91
Ozernaya Peshchera (Lake Cavern, USSR) 87
oxalic acid 49

Ökrös Hill (Budapest, Hungary) 73

Parajd (Transylvania, Romania) 92
Paranuzzi (Venetian Prealps) 58
partial pressure of CO$_2$ 107
passage section 95
pCO$_2$ 34, 36, 41, 46, 57, 111, 124, 126, 237
— of the soil atmosphere 41
pedogenesis 167
pedosphere 142
peneplain 122, 131
pelite 71
peneplanation 121
periglacial
— karst 109, 120, 121, 123
— morphological region 118, 235
permafrost ground 121
permeability 68, 69, 70
petrographic nature 86
petromorphology 54
petrovariance 25, 54, 115, 166
phosphate solution 50
phreatic waters 28, 75
phytedaphon 131, 149, 237
Piano di Ovindoli (Abruzzi) 58
Pierre St. Martin cavern (Pyrenees) 126
Pilis Hill (Hungary) 154, 174, 175
Pinar del Rio (Cuba) 132
pit due to evorsion 192
pitted plain 123, 236
plane 63
—, bedding 71, 135
—, structural 135
Planina Cavern (Slovenia, Yugoslavia) 225
plant
— root 49
— species 232
plastic
— deformation 88
— layer 206
plasticity 86
Plitvice lakes (Yugoslavia) 225
Poaná (Tabasco, Mexico) 58
Podgora (Dalmatia, Yugoslavia) 101
Podolian Platform 73, 87
points of outflow 169
polar
— karst 105, 107, 113, 116, 235, 236
— regions 232
polje 17, 96, 100, 127, 136, 210, 212, 234
—, inundated 208, 211, 212, 244
— rim 210
—, tropical 137
polymineral rocks 81, 93
porphyry-like texture 65, 66
position of the spring level 180
post-diagenetic dislocation 86
postgenetic
— corrosion 221
— recrystallization 74

post-glacial karst evolution 121
post-tectonic stage 87
potassium hydroxide solution 152, 157
precipitation 32, 106, 113, 130, 141, 235
—, infiltrated 224
preservation
— of natural values 227
— of the plateau feature 172
pressure factors 35
primary lapies relief 201
profile types 91
propionic acid 49
pseudokarst 116, 118, 122, 236
— of arid regions 116
pseudomorphs 51
pseudostructural cave 91
pseudotectonic fissure cavity 90, 91
Pteridium aquilinium 158
Puerto Rico 135
purple bacteria 50
Pyrenees 236
pyrite 49, 51

quartz 193
Quebec, West Scotland 105
Quercus pubescens 207

radiation 144
rain 161
— absorption capacity 237
rain-forest karst 134
rain-rill 201
rainstorm
— frequency 145
— torrent 130
Rana karst cavern (Italy) 95, 98
rate of
— absorption 48
— — and dissolution reactions 237
— denudation 104
— diffusion 48
— dissolution 59
— hydrocarbonate dissolution 48
reaction space 37
reaction time for dissolution 168
reafforestation 207
recrystallization 78
reduction in volume 84
reg 20
regions of geomorphology 117
—, glacial 117
—, periglacial 117
relief
— energy 25, 119, 130, 195
— evolution 243
— map 142
rendzina soil 51, 158, 183
reservoir 226, 228, 229
residual solution 236
residue 167
reverse faulting 88

Rhabdomonas 50
rhizogenic acid 41
rhizosphere 33, 130, 142, 150, 164, 198, 232, 239
— of various karst-lawn associations 164
Rhodothece 50
rhyolite tuff 91
rift faulting 96
rigidity of the rock 86
rill karst 138
Rio Champoton, Yucatan 105
Rio Grande (near Acacia) 105
Rio Usumacinta (Chiapas, Mexico) 105
river-laid alluvia 220
rock
— channel 138
— debris 193
— — comminuted by frost 123
— forest 139
— —, tropical 139
— pyramids 134
— salt 16, 54, 78, 92
— structure 66
— terrace 175
— — groove 191
— texture 63, 65
— —, differences in 233
— tower 134
rocky archway 208
role of climatic variance 129
root
— acid 110, 114, 235
— hole 201
— lapies 68, 127, 137, 150, 202, 222
— zone 164
root-level plane of the cave 175
rounded microforms 201

Salzburg Alps (Austria) 124
sand 55, 82, 182, 193, 226, 228
sand bank 182
sandstone 54, 82, 231
sandur 123, 236
Sas Hill (Budapest, Hungary) 73
savannah zone 109
—, tropical 134
Scandinavia 120
scour
— cavern 181, 182, 185, 188, 193, 217, 219, 242
— — formation 237
— channel 222, 242
— groove 190
second cavern level 185
secondary obstruction of the swallow-hole passage 208
self-insulation 228
semi-desert 130
semi-karst 71
senile stage of the cavern 181
series of doline (see doline string)

shaft cavern 124
—, corrosional 236
shear plus lateral compression 87, 88
sheetwash 21, 102
shiling 139
shrinkage crack 84, 91
shrub wood 142
Siberia 121
siderite 51, 76
sideritization 77
silica gel 55, 78
silt 182, 193, 226
sink-holes 17, 102
sinkhole (rows) 96, 134
skeletal karst 107, 120, 235
slaty-bedded limestone 86
slope of the streambed 227
Slovakia (CSSR) 223
"smell of rain" 33
snow limit 47
soapstone 67, 233
sodium chloride 52
soil 147, 202
— atmosphere 34, 41, 105, 107, 232, 235, 237, 238
— bacterial flora 145
— bacterium 113, 236
— biotope 105, 114
— degradation 203
— drying 237
— erosion 131, 201, 204, 205
— evaporation 106
— gas 32, 33
— — recovery 154
— humidity, local 150
— ice 236
— intensity 142
— microclimate 141
— microflora 145
— moisture 150
— organic acids 235
— removal 131
— respiration 106, 114, 141, 145
solar
— energy 21
— heat 145
solid residue 93
solifluxion 119, 234, 236
solubility 29, 52, 53, 56, 57, 59, 60, 67, 72, 74, 78
— coefficient 78
— of gypsum 81
— of limestone 60
— product K_1 26
—, variance in 59
Soyaló (Chiapas, Maxico) 58
sölle (soll) 122, 123, 236
specific structural condition of the rock 86
speleogenesis 89
speleology 16
sphinx rocks 20

Spitsbergen 118
spring 102, 169, 180, 216, 217, 243
— cave, inactive 174
— cavern 221, 222
— funnel 76, 174
—, hot 76
— level 180, 191
— outlet 221, 241
—, thermal 75
— tunnel 241
— zone 170
spring-outlet area 216, 221, 240
stalactites 28, 33, 202, 204
—, discharge rate of 202
—, dripping rate of 202
—, ice 79
steppe 142, 149, 162, 163, 239
stepwise retreating 186
Stokkvikgrotten Cavern (Sweden) 120
stratospecific preformation 126
stream 179
— with a free surface 95
streambed 175, 189, 207, 243
— dredging 225
— erosion 183
— —, linear 193, 209
—, fossil 188
stream valley
—, inactive 187
structural
— line 93
— orientation 96
— preformation 175, 184, 195, 234, 242
— postformation 195
structurally controlled cavern 91
sub-areal corrosion 123, 183
subcutaneous
— CO_2 production 164, 239
— lapies formation 201, 203
subnival karst 123, 125
subpolar karst 105, 109, 113, 236
subregions in the mountains 119
subsequent orientation 123
sulphate 51
sulphide 49, 51
sulphur bacteria 49
sulphuric acid 49, 76
surface
— erosion 141
— degradation 206
— temperature 237
suspended
— material 193
— karst aquifer 169
— valley 209
swallow cave 127, 139
swallow-hole 121, 127, 140, 185, 189, 191, 208, 209, 211, 212, 216, 217, 219, 220, 243
— cavern 209
—, flood-level of 220

swallow-hole
— formation 178
—, intake capacity of 208
—, multi-stage string of 242
— obstruction 209, 210, 218, 220
— section of the cavern 209
—, string of 185
Sweden 120
Szeleta well (Hungary) 126
synclinal 89
— axis 102
syphon 207, 221

taiga region 121
Tanana (Alaska) 104—106, 108
tangential stress 87
tectonic
— preformation 93, 95, 98, 120
— structure of the karst 96
tectospeleology 95
telescopic stalactite 206
temperate zone 170, 172, 175
temperature
— of solution 29, 38, 39, 41, 44, 74, 78, 124, 126
— of the air 34, 37, 113, 124, 130, 146
— of changeover 79
— of the soil 34, 48, 105, 142, 145, 146, 148, 232
— of water 34
temporary lake 213
tendency of surface evolution 200, 201
Tengerszem Lake (Jósvafő, Hungary) 226
Tennengebirge (Austria) 124
tensile stress 87
Teopisca (Chiapas, Mexico) 58
terra rossa 136, 158, 167, 171, 183, 206
terrace 184, 241
—, climatogenetic 217
— groove 184, 219, 243
— meander 219
— morphology 124
—, riverside 220
tetarata 124, 226
textural porosity 68, 69
texture of natural rocks 60
thermal water 175
thermokarst 103, 122, 123,
— doline 122, 236
thick-bedded limestone 86
Thiocytis 50
Thioploca 49
Thiospirillum 50
Thiotrix 49
through-cavern 174, 182
time factor 120
time for dissolution 26
time requirements of dissolution 47
Titel (Yugoslavia) 83, 84
titriplex 27

tjäle 109
— zone 119, 121
topoclimatic conditions 128
topsoil 161
Torrente Pentina (Venetian Prealps) 58
tower karst (see karst tower)
Transdanubian Hills (Hungary) 82, 223, 234
transpiration 129
trapezoidal cross-section of the cavern 186, 187, 242
triangular cross-section of the cavern 186, 187, 242
tricalcium phosphate 51
tropical
— cone karst 16, 140
— corrosion 114
— karstification 106, 109, 130, 131, 172
— regions 105
— vegetation 134
tropical karst 107, 111, 120, 132, 133, 140, 237
— cone 16, 140
— corrosion 235
— forms 132, 137
— process 103
— regions 104, 109, 113
tropics 50
tufa
— curtain 135
— —, tropical 140
— weir 124, 225
tundra region 103, 109, 121
—, mountainous 118, 121
—, subarctic 118, 119
—, periglacial 119, 121
Turmkarst 134
Tyrol 74, 76

Una river 15
uncovered karst 178
underground
— cavity 215
— channel 241
— drainage network 210
— karst 124, 236
— passage 208, 241
— river piracy 179
— section of a stream 208
— stream 182
— streambed 208
— stream channel 225
— —, regulation of 225
— valley 208
under-soil karstification 151

upper cavern 185
uvala 120, 127

Val de Brevine (Jura) 58
Val de Travers (Jura) 58
valley 220, 242
—, blind 220
— , erosional 177, 178
— formation by collapse 178
— glacier 118
— gorge 127, 178
Vaucluse-type spring channel 171
vegetal cover 113
vegetation zone 149
vertical digitation 191
Vietnam 134, 135
volume of water 197
Vöröstó uvala (Hungary) 172, 183, 184

wadi sculpture 129
Waldschmiede (Harz Mts) 80
warming
— by air convection 163
— by direct sunshine 163
Wartha—Lunge process 27
water
— infiltration 203, 205
— in stratiform 118
— passage 178, 180
water-storage capacity 131, 203
— of the soil 202
water-carbon dioxide 35
watercourse 179
water in equilibrium 43, 44
weathering
— due to inorganic acids 21
—, eluvial 167
—, physical 72, 149
Wetterstein limestone 56
wind erosion 231, 237
whirlpool hole 191

zonal climatic factors 20
zonality 103, 141
—, climate 103
zone
— of divergence 191
— of high-pressure 35
— of monsoon rains 109
Zuberec Cave (Tatra, CSSR) 97

Yugoslavian Karst 149, 157, 200
Yugoslavian poljes 208, 210, 211, 212, 243
Yunnan region (China) 138, 139